Albrecht
on Calcium

The Albrecht Papers, Volume V

by William A. Albrecht, Ph.D.
Edited by Charles Walters

About the Author

Dr. William A. Albrecht, the author of these papers, was chairman of the Department of Soils at the University of Missouri College of Agriculture, where he had been a member of the staff for 43 years. He held four degrees, A.B., B.S. in Agriculture, M.S. and Ph.D., from the University of Illinois. During a vivid and crowded career, he traveled widely and studied soils in the United States, Great Britain, on the European continent, and in Australia.

Born on a farm in central Illinois in an area of highly fertile soil typical of the cornbelt and educated in his native state, Dr. Albrecht grew up with an intense interest in the soil and all things agricultural. These were approached, however, through the avenues of the basic sciences and liberal arts and not primarily through applied practices and their economics.

Teaching experience after completing the liberal arts course, with some thought of the medical profession, as well as an assistantship in botany, gave an early vision of the interrelationships that enrich the facts acquired in various fields when viewed as part of a master design.

These experiences led him into additional undergraduate and graduate work, encouraged by scholarships and fellowships, until he received his doctor's degree in 1919. In the meantime, he joined the research and teaching staff at the University of Missouri.

Both as a writer and speaker, Dr. Albrecht served tirelessly as an interpreter of scientific truth to inquiring minds and persistently stressed the basic importance of understanding and working with nature by applying the natural method to all farming, crop production, livestock raising and soil improvement. He always had a specific focus on the effect of soil characteristics upon the mineral composition of plants and the effect of the mineral composition of plants on animal nutrition and subsequent human health.

Dr. Albrecht strove not to be an ivory tower pontificator trying to master and defeat nature, but to be a leader of true science and understand the wondrous ways of nature so we could harness them for the lasting benefit of all. A man of the soil, William A. Albrecht summed up his philosophy as such, "When wildlife demonstrates the soil as the foundation of its health and numbers, is man, the apex of the biotic pyramid, too far removed from the soil to recognize it as the foundation of his health via nutrition?"

Dr. Albrecht was a true student of the characteristics of soil and wasn't timid about his views—be they to a farmer in the field, an industry group or to a congressional subcommittee.

Respected and recognized by scientists and agricultural leaders from around the world, Dr. Albrecht retired in 1959 and passed from the scene in May 1974 as his 86th birthday approached.

About the Editor

Charles Walters was the founder and executive editor of *Acres U.S.A*, a magazine he started in 1971 to spread the word of eco-agriculture. A recognized leader in the field of raw materials-based economic research and sustainable food and farming systems, this confirmed maverick saw one of his missions as to rescue lost knowledge. Perhaps the most important were the papers of Dr. William A. Albrecht, whose low profile obscured decades of brilliant work in soil science. Albrecht's papers, which Walters rescued from the historical dustbin and published in an initial four volumes, continue to provide a rock-solid foundation for the scientific approach to organic farming. Additional volumes of Albrecht's papers were organized and edited by Walters for later publication—the result is shown here with this book.

During his life, Walters penned thousands of article on the technologies of organic and sustainable agriculture and is the author of more than two dozen books (and co-author of several more), including *Eco-Farm: An Acres U.S.A. Primer, Weeds—Control Without Poisons, A Farmer's Guide to the Bottom Line, Dung Beetles, Mainline Farming for Century 21* and many more.

Charles Walters generously shared his vision, energy and passion through his writing and public speaking for more than 35 years and made it his lifelong mission to save the family farm and give farmers an operating manual that they couldn't live without. The Albrecht Papers are an important part of this message.

Charles Walters passed on in January 2009 at the age of 83.

About The Albrecht Papers

When the first volume of these papers was issued, no one could foresee the possibility of recovering and publishing all the papers of this great scientist. For this reason the organization of these papers has not followed Dr. Albrecht's work in a calendar sequence, meaning the order of study and investigation. Instead the papers have been organized into topic themes. Here the papers have been grouped to best focus attention and allowed to reciprocate the values upon which all of Albrecht's work rests.

Some papers relating to the general subject considered here may have appeared in earlier volumes, some—likely as not—overlap and appear in later treatments. Nevertheless, an Albrecht Paper is valuable regardless of where it turns up. Enjoy and learn.

A Special Note

When this editor asked Dr. William A. Albrecht whether calcium was the Prince of Nutrients, he in effect said, "No, it is the King." It is not possible to scratch any Albrecht paper without finding a note on calcium, and it is not possible to discuss calcium without being led into the mosaic of the whole that Albrecht considered biologically correct farming.

Albrecht on Calcium

The Albrecht Papers, Volume V

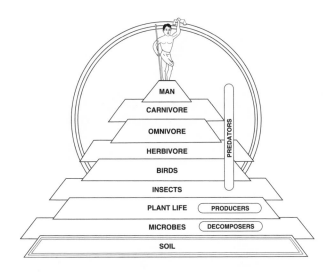

by William A. Albrecht, Ph.D.
Edited by Charles Walters

Acres U.S.A.
Austin, Texas

Albrecht on Calcium

Acres U.S.A.
P.O. Box 91299
Austin, Texas 78709 U.S.A.
(512) 892-4400 • fax (512) 892-4448
info@acresusa.com • www.acresusa.com

Printed in the United States of America

Publisher's Cataloging-in-Publication

Albrecht, William A., 1888-1974
Albrecht on calcium / William A. Albrecht., Austin, TX, ACRES U.S.A., 2011
    xvi, 292 pp., ill., maps, 23 cm.
    Includes Index
    Includes Bibliography
    ISBN 978-1-601730-22-0 (trade)

    1. Agriculture — crops & soils. 2. Soil management.
    3. Soil — plant relationships. 4. Soil fertility — calcium
    5. Plants — nutrition.
    I. Albrecht, William A., 1888-1974 II. Title.

    S593.A42 2011   631.4

**Dedicated to the
memory of C.J. Fenzau**

*A student of the Albrecht System,
a farm consultant and doer of the word.*

From the Publisher

A large part of the Acres U.S.A. mission is to preserve and promote the wisdom of those who came before us. Prof. William Albrecht was such a visionary. A collection of his papers was the first publishing entry toward this mission, that book being *The Albrecht Papers*.

Charles Walters, our founder and longtime editor — and my father — sought out Dr. Albrecht not knowing what lessons were there to be learned. The name Albrecht appeared in journals around the world, yet officials at the University of Missouri where the retired professor kept an office discouraged a meeting citing his age, poor hearing, and the like. Charles Walters visited anyway. What came from these meetings, which soon grew into weekly sessions, was a mentor/student dialogue. Albrecht, ever the patient pedagogue, dispensed the logic, elegance and simplicity of his agricultural systems to an eager mind. And Charles Walters, the publisher and writer, picked up the charge and spread the timeless wisdom of William Albrecht around the world to a new generation of farmers and agronomists.

It's hard to say whether Dr. Albrecht's work would have found its way to light through the efforts of others or if without the republication of Albrecht's papers they would have remained just that, papers to eventually fall into the dustbin of history.

Four volumes of *The Albrecht Papers* eventually came forth. Each had a style and character of its own and each brought new lessons from the master soil scientist to life, but only the most disciplined students of the soil tended to seek out and study these dense works.

Late in his career, semi-retired and legally blind, Charles Walters undertook the Herculean task of reading and sorting the hundreds of remaining papers and articles in Albrecht's archives. He completed that task a few years before his death in 2009. What was left to accomplish was the monumental task of converting damaged and faded copies of articles, some 80 years old, into formats compatible with modern publishing and readable by all.

From file cabinets full of faded photocopies came forth several new volumes of *The Albrecht Papers*, each with a specific focus and theme. It is our goal to produce these works in a timely fashion. In your hands is the beautiful collaboration of the visionary research of Professor William Albrecht and the deft editorial eye of Charles Walters. We hope you enjoy this new creation of William Albrecht and Charles Walters.

— *Fred C. Walters*

Contents

Foreword

I first encountered William A. Albrecht, Ph.D., on paper during my veterinary medicine days because of his connection with the discovery of aureomycin in the mid 1940s. Aureomycin literally leaped into the nation's headlines as an antibiotic similar to penicillin.

It promised to defend against death dealing viruses and as an answer to gram-positive bacteria. Aureomycin was discovered on an eight acre plot known as Sanborn Field at the University of Missouri, now a national historical landmark over 100 years old.

These 39 research plots have given up more of nature's secrets than any similarly sized piece of soil on planet Earth. At the time of Albrecht's death on May 21, 1974, most of these plots had been operated under his tutelage.

It was here that Albrecht learned nature's lessons and requirements. The papers presented in this volume reveal some parts of the record. They reveal some of the values and some of the fallacies and shortcomings of relations, the beneficial effects and some limitations of undigested farm manures, and the benefits and some misconceptions of legumes for soil improvement. The previous four volumes of Albrecht Papers have provided some of the bedrock rationale for limestone in crop production. The papers presented here merely enlarge the subject.

Through the years Sanborn Field told Albrecht more than a little about the acetic effect of some nitrogen fertilizers and the shortfalls after three quarters of a century of chemical fertilizers on soil properties and crop production. Albrecht asked nature about the possibilities of rejuvenating soil with non-legumes and plant nutrients, and nature gave her answers largely because Albrecht asked the right questions.

"If you really stop to think about it," Albrecht told me during one of our Socrates sessions, "All I have done here is write down what we've learned through the years about how everything connects." The prime connection was calcium.

The mere selection of Plot 23 for that famous aureomycin probe represented learned intuition. That plot had already accounted for face-reddening implications. Rotations under certain conditions were far from beneficial and even became outright harmful. Legumes could impoverish land as much as any non-nitrogen fixing crop. Fertilizer dealers found their premises demolished when they paused to listen to Albrecht.

Even this short inventory of information told the great professor that Plot 23 contained dynamite. That dynamite turned out to be *Streptomyces aureofaciens*, strain A377, the parent of all the aureomycins used in World War II.

Albrecht came to the University of Missouri as a microbiologist in 1916, having finished his graduate work at the University of Illinois. He was the seventh of eight children reared on a farm in Livingston County, Illinois.

Never satisfied with superficial answers to superficial questions, Albrecht pushed his way back to fundamentals.

In the early 1930s soil mining techniques had reached a climax point. The first government lime program surfaced under the Agricultural Adjustment Act. Possibly half the soils in the United States were helped by liming. "Lime and lime some more" became the catchphrase. "You can't overdo it."

As with most programs, this one was complied with political strategy, not science, and this caused Albrecht to come up fighting from his chair. There was more to reclaiming the soil than fighting acidity.

Albrecht had tapped foreign scholars. The classics—Russia's Sergei Winogradsky and Holland's M.W. Beijerinck—had proved that nitrogen fixation took place in the soil without any legumes whatsoever.

The essentials were found to be a balance of readily available nitrogen and the presence of carbohydrates, phosphates and calcium. Albrecht pondered the findings of Thomas Way of England. It was Way who in 1852 revealed that when soil absorbed ammonia, a corresponding amount of calcium was released into the drainage water. The exchange mechanism was seated in clay.

It was this point that Albrecht elected to explore. He knew that the exchange capacity of soil depended on both the colloidal clay and the organic matter.

"We took things one leg at a time," Albrecht said, "and wrote down the results." Often the findings went out as graduate student papers under the imprimatur of the Department, the student being the author, Albrecht the sponsor. Albrecht described his role as follows:

"I separated the finest part of the clay out of Putnam silt and loam soil by churning it in a centrifuge running at 32,000 RPM. After the clay had been suspended and settled for three weeks at the bottom, that clay finally plugged up the machinery. But we had thinner and smaller and smaller clay particles until about halfway up the centrifuge, there we had it clear as Vaseline.

We took the upper half of the clay. We made pounds and pounds of it. We took it into an electrical field and made it acidic. We took off all the cations so it was acidic clay. That was how we studied plant nutrition. We titrated back different elements in different orders. We mixed them, balanced them."

The papers presented in this book have to be absorbed with these few points in mind.

Albrecht was standing on the shoulders of giants. That's how he knew he had to begin with calcium.

"The shoulders of giants" is no mere hyperbole. The effect of calcium hydroxide on nodulation was first observed by a scientist named Salfeld-Lingen in 1900. He secured nodulation of peas only when limestone became a soil treatment. Em. Marchal worked with water cultures. He found that the salts of calcium and magnesium also formed nodulation. And E. Laurent and A.V. Donnan came to observe that lime stimulates nodulation formation. Other workers noted the effect of calcium and magnesium under both alkaline and acid conditions. The focal point of much research at the beginning of the 20th century was nodulation, but the purview expanded itself soon enough.

The Albrecht bibliography is rife with papers that seemingly exhausted the subject. The answers sought by early Albrecht studies relied on asking the right questions.

1. What was the effect of standard soil amendments on the nodulation of soybeans grown on various treated plots of certain soil in Missouri and Illinois?
2. What was the effect on soybean inoculation of calcium, phosphorus and potassium treatments individually on the above soils?
3. What was the effect of calcium on the viability of *Bacillus radici-cola* on the soybeans and on the nodulation of soybeans grown in solution?
4. What was the possibility of salt treatments of soybean seeds at the time of inoculation in order to increase nodulation?

Albrecht commented on these studies. "Professor Miller wanted me to put bacteria into the soil and I had to make the point that it took more than a fancy bull to produce a calf. The cow also had something to do with it."

By the early 1930s, soil-mining techniques in the United States had reached a climax point. As far east as Missouri the dust bowl fogged the sky. The east exhibited faltering production in terms of protein. The limestone connection beckoned!

"Your acidic clay is one that doesn't have the positive ions in it—hydrogen, calcium, potassium, magnesium, sodium and trace elements. I've got to have 65 percent of that clay's capacity loaded with calcium and 15 percent with magnesium. I have to have four times more calcium than magnesium.

See why we ought to lime the soil? We ought to lime it to where it feeds the plant calcium, not to fight the acidity."

The conventional ignorance concerning so-called sour soils almost goaded Albrecht into sermon-like activity. An explanation lies between the greens of the mustard family—kale, mustard greens, turnip tops and those of the goosefoot family (spinach, Swiss chard, beet greens and New Zealand spinach). The mustard group achieves nutritional superiority because of higher concentrations of calcium. Calcium papers reflect his wisdom. In *Eco-Farm, An Acres U.S.A. Primer*, I summarized and expanded the subject out of its airtight compartment. A general in-depth abstract concludes this foreword.

There are significant differences in vitamin C. Calcium is essential for body building and vitamin C is a protective food. Greens of the goosefoot family do not concentrate as much calcium as do the mustards. Moreover, calcium in the goosefoot family cannot be digestively utilized in the diet because of oxalic acid (oxalates). Oxalic acid combines with calcium to make nutrients in digestion. Indigestible oxalates are most pronounced when soils are neutral, when some soils have been corrected with calcium to a neutral point and not balanced as discussed by Albrecht.

Calcium has the leadership role among the nutrient ions that enter plant life. As protein concentrations rise, calcium concentrations also rise. With an increase in proteins, there is an increase in vitamins.

Soils limed to neutrality are nutrient deficient and contain toxic overloads of undesirable minerals. In the Albrecht equation a touch of acidity is preserved—about 10 percent. But the bottom line is that too much calcium or magnesium represent imbalance even if they adjust pH to the neutral point.

Other Albrecht lessons reveal that many high pH soils are built to neutral pH and beyond by sodium and potassium, yet remain calcium deficient. With these few words, I now invite the reader to join William A. Albrecht in his classroom via the agency of his papers on calcium. Each paper asks to be read more than once, for each reading seems to turn on the light on some fine point, some truth, some revealing Albrechtism.

— *Charles Walters, Editor*

CHAPTER 1

Lime Up to Date

FOR more than a generation now American farmers have been urged by soil scientists, agronomists and crop experts to apply some form of "limestone" to their soils to "sweeten" them. They were told that crops, with few exceptions, do better in an alkaline soil and, in theory, "sweeter" the soil, the bigger the crops. Farmers learned a new term, "pH"; they the pH of their soils and applied limestone for the sole purpose of reducing acidity. In the last few years some scientists have questioned this, insisting limestone should be applied primarily a plant food, and that some acidity necessary to all plant growth. The time has come to get up-to-date on our thinking about lime because the yardstick by which we measure the need for lime has proven to be inadequate. For some crops, such as clover and alfalfa, the reduction of acidity is desirable, but complete alkalinity is not. And we should think of limestone as a plant nutrient rather than as a sweetener.

Chemistry Review

To understand why this is true let's review our high school chemistry under the chapter on calcium, or limestone, as it is known agriculturally.

Limestone is actually a hard salt, the carbonate of calcium. We can make it in the laboratory quite simply by dropping a piece of metallic calcium into a jar containing carbonic acid (soda water), or by putting our breath, which contains carbonic acid, through lime water. Nature created an abundant supply of calcium carbonate, but she left us no instruction for its use on the soil. Consequently for many years as farmers we have used limestone with the wrong reason in mind.

Limestone and "lime" are not exactly alike. "Lime" is the oxide of metallic calcium, but since limestone and lime act so much alike in soil, what we say here applies to lime as well as to limestone. Limestone and lime are "Double Dealers". They do two things, and they do both at the same time. First, limestone puts calcium, a plant food, into the soil; second, limestone diminishes acidity or produces alkalinity. The putting of calcium into soil is a vital, necessary, and intelligent thing to do, but the so-called "sweetening" of the soil, or *complete* removal of acidity, is, in almost every instance, a wrong and costly thing to do. Limestone has the habit of removing acidity or adding alkalinity to the soil. We cannot break limestone of this habit of reducing acidity while supplying calcium.

At this point it will help us to understand the real purpose of limestone applications if we remember that farmers have always used limestone for its alkalizing ability, whereas credit should have been given to the calcium portion of the limestone for its crop-nourishing ability. We grow crops, but not just for the sake of the crops; we grow crops for the sake of their food value to human beings and animals which live on those crops. Humans and animals cannot live without calcium and the products it helps plants manufacture; therefore, we must see to it that our crops have the opportunity to absorb from the soil as much calcium as they require.

Let us get back to the discussion of the bad feature of too much limestone—that business about adding too much alkalinity to soil. When limestone comes in contact with the water in the soil the calcium portion of the limestone unites with that water to form what is commonly known as "limewater". Limewater is chemically known as calcium hydroxide with the formula $Ca(OH)_2$. The carbonate portion forms carbonic acid with the formula H_2CO_3, but this is not so active in the water, and allows the $(OH)_2$ of the limewater to dominate the activities. Water, in contact with soil, has the formula $H(OH)$, and thus we begin to notice a similarity between (OH) in the soil water and the (OH) in the limewater. We have learned that acidity and alkalinity exist at the same time. If we have more acidity than we have alkalinity, we say that our soil is on the acid side. If we have more alkalinity than we have acidity, we can say that our soil is on the alkaline side.

That pH Scale

Soil water, with its formula of $H(OH)$, is nicely balanced with one positively-charged H and one negatively-charged (OH). But when we begin to put limestone on the soil, the calcium portion of the limestone begins to associate itself with more and more of the (OH) portion of the soil water. The carbonate part is not so active; thus our soil becomes more and more alkaline. This is another way of saying that our soil becomes less and less acid. But where is the dividing line? Where is that point at which the soil stops being acid, and becomes alkaline, and vice-versa? In order to answer this question a scale was designed.

This scale begins at the figure 7.00 and runs in two directions. From 7.00 down to zero the soil becomes more and more acid; from 7.00 up to 14.00 the soil becomes more and more alkaline. The figure 7.00 indicates a neutral soil, which means that the soil contains exactly the same number of the alkaline OH units as it contains acid H units. The scale is called the pH scale.

Limestone does something else when, as a calcium carbonate it is added to soil. It forms some carbonic acid (soda water) as was pointed out above, but carbonic acid is a very unstable acid. It falls apart in a few minutes to lose part to the atmosphere, and this is why your glass of soda pop tastes flat if you let it get warm or if you spend more than five minutes drinking it. Thus we believe that attention should be focused upon the dangers of too much of the alkaline qualities of limestone, and action should be taken immediately to guard against bringing on too much alkalinity, for acidity in soil is vital and as necessary as a carburetor is necessary to an automobile engine.

All acids contain hydrogen; the "business end" of any acid is hydrogen. The chemical symbol for hydrogen is H, and the H in the formula of water, H(OH), is hydrogen. This is the element that is most active in taking the place of other elements to push them out into action. It pushes its way into a crowded molecule, other elements are forced out, and become food for plants.

Acidity Can be Added, Too

Now that we know that we need limestone in our soil, and we know that limestone has a bad habit of making soils less acid and more alkaline, what can be done about preventing or offsetting the undesirable alkalinity? There are several methods of accomplishing this necessary task. Some are quick; others are slow. Some are costly; others are cheap. But no matter what method we select we will be offsetting or preventing alkalinity by adding or by keeping some acidity, and when we keep or add acidity we are keeping or adding the vital hydrogen contained in that acid.

Prevention is simple. In putting limestone on the soil we must not add carbonate or alkalinity equivalent to the acidity originally present. We must keep some acidity on hand there. If excessive limestone is added to the point where no acidity exists, then acid must be restored to the soil. Theoretically, this could be accomplished by spraying dilute sulphuric acid on the soil. A slow method is to spread powdered commercial sulphur. Sulphur will do its work regardless of whether it is plowed under or left upon the surface. The sulphur slowly but constantly forms sulphurous acid, which is a milder acid than sulphuric acid; since we are after acid in our soil, to offset the alkalinity of the limestone, acid is what we are getting. Another method is the substitution of "gypsum" (calcium sulphate) for limestone. This salt will provide our soil with calcium, and at the same time will prevent the soil from going over on the alkaline side of the pH scale. Gypsum costs more than limestone, but gypsum needs no supplement to prevent the soil from becoming neutral or too alkaline. However, it is necessary to bring out the important point that limestone cannot be used excessively and successfully by itself; so let's get on with the story, and we will see why limestone, alone, will put your farm on the shelf.

The type of agricultural lime added to the soil is also very important. Calcitic limestone, for example, has the tendency to make magnesium unavailable to plants. The use of dolomitic limestone gets around this fault and also supplies magnesium, a very necessary plant food.

Minerals Released by H Action

Acid soils are soils which contain more of the acid H units than they contain of the alkaline (OH) units. Soil contains minerals, and in the minerals are metals such as potassium and phosphorus, cobalt, manganese, magnesium, copper, zinc, and iodine. These metals, weathered out of minerals by nature, are packed into the clay of the soil. Metals and hydrogen do not get along well together. In school we are taught that the hydrogen in acids will go after a metal, but what really happens is that a metal goes after the hydrogen in that acid. So, when we have an ample amount of the H units in our soil we can be certain that the clay will make a "deal" with the H units, and the deal is to exchange a unit of metal for a unit of H. At this point the metal is no longer bound to the clay. It "goes on the road", we might say, in search of a home. It has been pushed out to become active, and is thereby available for absorption by the root of the plant.

But look at what happens when our soil is neutral, which means there are just as many (OH) units in the soil as there are H units. Each H unit has a very strong liking for an (OH) unit, and since there are enough (OH) units to keep every H tied up, no deals for metals can be made with the clay, and no metals come out of the clay; therefore, the roots of the crops do not get as much metal as they need to feed themselves, and to feed humans and animals. Such crops are "empty" foods, because they cannot make sufficient protein, enzymes, vitamins and other essentials we have not yet discovered.

When our soil goes over to the alkaline side there is a surplus of (OH) units and even though the roots of a crop have the wonderful ability to excrete H units for the purpose of helping the plant to get metals into it, the plant starves because as fast as the roots excrete the H units, these H units are grabbed by the excess (OH) units to give nothing but water. Because limestone has the ability to create (OH) alkaline units, and because limestone puts vital, important calcium into the soil, the time has come for every farmer to pay close attention to the degree of pH of his soil whenever he applies limestone or lime to his soil, lest he make his soil neutral or alkaline, and the calcium he applied be less active than when acidity accompanies that calcium. An acid soil is a desirable condition. It is worth repeating here that acidity in soil is a fundamental and important principle upon which nature does her best to grow crops filled with food value.

High soil acidity, by *nature*, means low soil fertility. Consequently, it means also low-quality yields, and usually also low-quantity yields. Adding some single element of fertility may bring about high-quantity yields, but only plenty and well-balanced fertility additions to a soil left acid and not alkalized *completely* by that treatment can give high-quality as well as high-quantity yields. These are the facts that call for the help of soil testing. It is the soils of ample and balanced fertility *with some acidity* that make a high-quantity of high-quality products.

Litmus paper has been used, and still is being used, to tell whether soil is more acid than alkaline, and vice-versa. But litmus paper will not tell you how MUCH more acid than alkaline; neither will litmus paper tell you how MUCH more alkaline than acid. When your soil is tested an accurate pH testing kit which will show the difference between a pH of 5.5 and 5.6 and 5.7 and 5.8 and 5.9, etc. should be used. These close ranges are important because they will show you exactly what degree of acid is present to ward off the alkaline quality of limestone.

To apply limestone, or lime, in such quantities that we reach the point of excessive alkalinity, is very much like buying a new automobile, and then taking off the wheels to prevent the automobile from wearing out. It is true that the automobile will not wear out, but you have labored for something which will be of little use to you. Likewise, when we put limestone on soil, year after year, to the degree of bringing about the alkalinity of that soil, we are unknowingly reducing the yield, lower and lower, year after year, until we are operating at a loss instead of at a profit, and this is what we mean by the statement, "Limestone, by itself, will put your farm upon the shelf."

Accurate Soil Tests Needed

This new approach to limestone application will result in some radical changes in farm practices. A soil testing service much more accurate than is available at present is one of the first recommendations. A second must is to apply just the right amount of lime for the crop to be planted. For alfalfa and clovers and other crops that like soil on the sweet side, a careful balance should be the goal, a balance which will leave some acidity along with the alkalinity. It may be that after the acidity is reduced, a change to gypsum should be made, or sulphur or other acid-producing material should be applied.

The main thing to remember is that too much limestone can be applied, either at one application, or that constant applications year after year, without offsetting the alkalinity, can accumulate too much and the soil will stop, or diminish, in production.

We might sum up the functions of limestone thus: (1) To provide plant foods, (2) to *reduce* the excess acidity for the benefit of a few special crops.

Some soils are so acid that a form of limestone should be applied to reduce the acidity as well as to supply plant food. However, a soil may be acid and still have a high exchangeable calcium, in which case it would be unnecessary and useless to add calcium except as a plant food.

It is difficult for a person who has only a layman's knowledge of chemistry to understand how acidity and alkalinity can exist side by side in the same soil, since it is implied that one neutralizes the other. Pure water is an example of this; it contains exactly the same number of H units as it does (OH) units. There are many soils with a pH as high as 7.6 which raise fine crops. The Red River Valley in Minnesota and the Black Land soils of Texas and Alabama are alkaline and they grow excellent crops.

In these soils, however, there is sufficient acidity present for good plant growth. It is when soils are excessively acid or when not enough alkalinity exists, that calcium should be added to supply the alkalinity or reduce the acidity.

Few soils can be over-limed for field crops. Truck gardens and greenhouses sometimes are over-limed, but this is a question of imbalance rather than acidity destruction. The goal towards which every farmer should aim is the proper balance of acidity and alkalinity for the crops he is growing and the application of the proper amount of calcium for plant food.

CHAPTER 2

Limestone—The Foremost of Natural Fertilizers

LIMING THE SOIL has long been an agricultural art. It has now become a modern scientific agricultural practice. Putting ground limestone on the soil may well be viewed as a case of an old practice that has now come to a newer scientific understanding. It is only recently that scientific facts have given us comprehension of the soil and plant relationships that underlie the services which the limestone renders for the crop.

Limestone has always been associated with the production of leguminous plants. They in turn have always been considered good feed for young and growing livestock. We are just coming around to realize that the calcium supplied by limestone is a fertilizer, as the ancients probably also considered it. Calcium is, in fact, the foremost one of all the nutrient elements for animals and man that can be put into the soil to help it grow bigger crops, giving us better nutrition through them.

We use limestone to supply calcium, rather than to remove soil acidity. Acid, or sour soils, have long been known to be low in productivity. Seemingly like spoiled food about which we say, "It is poor food because it has soured." So we have come to consider "soured" soils as poor soils. This reasoning has appeared sound because we found that limestone, which reduces the soil acidity, also makes better crops. As a consequence of the observation of these two simultaneous results, namely, reduced soil acidity and better crops from applying limestone, our soils have been widely tested for their degree of acidity in the belief that the acidity was the cause of the soil's low productivity. Limestone has been the ammunition in the war on acid soils.

During our belligerency toward soil acidity, a very important fact escaped us. It was the recently recognized one, namely, that while the carbonate part of the limestone is removing the acidity, the calcium going with the carbonate is serving to nourish the crops. Delicate electrical instruments and refined chemical tests helped us to detect and measure the acidity, or the activity of the hydrogen ions that is the cause of it. Since hydrogen is the most active of all elements, and since there are more hydrogen than any other ions in the universe, we might well expect this to be the first one of which the activity would come under such accurate measurement. This attention which was focused so sharply on soil acidity resulted in disregard of the declining and deficient soil fertility.

Unfortunately, neither calcium nor any other plant nutrients have as yet submitted themselves to any such minute evaluations. As a result of these facts, the hydrogen ion or soil acidity has held prominence. This prominence resulted because hydrogen could be easily detected and conveniently measured, and not because of knowledge of its activities in the soils or in the plants. Its presence in the soil did not call attention to the absence there of the calcium, the magnesium, the potassium, and the other plant nutrients, all of which are more deficient as hydrogen is more abundantly present.

It was necessary, therefore, to use the physiology of the legume plants and to study their growth and chemical composition when they were produced on soils of which the acidity was nearly neutralized by limestone, or calcium carbonate, in contrast to these properties of those grown on soils likewise given the plant assay method that revealed the forms of calcium sulphate and calcium chloride, neither of which reduces the soil acidity. It was this plant assay method that revealed the fact that soil acidity is in reality a deficiency in soil fertility. It is a soil situation wherein the hydrogen of no nutrient service to the plants has come into combination with the clay to take the place of several nutrients that are there in productive soils. This method demonstrated also that legumes will grow on a soil that is acid provided it supplies amply the fertility or stock of plant nutrients needed.

Unwittingly we have carried calcium as a fertilizer along when we were applying its carbonate as the remedy for soil acidity. The same has also happened for our unrecognized benefits in "correcting the acidity of commercial fertilizers." More fortunately, however, the dolomitic, rather than the pure calcium limestone, has been the "neutralizer for fertilizer acidity." Consequently, both calcium and magnesium have been coming along with the nitrogen, phosphorus and potassium (N, P, K) in fertilizers, though probably more because dolomite has higher "neutralizing value" than because of the planned desire to add these two extra nutrients for which no additional fertilizer charges are made. This is a case where calcium has been going ahead of—while going along with—the other fertilizers, even though it was not regarded as such in the designing of commercial fertilizers.

The fact that calcium has been the major component of a fertilizer, like superphosphate for example, has reacted to the pronounced benefit of lateritic or red soils so common in the South. These soils have little absorbing or exchanging capacity. Consequently they do not absorb or retain much hydrogen or acidity. There has been no "war on soil acidity" in the South. There is, however, a serious need for calcium as a fertilizing help in better animal and human nutrition coming from the soils and as a help for those plants which synthesize the proteins and other chemical complexes of higher food values. While tropical soils do not invite the use of limestone in a war on their acidity, they do demand limestone to supply calcium as a fertilizer in its own right.

Ash analyses of plants leave confusion about the services of calcium. Unfortunately for the services which mineral nutrients coming from the soil render in the plants, the chemical analyses ignite them to destroy their organic combinations. Such procedures measure mainly the percentage of the ash constituents in the dry plant tissue. This gives no concept of the many organic compounds of plant construction into which the calcium, for example, may have been combined, or in the syntheses of which this nutrient plays an important part. It leaves mainly the idea that the plant hauls either a large or a small load of calcium and other minerals from the soil.

Ash analysis is no measure of the functions performed by the chemical elements. It fails to point out in what period of plant growth the calcium and other minerals are taken from the soil in major or minor amounts. It has not given calcium its decided importance in the very early life of many plants. It has not emphasized the help of calcium in moving other nutrients into the root of the plants, which Professor A. C. True of the University of Pennsylvania has called a "synergistic effect." It has given undue importance to potassium, for example, as a fertilizer for potatoes because of emphasis mainly on the potato tubers. It has left unemphasized the facts, (a) that the tops of the potato plants carry more calcium than does a legume crop like red clover, and (b) that lime may be necessary as a fertilizer for potatoes more often than commonly surmised. It is such incomplete chemical analyses, with their attention to the ash constituents only rather than to the more complete organic compounds, that have given the confusion about potato scab in relation to soil acidity, instead of its connection with deficient nutrients, even with respect to calcium.

Ash analyses may measure the mineral elements of soil origin, but such measurements fail to mean much when the more efficient function by the plant in synthesizing important compounds is not necessarily dependent on a larger amount of one single plant nutrient taken from the soil. Unfortunately, such chemical measures do not inform us as to what constitutes the properly-balanced supply of all nutrients at any time, nor how that balance must be modified for highest plant efficiencies in different periods of growth. It is such ash analyses that have failed to classify calcium as a fertilizer of even greater deficiency on many soils than are phosphorus and potassium. Yet both of these latter two are so common in and emphasized by the mixed goods of commercial soil treatments, the calcium contents of which get no mention on the label or in the sale.

Soil acidity must be removed by fertilizing with calcium, plus other nutrient elements. That soil acidity should have come under condemnation by the recent scientific attacks on it seems strange, now that we look at the pattern of life on the globe and find it most concentrated, not on the neutral and alkaline soils, but rather on the acid soils bordering those that are calcareous. Agriculture has reached its high food output by the help of grazing animals. Grasses as feed for grazing animals are most common and most nutritious on soil developed under moderate annual rainfalls. Grasses grow under a distribution of rainfall which leaves a droughty period of the growing season that spells destruction of the trees but not permanent extinction of the grasses. Such rainfall distributions develop acid soils but do not leach the soils of their adsorbed supply of calcium and other bases. Such rainfalls gave us the prairies that are acid soils but that are also stocked with plenty of calcium, as was the virgin soil of the corn belt. Man and his companion animals for his support have multiplied most rapidly and concentrated themselves most highly, not on soils that are neutral, but rather on those that are acid in their reaction. Yet we have recently gone forward under the belief that soil acidity is highly detrimental and should be completely neutralized. Scarcely have we cherished the thought that soil acidity might even be beneficial, as the locations of higher concentrations of populations and their better agricultural support suggest.

When soils are a temporary rest stop of rocks and minerals on their way to the sea and to solution under increasing rainfalls encouraging their faster travel in that direction, we must credit carbonic acid as the natural agency that is mainly responsible for the rock and mineral decomposition.

When carbonic acid breaks down the rock, another kind of acid, namely, a soil acid must of necessity be the result. Nature has long been using acid reagents to decompose rocks and minerals of which the end products are nourishment for vegetation. But it has only recently been recognized that the soil acids or clay acids in our productive soils are the agencies that are weathering rocks and minerals to release their nutrient contents to the absorbing clay and thereby for exchange to the growing crops. Soil acidity is an integral part of the chemical mechanisms within the soil by which the mineral reserves are broken down to fertilize the crops.

Surely, then, we must recognize in these facts the need for the soil to be acid. At the same time we must recognize the necessity for that soil to contain mineral reserves, among which limestone is the foremost. This must be there to provide calcium for plant nourishment while this stone is being decomposed on contact with the soil acid. In such a concept of the function of soil acidity, its partial removal is a means of fertilizing the soil and crop with available calcium through the service of this acidity in breaking it out of the limestone rock. Viewed in this light, the application of limestone to the soil is a case of applying calcium as a mineral fertilizer for its mobilization from inert rock form to active form on the clay by means of the acidity of the soil. Surely, then, we would not remove from the soil this mobilizing agent and thereby lose its valuable services.

Can we use too much limestone on the soil? Now that the soil acidity is considered a means of decomposing the soil minerals to make their fertilizing contents available to plants, it is evident that a productive soil is one which contains not only hydrogen or acidity, but one which is also supplied with the elements that are nutrients or fertility. Just as our application of limestone is a means of letting the soil acidity mobilize the stone's contents of calcium, so many other minerals with fertility contents may be applied to the soil and made available by the soil acidity. Rock phosphate is an example. Other minerals may come into use later as fertilizers under this same category. It was from a mixture of such rocks and minerals that soils were originally developed to form the clay residues and to load these with the many nutrients that give our productive soils.

When the plant roots are exchanging their hydrogen or acidity to the clay of the soil for its fertility contents, we may well visualize the fact that they might remove these so completely that the soil becomes infertile and highly acid. Then if we should put limestone on such an acid soil until all of its acidity is removed, would this make it a highly productive soil because it was now neutral, and because that neutrality was obtained by loading it with nothing but calcium, of which the associated carbonate in the limestone had neutralized the acid after the calcium had displaced it from the clay? If a soil is neutral but completely saturated with only one element—even if it be a plant nutrient ever so extensively taken by plants and animals as food—is that soil going to be any more productive than when completely saturated with the non-nutrient hydrogen that makes it very acid? Alkaline soils are not necessarily productive merely because they are not acid. They are often deficient in some elements of fertility, just as acid soils are deficient in some. Thus a very acid soil made completely neutral by liming as the only treatment becomes a hazardous condition in that the acidity, or hydrogen, on coming originally into the soil, displaced too completely many other nutrient elements as well as the calcium. Very acid soils, then, need other fertilizers besides the calcium we provide by applying the limestone.

Calcium has been the foremost deficiency in fertility on extensive soil areas. That limestone has been the most effective fertilizer is indicated by its use to the total amounts of more than ten million tons in the state of Missouri, for example, in less than ten years. The amounts of all other fertilizers used has not been one-fifth that of the limestone during their maximum use. But now that the calcium shortage in the soil has been remedied to strengthen that one weak line, the next item representing the next weakness will need to be strengthened.

On soils limed now for some years, the potassium deficiencies are being indicated more commonly by crop symptoms. Corn stalks are not so strong and may break over. The ears of the corn are less solid or more chaffy where heavy liming and consequent reduction in the degree of soil acidity are bringing on deficiencies of manganese. This deficiency in the crop may possibly reach greater importance as liming is more generously used, and when we recall that perosis of chicks is caused by deficiencies of manganese in their ration. Manganese, commonly considered among the minor nutrients, takes on major importance if its deficiency in the soil can reflect troubles in the animals by way of the crops they consume.

Boron and iron, too, are demobilized when the acidity of the soil is much reduced. Alfalfa, root crops, some vegetables and other crops require more boron than may be found available in a soil that has been given heavy dosages of limestone. Whether the excessive carbonate or the excessive calcium is responsible for the trouble has not yet been learned in all these cases. Nevertheless, the trouble is prevented by caution against believing that if a little limestone is good, much more of it will be better. Calcium used alone is not able to offset the shortage of other nutrient elements. Plant nutrition demands calcium in generous amounts for its direct services, and also for many benefits it exercises in mobilizing other nutrients. Nevertheless, soil acidity is also required. It, too, has much mobilizing power for nutrients toward which excessive calcium and neutrality of the soil exercise quite the opposite or a demobilizing effect.

Calcium must lead the parade for other fertilizers. Calcium plays a prominent role in—and is always associated with—protein production by plants. Amino acids, the building blocks of proteins, are not synthesized by animals and humans. They are the synthetic product of plants and micro-organisms but most commonly by those kinds of these producers for which liberal supplies of lime are requisite. Animals and man are always in the struggle for proteins. On the contrary they obtain carbohydrates more easily. On the calcareous soils of the prairies, rather than on the lime-deficient soils cleared of their forests, do we find production of animals less difficult. Animals are grown on the former and fattened on the crops from the latter. By the same token do we have poor reproduction and growth of animals on soils that, through crop removal and neglect, have been depleted of their calcium and the other fertility elements that are associated with it in fertile soils. Lime is first on the list of needs for soils that are to be kept high in animal production.

It was on those soils containing acid properties in the surface horizon, but calcium in their deeper layers, that the bison originally supported himself. It is on these same soils that production of beef and mutton rose to the magnitudes of which we boast. It is on the soils of greater deficiencies in calcium and other fertility constituents where the hog of mainly fat output is the king. Humans, too, may be fitted into the soil picture with more tooth troubles on calcium-deficient soils, as the draftees for the Navy demonstrated. Calcium, which constitutes 40% of limestone, makes this rock an important fertilizer for the soil in service to man as well as to plants and animals.

Limestone is no longer merely a soil conditioner in terms of the control of the degree of soil acidity. It is the provider of the foremost element for fertilizing effects. It is the mobilizer of other nutrients. It is the catalyzer in the process of synthesizing proteins. It has been delivering these services ever since it was a part of the art of agriculture, dating back some 40 centuries. But, unfortunately, only recently have we realized that calcium is only one of the essential nutrients needed by plants and that many others must come along with it for most efficient crop production. Nevertheless, when animal and human nutrition are taken as the goals of crop production, calcium heads the list of the nutrient elements and stands out as the one demanded in largest amounts from the soil. In terms of human foods for their quality dependent on the soil, limestone is the contributor of calcium and is the synergistic agent for other nutrients; which services make it the foremost of the fertilizers.

CHAPTER 3

Limestone—A Fertilizer

MAKING LIMING PAY BETTER ought to have more attention now that we are using this soil treatment to feed calcium to plants rather than to fight soil acidity. This shift in purpose of liming points to possibilities in reducing the labor and financial load. Serving the single year needs of a crop for lime to make it better feed for livestock ought to be more encouraging than trying to remove completely a soil condition arising from many years of soil neglect.

Better feeding values in forages and healthier animals on soils treated with lime are recognized now that we have learned more about the services of calcium, or lime, to plants. In evaluating feeds as they supply proteins, carbohydrates, minerals, and vitamins one might not readily comprehend how calcium is connected with any of these items except, possibly, the minerals. But we know that calcium goes right along with nitrogen, the key item in protein. More nitrogen goes into plant protein only as more calcium is supplied by the soil. Then, too, phosphorus, which like nitrogen is also a part of the protein, is moved into the crop through addition of lime to the soil. This helps us to understand how calcium makes protein, even if it doesn't come through as a chemical part of this nutrient complex. Lime in legumes is the force that moves phosphorus from the soil and nitrogen from the air, so the plant can run not only its protein and mineral factories, but also can be a better factory for possibly other complexes, such as vitamins, which make the big differences in the feed from limed soils when its full value is reflected in the animals that eat it.

We are so accustomed to thinking of legumes taking nitrogen from the air that we can scarcely imagine that they could fail in this process. Careful chemical studies show that unless they get lime liberally they don't use air nitrogen. Can you imagine that soybeans could grow to be almost two feet high without taking nitrogen from the air? Would you believe that even some of the nitrogen and minerals in the seed were lost back to the soil by this crop? Under such soil conditions the resulting legume forage crop has less minerals and less protein in it than was in the seed at planting time. This has happened on soil too low in lime. Only when liberal lime allotment was offered by the soil and taken by the crop were the minerals from the soil and the nitrogen from the air moved into the crop to make it a real feed in place of so much woody packing for the poor animal's paunch. Lime must get into the plant and serve there as a tool in fabricating the complex substances the plants make out of nitrogen, phosphorus and other plant nutrients.

Thus, legumes can be feeds, not merely because their pedigree labels them as such. Rather they are nutritious according as they have calcium within their plant tissue to help carry out their plant functions, and not necessarily because the lime application has corrected soil acidity. Feeding plants lime makes it possible for them to feed the animals with forage of nutritious value.

Young plants must get lime early in their life. This was demonstrated in studies by Dr. H. F. Rhoades, now at the University of Nebraska. When soybeans were started ten days in limed sand and transplanted to soil, they grew much more successfully than those transplanted from unlimed sand. Young plants without lime often die and look as if they had been hit by a fungus to make them "damp off." Raising the delivery of calcium to the plant removed this "disease," so when plants are "taken" by fungus disease it may not be so much the epidemic as it is a lack of vigor.

Have we been thinking enough of the health of the plant as it depends on our supplying its needs in soil fertility, of which calcium is the foremost item? Good feeding of the plants enables them to resist disease. Haven't we possibly been throwing seed away, complaining about the failure of plants to fight off disease; haven't we been purchasing disease-combating chemicals in place of recognizing this situation as indicating a fertility so low, first in lime, then in phosphorus and even other nutrients, that the soil delivery of those nutrients is too slow in the spring? In such cases the seed supply presumed to carry the plant into the warmer part of the growing season becomes exhausted before the soil delivery of nutrients is in higher gear. In place of taking up a fight against plant disease, perhaps we might well look to lime for help in "eliminating" weak plants by making them healthy and thus "immune" to disease because they are well fed.

CHAPTER 4

Lime the Soil to Correct its Major Fertility Deficiencies

LIMING THE SOIL, so that this practice can build up the fertility reserve of calcium (and magnesium), has gone unappreciated all too long. Instead, we have persisted in the erroneous belief that the benefits to crops from liming result from the reduction of soil acidity by the applied carbonate. We are gradually realizing that our productive soils, under annual rainfalls abundant enough to give larger crop yields, must contain more of calcium (and of magnesium) in the exchangeable (available) form than any other fertility element. The laboratory gadgets for measuring soil acidity in degree—and in total—have absorbed our interest so completely, and for all too long a time, that they kept us from recognizing the services by limestone in the nutrition of the crops in the field. We failed to connect the activities and ratios of the fertility elements, exchangeable and active, in the soil with the nutrition of the plant. We were oblivious to the facts (a) that calcium is one of the elements which the growing plants must find in the soil very early, and (b) that it seems to serve in setting up the conditions by which the other nutrient elements and compounds are mobilized into the roots for crop growth. We are gradually coming around, however, to see that by liming the soil we are fertilizing it with the two major nutrient elements; namely, calcium and magnesium. Accordingly, this practice is taking on a new classification and a greater significance.

Now that we view most of the plant nutrition processes as a case of the positively charged elements held on the clay exchanging from there for the non-nutrient hydrogen, or acid, coming from the plant root, the extensive soil testing is pointing out that crop production requires larger amounts of the exchangeable calcium in the humid soils than of any other fertility element. Calcium is especially important in the production of proteins. These are the only compounds capable (a) of giving cell multiplication or growth, (b) of protecting the plants against disease, etc., and (c) of reproducing them by seeds. It is required by legumes for this reason more than for the "suitable degree of soil acidity" of which the carbonate of calcium might have been the producer. Lime is important because its calcium (and magnesium) nourish the crops.

In order to appreciate just how much exchangeable calcium a productive soil contains, let us consider the soil test results from a good silt loam, a corn-belt soil like the Marshall of north Missouri or Iowa. This has a total exchange capacity of near 18 milligram equivalents. This figure tells us that such a soil could hold by adsorption, and for possible exchange, 18 milligrams of active hydrogen—a non-nutrient and acid—per 100 grams of soil, or the equivalent in other positively charged ions. This would be 18 pounds of hydrogen per 100,000 of soil or 360 pounds of hydrogen per plowed acre of 2,000,000 pounds. For good crop production, it is considered well that about 75% of the soil's exchange capacity should be taken by calcium, and from 7 to 10% by magnesium. These make up the maximum two of all the nutrient elements held by the adsorptive and exchange capacity of the soil, or nearly 85% of the total capacity. For potassium, the next item in order, the figure is 2 to 5%. This leaves but 10 to 16% of the soil's exchange capacity for all the other necessary positive ions of nutrient services to the crops.

In terms of pounds per acre of soil of plow depth, or 6 to 7 inches deep, these percentage saturation values as replacements in equivalents for hydrogen or acidity represent (a) 5400 pounds of calcium, (b) 302 to 432 of magnesium, and (c) 280 to 700 pounds of potassium. Even with these amounts occupying the soil's absorbing power, it would have capacity remaining to hold the other nutrients in ample amounts, especially the trace elements, and then also some capacity for hydrogen, or acidity, as the favorable soil condition. Plants are nourished better in the presence of some soil acidity. Let us note that the amount of exchangeable calcium in this series is more than ten times the maximum of the nearest amount of any one of the others. By finding such calcium values in terms of the requirements for plant nutrition, we begin to get some basic concept of the importance of liming for the calcium supplied to feed the crop rather than for the carbonate incorporated to fight the soil acidity.

All of this may well serve to classify the liming of our humid soils into the category of farm operations more technical than those of merely dumping any kind of limestone on the land, and of proceeding under the belief that "If a little is good, more will be better." It puts liming into the group of skilled operations calling for a clear-cut diagnosis of the soil's condition before treatment is undertaken. Testing the particular soil for its shortages in calcium and magnesium in order to build up its supplies of these by either a calcic or dolomitic stone, or both, makes liming a prescribed nourishment of the crops. This is a treatment different from one of using the carbonate of any stone, regardless of whether calcic or dolomitic, merely to reduce the degree, or the total, of soil acidity.

Viewed from the vantage point of plant nutrition, liming the soil becomes the application of fertility elements of quantities nearly ten to twenty times as large as any of the other elements commonly used in commercial fertilizers. It becomes then a major fertilizing performance. Surely under such large amount applied according to soil test, and under the concept of lime as our foremost fertilizer, the business of limestone production and distribution should feel itself playing the major role in maintaining the fertility and productivity of our soils. Unfortunately for the liming of the soils, as for the other fertility restorative treatments, its services in food production for all of us, rather than for profit only to the farmer, are not yet recognized nor appreciated. The 85% of us in the urban portion of our population do not yet feel any obligation to help resources coming to us gratis from out of the rural area. We are set up in urban commercial businesses and industries of which the laws, economics and taxation procedures are so formulated under carefully lobbied legislation that our capital investments in them are self-perpetuating. Even for the minerals or rocks taken out of the limestone quarry, for example, the owner-investor may be allowed a depreciation, or depletion, figure as high as 15% of the income. For the owner-investor in an oil well, it may be a larger amount. The capital investment in these mineral businesses is soon recovered.

But for the mineral fertility taken out of the soil and delivered in the crops to the urban population without charge for it, there is as yet no economist or authority on taxation suggesting the justice of a depletion allowance to the landowner, or investor in that kind of real estate, for the perpetuation of his capital in his farming business. His investment in the minerals in the soils for the food production for all of us is being liquidated gradually under an economic thinking (or the lack of it) which contends that the farmer is thereby taking a profit. On the contrary, he is compelled to throw his financial, and our national, security by installments into the bargain every time he makes a sale of his products. Those of us on the urban receiving end of that transaction get those installments gratis and flush them into the sea. We are parties to the crime of soil fertility exploitation, but yet are crying against the rising costs of living. We are slow to see that such short sightedness (or absence of any sightedness) in our economic, agricultural, and other policies toward the fertility resources in the soil are undermining seriously our national security. All this is the more serious with a growing pressure on the soil's production potential by our own increasing population to say nothing of that by the rest of the world calling on us to share that potential with them.

Liming our soils deserves consideration as an operation undergirding our future security in food, and particularly those foods of high protein content. We have long known that lime is needed for legumes. We are slow to see that need as one for the production of protein, rather than the tonnage, yield of the crop. It is lime via that route that gets us our meat, milk and eggs. Viewed in this light, one cannot escape the question whether we dare expect the farmer to continue liquidating his fertility assets under the false concept of taking a profit and at the same time ask him to purchase large amounts of calcium and magnesium to aggravate his rate of liquidation all the more. Isn't it about time that as a basic agricultural policy we design the required machinery of economics and taxation to guarantee the self-perpetuation of the farmer's fertility capital which must feed all of us, both urban and rural?

Perhaps now that the fertility restoration by liming the soil is moving itself into the more exact category of soil chemistry for the nutrition of our plants, our animals and ourselves, should not the maintenance of the soil fertility and thereby of agricultural industry be interpreted by the same views in economics and taxation as those prevailing in other industries?

Perhaps we can bring about self-perpetuation of our soil fertility capital under the agricultural business in the rural areas in the same manner as perpetuation prevails for monetary capital under all businesses in our urban centers. If that situation is consummated, then liming the soil for calcium's sake will become big business by meeting the major needs in our soils; namely, lime and other fertility-restoring helps through which there can be guaranteed greater national food security for the future of all of us.

How shall we get lime or calcium into the plant and how much will it take? If all that we needed to use were that which gets into the crop, the figure would be less than 150 pounds of limestone a ton of clover hay produced, or less than two-thirds of this figure for a ton of soybean hay. We still can't get the lime into the plants by external application. We can't rub it on. It must come through the roots and they must take it from the soil. Delivery to the plant by this soil route is far more effective when a little of the soil is heavily loaded with lime, than if all of the surface soil has the limestone thinly scattered through it. Non-legumes such as bluegrass and redtop, as well as legumes, get their lime or calcium much more effectively if the upper two inches of soil are heavily dosed than if this same amount of limestone is mixed into the soil to a depth four times as great. Soil that has become sour has a tremendous power to hold lime. Plants can't take from it all the calcium it has. Studies to date give a low efficiency in lime recovery by plants unless the lime is used so as to saturate the soil in the root feeding zone. We are then forced to think of the practice that loads a little of the soil completely rather than all of the soil only partially, if the investment in limestone is to give us maximum return.

Studies of the practice of drilling limestone as a fertilizer have demonstrated that as little as 600 pounds on a soil needing more than 2 tons to sweeten it can establish sweet clover regularly in a rotation, though more limestone is better. The stand of sweet clover from drilled limestone holds out against winter-killing when that sown without limestone fails. The composition of the crop in terms of forage feed, and its effects as a soil-improver on the corn crop following, are all evidence that giving the crop its calcium without neutralizing the acidity is coming to be the real function of liming, and that economical and effective use of limestone means that it may well become a fertilizer in our thinking and in its use.

The art of liming is old. The science of it is new. Our science has led us astray and we are just now getting back. Nature always has been consistent in demonstrating the effects on plants by liming, but we have not been so consistent in explaining how these effects came about. We have looked to the wrong one of two things going on at the same time, as the real cause. When we use limestone we put on calcium combined as a carbonate. The carbonate neutralizes the soil acid. We have misconstrued this phenomenon as the cause of plant improvement when we should have been thinking of the addition of the calcium to the soil as the causative factor. Since sodium carbonate which removes the acid doesn't help the plants, while calcium chloride helps the plants but doesn't correct the acidity, we know now that liming is not a matter of fighting soil acidity but one of giving the plants calcium, their much-needed nutrient on our humid soils.

Thus, we can put liming into the fertilizer category and look to lesser applications per acre to serve its fertilizing function. But we must remember that nature has been taking the lime out of our soils for many years and a teaspoon dosage now won't do the work completely. We need to give many of our soils a heavy liming to offset this neglect and then we can go to regular lighter applications of 1,000 pounds an acre by drill in place of tons by spreader. As we go to using lime to feed plants so they can feed and protect our animals against starvation fevers, we see prospects of making this operation economical enough in money and labor costs so we will adopt it for use as regularly as we scatter a legume seeding.

CHAPTER 5

Blast Furnace Slag—
A Soil Builder

THE TERM *CONSERVATION* implies so much, and is taking on so much importance, that many folks are asking whether the soil might not be built up in fertility by using some of our industrial wastes. Numerous inquirers, interested in soil organic matter, have asked about city garbage, and septic tank sludges recently. Also, inquiries have come in concerning the value of blast furnace slags, the wastes from making steel. Such slags should be considered, though their variation in composition demands that one know something about them, and about the fineness of the materials. They are the residue from putting limestone, feldspars and other minerals in with the iron, to serve as fluxes, to purify it. The carbonate part of the limestone burns off to let it become quicklime, calcium silicate, or calcium phosphate, and other combinations possible at those high-furnace temperatures.

Slags are the rock-like residues dumped out after the molten iron has been drawn off. They are of fertilizer value, therefore, as carriers of phosphorus as well as calcium, with much of the latter in silicate form. In making some steels, manganese and other "trace" elements are often present, too, in this complex silicate rock. Sometimes the hot-rock is slaked and granulated by spraying with water, or it may be cooled and crushed. Either treatment aims to make it serve as a lime substitute for soil building.

Since, like many other original rocks, it is a silicate, therefore, it weathers down slowly. Its use is, then, a case of adding "sustaining" fertility to the soil rather than as a "starter" fertilizer. By its decomposition it adds not only calcium, some phosphorus, and "trace" elements, but also some silica. This is a clay-builder for the soil which would be helpful on sandy soil with "too little body," or not enough capacity for adsorption and exchange of nutrients to the plant roots. In the slow reaction, by this kind of lime, there may be more of a safety factor than when lime carbonate is too generously used under the belief that "if a little is good—more will be better." Since we lime soils now to supply calcium (and magnesium) as fertility, rather than to remove the acidity, the blast furnace slag has been shown by tests to be a good way of building up the soil in calcium (and magnesium). We can, therefore, practice conservation with profit by using this waste from the steel mills to build up the soil.

The fineness of the slag, into which it is ground—as for limestone— becomes a factor in its rate of being effective in crop nourishment. Also, its lime content (calcium and magnesium) must not be too low (preferably near 45%) if its effects are to follow more promptly after its application on the soil. These may be greater because it is not so much of a reagent to reduce the soil acidity as it is an active silicate providing calcium. Combined as a silicate rather than as a carbonate, it is more of a buffer in that it does not bring on, or permit, sudden shifts in the degree of soil acidity under heavier applications of it. In terms of the microbial life of the soil, its application is no shock because of any salting effect. Yet it stimulates (a) nitrification, as the change of ammonia nitrogen to the nitrate form; (b) the speedier oxidation of the carbon compounds; (c) the fixation of nitrogen by microbes living independently of the legume plant roots; and (d) all the other biological soil processes which distinguish a live soil from a dead one.

The employment of blast furnace slag as a fertilizer for the fields, and as an aid in composting, has been a practice in the art of agriculture by some folks long before recent scientific studies, tests, and partial commercialization gave its use greater sanction as a soil treatment—using this accumulating waste from the dump heaps of steel mills. We can use such material not only for true conservation but also with assurance that it builds up the soil for more nutritious crops.

CHAPTER 6

Drilling Powdered Agricultural Limestone

RECENT ADDITIONS TO our knowledge of sour soils and of the requirements for successfully growing legumes, indicate that the practice of applying two to three tons of coarsely ground limestone per acre in order to grow certain legume crops bids fair to undergo modification. The well-recognized necessity of liming the soil long in advance of seeding the legume crop is evidence of the sluggishness with which the common agricultural limestone becomes effective. Though relatively insoluble, limestone becomes much more soluble when extremely finely divided. The wider recognition of this fact and the fuller understanding of the functions of limestone in growing legumes are contributed to the impending changes in our liming practice. It has been recently emphasized that the one of the beneficial effects of liming is due to the fact that it supplies the element calcium. Sour soils present a problem not only because of their sourness, but also because of their deficiency in this plant nutrient. This suggests that the lime of the Romans and other ancient agricultural nations may well be called "forgotten fertilizer." Laboratory studies and field trials suggest the fitness of this newer cognomen, when they demonstrate that 300 pounds of finely ground limestone, drilled with the legume at seeding time, is enough to establish red clover, sweet clover, and other lime-loving plants on soils giving tests of two to three ton lime requirement. Farm trials in cooperation with the Missouri Agricultural Experiment Station, dating from 1926 and in gradually increasing number, suggest the wisdom of giving consideration to finely ground limestone as a fertilizer as well as a soil-sweetening agency.

Trials of limestone of different fineness have always indicated that the extremely fine material is the most important part of the limestone. Early experimental data by the Pennsylvania Agricultural Experiment Station and others following have pointed out that only when limestone is ground finely enough to pass a hundred-mesh sieve, does its effectiveness approach that of the soluble hydrated lime or quick lime. During the early development of the agricultural limestone market, the product offered was of widely varying fineness, for the problems of crushing the stone prohibited much else. It was a by-product. Now science points to the need for a specially prepared material whose effectiveness demands that it be very finely ground. At present with newer types of stone-crushing machinery which can produce at low cost a limestone ground finely enough to pass a hundred-mesh sieve, and with an entire rearrangement of our economic household in progress, we may well contemplate changes in our liming practice. We may well consider this powdered limestone ground finely enough for most of it to pass a hundred-mesh sieve as the standard product for general use. Its economy is an especially weighty argument for its adoption, since its rates of application are low enough to cut the cost of material to one-half, and the amount handled to one-tenth. Savings in cost of transportation, the convenience of handling a bagged product, and the reduction of the labor of application to a one-man basis instead of a community affair, will direct attention to this newer practice of using the powdered or hundred-mesh limestone.

The powdered limestone must be drilled into the soil. The old methods of spreading limestone broadcast will not suffice. By drilling it, certain areas within the soil are given a concentrated application from which the plant may take its supply of calcium, while adjacent soil areas are not subjected to the radical changes in chemical and biological conditions that would be created by complete neutralization of acidity. The fertilizer drill presents itself as the logical machine for drilling this fine limestone, and wherever it is available its use is recommended. The scarcity of fertilizer drills in some sections of the country raises the question, "Why not drill it with an ordinary grain drill?" The problem of distributing limestone powdered finely enough to pass a hundred-mesh sieve has recently been given some attention in the hope of learning something about its drillability, and the possibility of drilling it with a regular grain drill, as well as the fertilizer drill. The tests reported in this paper indicate that the ordinary grain drill may help solve the distribution problem created by the change from coarsely to finely ground limestone in agricultural practice.

A test was run on the fertilizer distributing part of a superior combined grain and fertilizer drill equipped with the finger or star-wheel type of fertilizer feed. The stone, furnished by the Columbia Quarry Company and ground by a crusher using air draft to separate the fine material had the sieve analysis as given in table 1. The method of testing consisted in filling the fertilizer hopper with the powdered stone, hauling the drill with a tractor for a distance equivalent to one-tenth acre, collecting the stone delivered by each delivery opening in a separate container attached just below the drill box, weighing this, and making calculations on the acre basis. The distributing fingers were set at the high speed (gear 6), and the test run with different gate openings. The results are shown in table 2, which compares the amount of stone delivered to the amounts of fertilizer that would be delivered according to the sowing table furnished with the drill. The weight of stone delivered in the test varied from 70 to 81% or an average of 75% of that given in the fertilizer sowing table for the different gate settings. It should be borne in mind, however, that the sowing tables for fertilizer furnished with a drill, can be only approximately at best as different fertilizers vary considerably in weight and drillability. In drilling finely ground limestone through a drill, the rate of application can be determined approximately by noting the acreage covered, as indicated by the drill surveyor, while a known amount of material is drilled.

Attempts were made to drill fine limestone through ordinary grain drills, both of the internal double-run type and of the fluted-roll type of force

Table 1

Fineness of Powdered Limestone Used

Mesh of test screen	Per cent caught on test screen	Per cent passing through test screen
40	2.0	98.0
60	0.3	97.3
80	1.1	96.6
100	1.6	95.0
200	16.8	78.2
300	46.2	32.0
Through	32.1	

feed. It was found that this fine, fluffy material would not feed through. Tests were next run on a McCormick-Deering drill equipped with agitators. The drill was of the double-rod type, with three-finger spider stirrers on the lower rod and with two-arm paddle throats beneath the fluted rolls open, and with them closed. The results are shown in table 2. The tests indicate that this drill can be easily made to deliver 200 to 350 pounds of this powdery material by setting it the same as for 6 to 12 pecks of oats per acre. Since it would be difficult to get agitators for some of the older grain drills, a homemade agitator was made and tested in a Superior grain drill, this particular drill being equipped with the internal double-run type of force feed. The agitator was made essentially as follows: A one-inch gas pipe was run lengthwise on top of the drill hopper and mounted in improvised

Table 2

Rates of Delivery of Hundred-Mesh Limestone by Different Drills

Superior Drill (Fertilizer Side)*			McCormick-Deering Drill (Grain Side)**			
					Limestone rate, lb Throats	
Fertilizer gate opening	Fertilizer rate, lb	Limestone rate, lb	Oats rate pecks	lb	open	closed
3	115	86	4	32	106	116
5	200	163	6	48	182	200
7	300	233	8	64	225	245
9	400	284	10	80	242	329
12	490	361	12	96	242	354
15	550	390	14	112	266	371

Superior Drill (Grain Side)***		
Gear	Oats rate, quarts, per acre	Limestone lb per acre
3	81	192
5	108	217
9	162	288
13	216	316

* Gear 6.   *Note: 1 U.S. dry peck = 8.81 litres*

** Fluted-roll, force-feed type. Agitator in grain box.

*** Internal double-run, force-feed type. Set for oats. Homemade agitator in grain box.

wood bearings. The outer end of this pipe was equipped with a crank so that the pipe could be oscillated back and forth in its bearings. Vertical arms were attached to this pipe and allowed to project downward beside each of the drill runs in the bottom of the hopper. The first design of this agitator failed to work because these vertical arms did not work in close enough proximity to the wheels which carry the seed through the runs.

During the test, the agitator was worked back and forth by hand twice for each revolution of the ground wheel of the drill. Very little effort is required to operate the agitator, and doubtless wood blocks bolted to wheel spokes could be made to operate it. The results of the test are given in table 2, and indicate that the internal double-run type of force feed will drill fine limestone when a suitable agitator is used in the drill hopper.

With coarse limestone for our past experience, the opinion naturally arises that the drilling of limestone through the regular seed runs of grain drills will cause excessive wear and consequent inaccuracies in subsequent drilling of grain and seed. The trials reported here did not include tests on this point, though such are contemplated. The finely ground limestone, however, is widely different from the commonly used, coarsely ground agricultural limestone. This finer material is impalpably fine, and resembles flour more than it does the common agricultural limestone. Its fluffy nature and ease of agitation through failure to pack as does the coarser material suggests that any wear on the drill by such material would be relatively small. Further, it is of neutral reaction—neither acid nor alkaline—with no corroding effect on metal. While there may be some wear, the seriousness of this remains to be established by experiment or experience. In all of the trials there was a surprising uniformity in the rate of delivery per spout, and calculations based on the lowest spout rate and the highest spout rate were never widely different. The variations were certainly within the limits of accuracy commonly demanded in such farm operations.

The results of these trials as given in table 2 indicate that present drilling machinery will distribute the finely powdered limestone effectively and in rates that easily accommodate the amounts suggested by soil experiments with this fine limestone.

CHAPTER 7

Drilling Fine Limestone for Legumes

THE IMPORTANCE OF LIMESTONE as a soil treatment, especially for legumes, has come to be widely appreciated, but its use has not become a general practice. The labor required to deliver and to apply two or more tons of 10 mesh material per acre is often too large to fit into the farm scheme except at periods of slack labor. Moreover, the maximum effectiveness of this coarsely ground material is delayed until six months or a year after its application. Finally, the wide variation in the quality of such stone available, especially in its content of material fine enough to pass a 40 mesh sieve and be effective during the first season, gives a correspondingly wide range in its effectiveness and in amounts necessary for good results. All these are handicaps in the wider adoption of liming as a regular farm practice and they have pointed to the need for a simpler method. This has been found in the plan of drilling smaller amounts of the more finely ground limestone with the seeding of legumes. It should not be understood that the plan of using larger amounts of ordinary limestone is not as valuable as ever, but the use of time limestone permits liming under many conditions where heavy liming is not commonly practiced.

According to the common conception of the function of limestone, it is applied to the soil as a means of removing, or correcting, soil acidity. Experimental studies at the Missouri Experiment Station, however, show that limestone, or calcium carbonate, renders two services. One of these is the removal of the soil acidity that is accomplished by the carbonate part. The other is that of supplying calcium as a nutrient to the plants. In the past, emphasis on the removal of acidity has so completely overshadowed the importance of supplying the much needed calcium for plants, that this latter function of lime has not been fully appreciated. Experiments have shown, however, that in terms of better plant growth, the application of calcium to the soil is more important than the removal of acidity. Compounds of calcium other than its carbonate, which do not remove soil acidity, will often serve in place of limestone. Conversely, however, carbonate compounds that will remove the acidity but do not contain calcium do not have significant influence on plant growth. Since limestone is the cheapest source of both calcium and carbonate, such other compounds have not been substituted for it and these facts were not observed in practice. Thus, in using calcium carbonate to remove the soil acidity, the calcium needs of the plant have nevertheless been met without ascribing to the limestone application for this particular and important function.

Studies on calcium as an important nutrient for legumes have shown that the amount of this element required by these plants is large in comparison with the needs of non-legume plants. For 25 bushels of wheat and a ton of straw, only 5 pounds of calcium are needed. For 50 bushels of corn and a ton of fodder a like amount must be provided. To produce two tons of clover hay—about the crop that might be expected on 50 bushel corn land—the soil must supply 80 pounds, or 16 times as much calcium. A two-ton hay crop of soybeans, often considered able to grow on sour soil, requires 55 pounds of calcium. Legumes make large demands on the soil for calcium in comparison with other crops, and for this reason they represent the first group of crops to show disaster from a depleted supply of calcium in the soil.

In terms of the amount of limestone required to supply this required calcium, however, the figure is small. Pure limestone contains 40% calcium, or 40 pounds per hundred, hence a crop of 50 bushels of corn and stover would take calcium from the soil, equivalent of only 12 1/2 pounds of limestone. Red clover, a much heavier feeder on calcium, would take for a two-ton crop, the calcium that would be supplied by 200 pounds of pure limestone. Soybeans at the same acre yield would need about 150 pounds. Thus the actual calcium needs of the crop can be supplied in relatively small quantities of limestone if it can be delivered to the plants in such a way that they can use it fully. In respect to the crop needs of calcium, therefore, we may think of limestone in terms of pounds rather than tons, provided this is delivered to the plant in usable form.

When the limestone needs approach such small figures per acre the liming treatment becomes similar to that of applying fertilizer. Then, too, since it becomes a matter of getting the lime, or calcium into the plant, it further approaches fertilizer in the matter of providing limestone of ready solubility. Limestone is similar to fertilizer in still another respect, namely, that the effects of the lime are marked in the early life of the plant. Experiments have shown that legume plants given lime are larger and more able to take nutrients from the soil in their early life, when given access to lime for only the first ten days of their growth and then transplanted as seedlings to acid soil, than when lime is withheld. Also they are more active in forming root nodules and earlier as well as superior in nitrogen fixation.

As a rock, limestone is usually considered insoluble, yet this is not the whole truth when one recalls the numerous caves dissolved out of limestone by running water. When finely ground, of course, limestone becomes more soluble in the same way that powdered sugar dissolves more quickly than rock candy, yet both are the same chemical composition. When limestone is ground into a powder that is fine enough to pass a sieve with 100 holes per linear inch, or 10,000 holes to a square inch, its action in the soil is practically as rapid as that of the water soluble forms of lime, namely, quick lime and hydrated lime. The finer grinding of limestone with this resulting increase in solubility make it behave like a fertilizer in speedy effects.

By drilling finely ground limestone into the soil at the time of seeding the crop, the approach to fertilizer is still closer in method of application and in use by the small plants in their first stages of growth. The effectiveness in starting legumes by drilling these smaller amounts which do not remove the acidity of the entire soil layer, points to the fact that it is not necessary to correct all the soil acidity before legumes can be grown. Finely ground limestone has started sweet clover on soil whose degree of acidity was quite high, (pH 4.9, requiring more than two tons of coarse limestone on a silt loam), and this acidity was slightly changed in no greater distance than two inches from the drilled stone. Even with heavy applications of limestone, legumes succeed when not all the soil acidity has been removed. In fact it has often been observed that clover will succeed in consequence of applications of coarse limestone on soil whose test after treatments still shows considerable acidity. Such soils are evidently delivering enough calcium to the plant for successful growth even though they are still acid. When plants can be transplanted from limed to sour soil and are better there because of the short early period in the presence of limed soil, and when nodules are produced in the soil at some distance from the streak of limestone applied by the drill, as has been common observation, it is clearly evident that lime can serve the plants without neutralizing the acidity in the entire soil area. It is highly probable that it would be disastrous to plant growth in other respects if many soils were suddenly neutralized completely. Potato scab is encouraged by neutral soils and the potato grower may well consider fine liming as a means of growing legumes for organic matter addition to his soil without bringing on the scab disease that results from correcting the acidity completely. Excessive liming has given bad effects in a sufficient number of cases to lead us to believe that some degree of acidity is desirable. Under such circumstances limestone behaves as a fertilizer in that it supplies the calcium needed by the plants, and can be handled on this basis in farm practice on many soils without necessarily completely neutralizing the soil.

If limestone is to be rapid in its action it must be finely ground. Much pulverized, or powdered, stone is now available as a consequence of improved methods of separating this fraction during grinding. Likewise channels that formerly consumed such output are now using less, so that it is available at prices more conducive to agricultural use. Some quarries are providing stone of such fineness that all of it passes the 100 mesh screen, while many have 40 mesh, or 30 mesh, stone. These latter contain no particles larger than those which will pass screens of such size and usually have about one-half, by weight, fine enough to pass the 100 mesh screen. These also lend themselves to drilling better than the 100 mesh material which does not flow through machinery easily.

The regular 10 mesh stone commonly broadcast at heavy rates might also be drilled according to this plan but it contains such a small portion of finely ground powdered stone that it is slower in its action. If larger amounts can be drilled so as to put into the soil as much powdered stone as is added by the finer material, similar results may be expected. Such large amounts cannot be handled so easily through the drill, nor with so little wear on the machinery. It seems doubtful economy to drill the coarser stone in place of the 40 mesh and finer material. For drilling purposes and effective results the finer stone should be considered.

Beside limestone, there are other compounds which can supply calcium and are often available. Acetylene plant waste is a form of very finely powdered lime hydrate that on drying and exposure to air will change to calcium carbonate. It will serve effectively as limestone, though its fluffy nature prohibits easy drilling unless there is an agitator in the drill box. Lime tailings, residues from burning lime, are another by-product that deserves consideration. Lime hydrate in the commercial form will also serve. It carries as much calcium in 74 pounds as limestone does in 100 and one will need only three-fourths as much of this as of limestone. Granulated quicklime may also be used, but is not as convenient to handle because of its caustic nature and like the hydrate may disturb germination if put into close contact with the seed in the soil. About 56 pounds of this are equivalent in calcium value to 100 pounds of limestone. When quicklime air slakes completely and changes from the stone to the powder form, it may also be used. Then it has no weight advantage and 100 pounds are required for the equivalent of 100 pounds of limestone. It also has the same chemical composition. Its fineness introduces difficulties in drilling it effectively. Other kinds of lime and lime wastes may be considered and can be evaluated on basis of their calcium supplying power. Many of these miscellaneous forms of lime deserve more consideration as a soil treatment.

If smaller amounts of finely ground limestone are to be successful in supplying plants with calcium and establishing the crop, the limestone should be drilled into the soil. Broadcasting such small amounts as 500 pounds per acre is not significant in its effects. Yet when this same amount is drilled, each drill row represents small soil areas where the limestone is concentrated and the soil along the row is more highly saturated with lime. Experimental studies show that the higher the degree of saturation of the soil by lime, the more readily does the plant secure the lime. Thus, the plants find in the drill row this favorable condition for supplying lime and will grow there. As is true for wheat and other drilled grains, so it is true for legumes—their establishment in the drill row only usually means plenty of plants per acre and a good stand.

Finely ground limestone need not be drilled deeply. It moves slightly downward in its reaction with the soil. Even if put right on top, it will be fairly effective but in this case the wind scatters it to reduce its effects. It is unnecessary, however, to make the drilling operation a heavy load by setting the drill deeply into the soil. If a quiet or non-windy time is chosen, the drill can be run shallow, the limestone delivered in a very narrow strip into the soil with light cover, and narrow, highly-loaded streaks of soil through the field provided. There the plants can early find their needed lime supply and get off to a good start. This early growth is essential in the life of the clovers if they are to get their roots down into the lower soil and establish themselves in competition with the nurse crop of wheat or oats for the soil fertility and moisture. Only as they do so can they survive the summer and make a paying crop later. Lighter applications of limestone cannot be promptly beneficial if scattered enough through the entire surface soil. They can be helpful, however, if drilled into the soil.

Since fine limestone is considered much like a fertilizer, naturally the season for drilling it might be expected to be that time when the legumes are seeded. It has been found a good practice to drill the limestone in the spring when the clovers and other lime-loving legumes are sown. The fertilizer attachment of the grain drill will deliver the limestone, while the grass seed attachment delivers the seed. In this way one operation over the field completes the seeding. If the drill is not run into the soil deeply, the seed may be delivered down the spout and the seeds and limestone put into immediate contact. If the seeds are covered too deeply by soil or heavy droppings of the dry powdered stone, the germination and stand may be disturbed. The seed delivery spouts on the drill may be detached from the sprouts leading down to the drill shoe, and the clover seed scattered on the surface of the soil. The seed spouts may also be extended to scatter them behind the drill, where they will fall into the drill furrows immediately over the limestone and be covered well enough by the first rain.

When drilling the fine limestone in the spring season, it should be done as early as possible because of the well known need for seeding clover early. This is sometimes impossible because the soil is too wet to permit going over it with the drill, and the wait for suitable soil conditions delays the seeding until the nurse crop is so large that the clover will be smothered out, or fail because of moisture shortage. It is not necessary that the limestone and the seed go on together, provided the soil is not cultivated or disturbed between these two operations. Consequently, the fine limestone may be drilled during the winter when soil conditions permit. The broadcast clover seeding may follow at the proper date. This will serve practically as well as drilling the two together.

As heavy applications of coarse limestone are often made in connection with wheat seeding in the fall, so the drilling of the finer limestone may also be done at this season. The limestone may be drilled like a fertilizer directly with the wheat. Since the wheat and limestone cannot be mixed and seeded together through the grain section of the drill very successfully, the stone should be put on with the fertilizer attachment. Limestone so applied in the fall will be effective the following early spring when the clover is seeded broadcast in the customary manner. If fertilizer is to be applied for the wheat this may be mixed with the limestone and both put on at the same time. Such a mixture may also be drilled with the clover seedings. There is no serious danger from the interference of one with the other. On the contrary, there may be improvement in the effect of the fertilizer as a result of the presence of the limestone. Likewise, for the limestone effect on the wheat, this will not be detrimental but may be helpful. Inoculated soil may also be mixed with the limestone as a means of inoculating the following clover seeding.

As for the time when fine limestone may be drilled most conveniently and effectively, the fall seeding season is a good one where wheat or barley is the nurse crop. If oats serves as such, the limestone may be drilled similarly with the oats in the spring and the clover broadcast later. When the legumes are seeded alone, then the limestone may well be drilled at their seeding season.

"How long will the fine limestone last?" is a common question when one contrasts this method with that of broadcasting a heavy application of coarse material that is effective to the legume crops in more than one round of the rotation. Legumes are the first among the crops to need lime, consequently, the fine stone is drilled with the legumes. The effect will last longer than this one crop if the soil is not disturbed. Sweet clover has reseeded itself after a start with fine lime, showing that the effect can carry over to the third year. When only the small soil areas represented by the drill rows are treated and the ground plowed afterward this small amount of limed soil is too thoroughly scattered through the great soil mass to lend much effect. When the next legume crop comes around in the rotation another limestone treatment should be used. Because broadcast heavy liming is an arduous task and represents a significant investment, one naturally hopes that its effects will last a longer time than for one single year of rotation. Drilling the fine lime is a simple, one-man operation of moderate cash outlay and it might be considered as a part of the treatment for every legume seeding.

The most effective method of drilling fine limestone is by means of the fertilizer attachment on the grain drill. This will handle limestone effectively though one cannot expect even this machine to operate without attention. One must always make sure that the stone is not failing to get down into the distributing machinery satisfactorily. It is also necessary to learn the rate of delivery. Some careful tests have shown that very fine limestone was delivered at only three-fourths of the rate as given for the particular set of gears and gate opening specified for that of fertilizer. If one is to drill 500 pounds of the finer stone it may be necessary to set the machinery at a higher figure than that for fertilizer delivery.

The ordinary grain drill without fertilizer will distribute fine limestone if some agitating device is used. Some grain drills are already made for, and can easily be equipped with, an agitator in the grain box so that they will serve to drill fine limestone. In testing such a machine with 100 mesh limestone, it delivered 200 pounds per acre when set for six pecks of oats, and 350 pounds per acre when set for 12 pecks. Another drill equipped with a home-made agitator tripped by a block on the wheel, delivered slightly less than 300 pounds when set for 9 pecks of oats. Such machinery is not as convenient as the fertilizer section of a grain drill, but will serve and can be used to drill the stone. As coarser stone is used, the wear will be greater, but this is not a serious matter and should not prohibit drilling limestone by this method. It is important, however, that the drill be cleaned thoroughly thereafter.

As the declining fertility of our soils becomes more widely recognized and the use of fertilizers to replace it becomes a more general practice, the fertilizer drill will be a more common machine for applying limestone as well. In respect to farm machinery, the fine limestone drilling methods will fit into the already common stock of farm equipment and call for no special machinery of limited use.

It is not uncommon experience in Missouri to find that an application of limestone alone does not secure a stand of clover. This has been true with heavy applications of limestone, but has come under more careful observation and with more emphasis in trials with fine limestone in conjunction with fertilizer treatments. Clover requires more than limestone for its successful stand and growth. It is true that liming increases root nodule production and, through the nodular bacteria, helps the plant to get its nitrogen from the unlimited supply in the soil air. In respect to this one nutrient, beside calcium, liming increases the supply of nitrogen for the legume plants by their improved nitrogen fixation. Limestone cannot substitute, however, for soil shortages in phosphorus, potassium, moisture or any other items required for plant growth. The addition of phosphorus to limestone has shown itself beneficial. The addition of potash is also noticeable in its effects so that on many soils of the state, the level of this nutrient is so low as to deserve consideration. Farm manure will supply some of this shortage and should often be used for this reason in conjunction with liming for a legume stand. Resistance to drought by clover was increased as limestone was supplemented with other treatments, possibly because these produce greater plant vigor and a deeper tap root. These illustrations indicate that more liming is often required, and that if fine limestone has been drilled with the clover seeding which fails, that failure should not be wholly ascribed to the fault of the fine liming method. Rather, some other soil deficiency may be responsible. The fine liming method will supply the needed calcium, and will increase nodule production and consequent nitrogen fixation, but it cannot take the place of other requisites for this crop. When used alone fine lime should not always be considered as a guarantee for a good stand and crop of clover.

As the soils in the regions of great rainfall and heavier crop production have become low in lime—now being especially recognized by clover failures—so have they also become correspondingly low in other nutrients not so grossly removed by plants. The soil deficiency in these is just as disastrous since the crop is impossible unless each of the required nutrients is amply supplied. The use of fine lime drilled with wheat has sometimes improved the wheat crop, pointing out that the soil was low in calcium even for wheat, and doubtless for corn and other crops that require but small amounts of it. Liming ahead of corn has improved this crop, probably by indirect as well as by direct effects through the calcium supplied. Oats have sometimes been improved by liming and reports of improvement in soybeans from limestone drilled with them are not uncommon. Its benefit on oats and wheat nurse crops, suggest similar effects from it on barley serving the same purpose, especially since barley is the most sensitive of the small grains to the lack of lime. The low supply of lime that may be disastrous to the extent of complete crop failure for legumes, is therefore injurious to many other crops.

This declining supply of soil fertility may be responsible for clover failure where it is grown with a nurse crop as contrasted to success where grown alone. The fertility supply of the soil may not be sufficient for two crops. Illustrations are not uncommon of clover in wheat drilled around shocks of corn fodder. In such cases the clover may be large next to the shock where nutrients were leached from the fodder into the soil by rain, while farther from the shock where no wheat was drilled and the clover grew alone it will be somewhat smaller. It will usually be still smaller within the wheat crop. The improved growth of clover around the shock from which the added fertility was leached into the soil, points out that the fertility of the soil is low for clover, but especially so when it must grow in competition with the wheat for this limited fertility supply. Farm experience in growing clover alone successfully is testifying to this situation. When grass takes alfalfa, this is also a testimony that the fertility level will not meet the high demands for good alfalfa that would smother the grass.

We are expecting too much of many soils when we seed a nurse crop and clover too, and expect both to succeed on the low level of soil fertility offered them.

This declining fertility level is evident in spite of the fact that a liming treatment, especially a heavy application, helps much in making other plant foods more effective. It is now known that liming helps the plants to obtain more potassium. Also it is instrumental in making a phosphorus treatment more beneficial. On limed land phosphorus is usually more effective than on unlimed soil. Lime also helps the plant to get nitrogen. It aids the plant in making much better use of the limited supplies of these other nutrients. It does not add these to the soil, hence the already low supply will be more rapidly depleted by liming. If, however, clovers can be grown and larger crop yields result, the restoration of the fertility should be quickly undertaken when this soil need is fully appreciated. As we use more limestone, attention must likewise be given to other deficiencies of soil fertility which this practice will help bring to our notice, and for which limestone cannot be a substitute.

To date the drilling of the finer limestone has been tried with successful results by farmer cooperators in many parts of the state. The soil types represented include the following: Boone, Cherokee, Crawford, Decatur, Edina, Gerald, Grundy, Knox, Lebanon, Marshall, Memphis, Oswego, Putnam and Summit silt loams; the Shelby and Lindley loams; Clarksville and Baxter gravelly loams; Lintonia fine sandy loam; and Wabash clay loam. By no means have all soil types been included in this rather extensive list, but those of level topography, heavier subsoil and significant degree of acidity have been grown to acid sensitive crops by means of lighter applications of limestone drilled on them. They testify to the success of this practice on those soils most difficult to seed to clover. Not only red clover, but sweet clover, and in some cases, alfalfa has been started by this treatment. Unfortunately, liming cannot offset bad seed, summer drought or infertility, but it can care for the calcium deficiency, or lime need, on many of the prevailing soil types in the state.

In terms of cost of the limestone, the drilling of a quarter ton of finer limestone is less than that of broadcasting two tons of 10 mesh material per acre. With the price of the former at $5.00 per ton at the quarry and a delivery charge of $1.00 per ton within a radius approaching a hundred miles. A 500 pound, or quarter ton application should call for a cash outlay of $1.50 per acre. For two tons of 10 mesh material such a cash outlay would allow only 75 cents per ton delivered on the farm. Costs of this coarser material have usually been much greater than this, so that drilling finer limestone should not exceed—and will usually be less than—the per acre cost of coarser material at the two ton rate.

In terms of the labor of distribution, the drilling method effects a real saving. To drill 500 pounds per acre on 20 acres is a one-man labor load, totaling five tons of material, while the corresponding labor load of 40 tons broadcast might require the help of the neighbors. It is this labor requirement that should be considered as the significant advantage of the finer limestone, and that makes this method lend itself to bringing limestone to soils where the other method might mean too great an initial cost. The smaller amount of limestone means less initial cash outlay; it permits the stone to be hauled to greater distance from railroads or delivery points, and makes possible liming within the farmer's own labor. The one-man labor load and smaller amounts of stone required make delivery possible at any time with storage for later use. When its use becomes more widespread, the stone may be stocked more generally by local dealers and thus still greater economies effected. Under such conditions, its costs when used regularly in every rotation should not exceed the costs of heavier applications of coarser stone applied less often.

This method of handling the liming need of the soil reduces it from a complex problem of large cash outlay and extensive labor, to a regular farming practice that can be geared into the routine farm program without its disruption. On such a basis the drilling of fine limestone may be accepted as a regular part of the legume seeding whenever it comes around in the rotation just as fertilizing should be a part of wheat seeding. Under such conditions more legumes can be successfully grown, more fertility restored to the soils and higher profits returned by the land.

CHAPTER 8

Lime for Backbone!

THE BUSINESS OF FARMING depends much on using the soil as the main factory. Our attention has been so completely absorbed above the soil that the real basis of "growing things" has not been commonly examined on each farm for its possible success and security. With animals playing a larger part in the final accounting of profit and loss, however, we are beginning to recognize the possibility of doing something to feed our animals better by treating the soil with some added fertility. And animals tell us, unfortunately, that as meat producers they are not as certain of profit today as they used to be not many years ago.

Much of this uncertainty may be traced right back to the declining fertility supply in the soil. When a 70% calf crop cuts into the margin of safety in the farming business, we are inclined to blame the bull. We have been told that he is "half the herd." When only one animal needs to be sacrificed to correct a 30% trouble, we are apt to dispose of the bull and pin our faith anew on another one that may not give us even a 70% calf crop. Reproduction is a delicate physiological performance. The fecundity in it, by both female and male, is influenced more by the soil than by the pedigree. Soils with depleted fertility and producing forages that are consequently deficient in minerals means that shy breeders and aborters will be more numerous. Losses through those channels alone, if corrected, may push the balance sheet in the farming books from the loss to the profit side.

During wintertime, feeds that are mainly of fuel value are not of great help in foetus production, which demands calcium and phosphorus in liberal amounts. When a cow calves and goes into milk production, the demand on her body for daily delivery of calcium and phosphorus goes even higher. Some soils are too deficient in these nutrients to enable the cow to go through the pregnancy period without developing acetonemia in late stages. Should she carry her foetus-building business through under strain, by sacrificing much of her own skeletal calcium and phosphorus for the offspring, she may yet break down in milk fever when the demand for the minerals arises.

"Pregnancy disease" among ewes is similar testimony when those with twin foetuses are more commonly taken with it. Rickets in calves, in spite of sunshine for vitamin D and of ample volume of milk, are occurring on soils from which the fertility has been highly exhausted. This exhaustion has reached a degree where the product of the milk is not necessarily of unvaried food value, which, even in milk, depends on the soil from which it is produced.

Animal deficiencies are pointing their fingers back to the soil and not to the drugstore. Plants given calcium and phosphorus via soil treatments do more than convey them to the manger. Plants manufacture essential food products, many probably still unknown as to composition and bodily service. They may be the means of making the animal sleek in the spring before the soil factory runs out of its raw materials. It may be the lack of these that gives us poor animal appearance commonly ascribed to fly troubles by August.

Fortunately for better feeding values in the grains and forages for our livestock, and in the vegetable and animal products for human consumption, we are gradually putting the essential nutrient elements, calcium and phosphorus, back to the soil in a larger soil improvement program.

Calcium and phosphorus, or limestone and phosphate, as their compounds are called, need to become household words in the soil fertility list. There is no substitute for them, except as we will accept starvation. Lime needs to be used more often. Lime or calcium is first of the items on the chemical list in the business of farming. It has gone ahead of nitrogen now that we know that the legumes given calcium and phosphorus can serve us to run nitrogen-fixing plants on every farm.

Though plants and people may be mainly carbohydrates and fats, both of which originate in fresh air and sunshine, it nevertheless takes some soil minerals to put a backbone into them—so badly needed by all of us now. It is soil and its mineral output that makes us "personalities rather than puddles." As fast as we realize that what must be put into the soil determines what we get out of it, we can optimistically view the future. The soil is still our best support. It is still the basis of our biggest business.

CHAPTER 9

It's the Calcium . . . Not the Alkalinity

NORMAL DEVELOPMENT OF PLANTS like any other growth performance, is distinctly a matter of proper nutrition. Nodule production on the roots of the soybean plant and its use of nitrogen from the atmosphere to let this crop serve as a protein-producing, and a nitrogen-fixing factory on the farm, are determined in the main by the nutritional levels or the fertility conditions of the soil.

Of the 14 chemical elements required to construct plants, 11 must be supplied by the soil in cases of the non-legumes. One less, or 10 are demanded from the soil by the legumes. The legumes, in the same manner as the non-legumes, use carbon, hydrogen and oxygen provided by air and water. In addition, and quite different from the non-legumes, they can take a fourth nutrient—nitrogen—from the air provided they are operating in cooperation with the proper bacteria on their roots commonly supplied as inoculation.

Much of the attention to the behaviors of legume plants and their accompanying bacteria has centered about the fact that legumes can draw, on the weather, as it were, for four of their nutrient requirements, while non-legumes are limited to three. Little attention has gone to the fact that legumes must still obtain ten (possibly more) nutrient elements from the soil. Demand made on the soil by the legumes for these elements is greater than by the non-legumes because the mineral content of legume forages are of higher concentrations. These demands are more significant because on these increased mineral content drawn from the soil fertility store there depends the effectiveness with which the root nodule producing bacteria will work.

Because the soybean can go, via bacteria, to the atmosphere for its nitrogen supply, we must not fix attention so completely on this escape from one responsibility as to forget the ten others that still lie in the soil. Studies to date have not given sufficient importance to all the soil-borne plant nutrients as these influence inoculation, nodule production and nitrogen fixation by legumes. Critical attention has gone to some, namely: calcium, phosphorus, magnesium and potassium, the four most prominent in the soil fertility list. Consider the importance of these in connection with the soybean.

Since long ago the art of agriculture has been pointing to the need for lime by many soils if they are to grow legumes. Nodulation of soybeans is generally improved by the practice of liming. It is only recently that science has begun to understand the function of liming for better cooperation between the plants and the bacteria. The scientist's first suggestion as to the role of liming soils in giving better legume growth was that lime was effective because it removed soil acidity.

This explanation is about to lose its adherents, in the face of the accumulating evidence that liming serves because it supplies the plants with calcium, one of the foremost soil requirements for both legumes and non-legumes.

Legume bacteria, too, have been considered sensitive to soil acidity. Failure of inoculation has often been ascribed to injury to the bacteria by the soil sourness. Successful inoculation, or ample nodule production, however, involves more than the idiosyncracies of the plant and bacteria. It involves, most decidedly, the soil as it nourishes both of these properly and sufficiently to make their joint activities result not only in a crop of larger tonnage but one of increased concentrations of proteins and minerals.

Since the soybean must be provided with its specific nodule bacteria when seeded on a soil for the first time, naturally the practice of inoculation of the seed is a recommended one. Failure of inoculation to produce nodules in many instances has brought blame on the bacterial culture, which, like water over the wheel, was past recovery or beyond defense when once distributed throughout the soil. It seemed a logical hypothesis that defective plant nutrition because of soil fertility deficiency might be prohibiting effective inoculation.

In order to test the nutritional value of liming for the soybean plants as compared to the role of lime in neutralizing soil acidity as these two effects encouraged better nodulation, calcium as a chloride was drilled with soybeans in comparison with similar drilling of calcium hydroxide.

Though the latter neutralized soil acidity while the former did not, but treatments brought about effective nodulation, deeper green color and larger plants of more stable cell structure. The nodules were not necessarily located in the soil areas into which the calcium compound was deposited. Roots in the acid soil areas bore nodules. Here was evidence that liming was improving the results from inoculation because lime was providing calcium.

In order to separate the nutritional value of calcium for the plant from those for the bacteria, more detailed tests of the soybean and its calcium needs were undertaken. It was readily demonstrated that calcium was more important than magnesium or potassium in the early life of the soybean plant.

A deficiency supply of calcium encouraged attacks on the plants by a fungus resembling "damping off," and brought failure of inoculation.

To determine the minimum amounts of calcium required per plant for effective establishment of the stand, calcium was used in the solution form and in the form absorbed on colloidal clay. The latter method permitted variable amounts of clays at different degrees of acidity (pH). It thus permitted controlled amounts of calcium at any pH or degree of acidity desired. These trials demonstrated that the soybean's early growth was dependent on a significant supply of calcium more than on a particular degree of soil acidity. Nodulation could not result later unless liberal levels of calcium were provided early to carry the plant to the inoculate age. More detailed separation of the calcium as a nutritional element from its role in modifying the soil's reaction as this influences nodulation was undertaken by using clay neutralized to different pH values or degrees of acidity through titration with calcium hydroxide.

Constant amounts of calcium were provided at different pH values by taking the proper amount of clay at a particular pH. Thus by placing these different amounts of the clays of different pH values into sand for soybean growth, there were provided soils of variable pH but of constant supplies of exchangeable calcium. Plant growth and nodule production showed clearly that even though the soybeans reflected their response to differences in soil acidity, they reflected far more their growth and nodulation response to the amount of calcium provided.

Nitrogen fixation, or an increase of nitrogen in the crop over that in the planted seed, did not occur even in a neutral soil unless the supply of calcium was ample. It occurred in acid soils containing liberal supplies of exchangeable calcium. Here, then, was distinct evidence that if inoculation of soybeans is to be effective in making this crop serve for soil improvement, the soil must deliver calcium to these plants.

We may well imagine competition between the soil and the plant for the lime. The absorbing power of the soil for nutrients like calcium, potassium, magnesium and other substances is appreciable. It was demonstrated by means of better soybean growth, nodulation and nitrogen fixation, that placing the calcium on a small smount of soil to saturate it highly is more effective than is placing it on much soil to increase the soil saturation only slightly.

These effects from variable degrees of saturation of the clay by the plant nutrient demonstrated similar results regardless of whether the variable calcium was accompanied by acidity or by neutrality. The soybean growth proved that it was not the acidity that disturbed plant growth, but that it was the deficient soil fertility commonly present when soils become acid. Likewise it demonstrated the more efficient use by the plant of the applied calcium in a soil more highly saturated by it. It also suggests a higher efficiency for drilling soil treatments than for broadcasting them.

That calcium is needed for the legume bacteria as they live independently of their host has become a well known recognized fact. With limited lime supply they become abnormal, and fail to inoculate. But given plenty of calcium, they grow well and are effective inoculators.

Unless both the plant and the bacteria have access to calcium, effective inoculation cannot be expected. Lime for a legume—even an acid tolerant plant like the soybean—plays a helpful role because it nourishes the plant rather than because it removes soil acidity. Even an acid soil must supply lime for successful inoculation and growth of the soybeans.

Phosphorus, like calcium, is a requisite if soybeans are to be active in nodule production and in nitrogen fixation. But its importance and behavior are closely related to the amount of calcium. Unless calcium is amply supplied, soybeans are poorly nodulated, and are poor nitrogen fixers for soil improvement. In fact they may even lose phosphorus back to the soil, so that the final crop will return less phosphorus when harvested than was in the planted seed.

That magnesium should be helpful toward better soybean inoculation has not come to our attention because relatively little magnesium is required by the plant, and most soils are not seriously deficient in this nutrient. This element is effective on soybeans, but probably indirectly as well as directly. It makes calcium more effective and thus illustrates the fact that fertility elements work together. These effects suggest an interstimulation among the elements, so that the final results can not be considered merely as additions of the values of their effects when applied singly.

Improved inoculation may be also dependent on the potassium supply in the soil. Experimental studies demonstrated increased nodule production and better growth as potassium deficiencies of the soil were remedied. With more liberal amounts of potassium, however, particularly in contrast to the amount of calcium, inoculation may be less effective and give reduced nodulation and nitrogen fixation. Excessive potassium in relation to calcium makes the soybeans produce more tonnage, but they fix less nitrogen and become more clearly non-legumes than legumes. They move into the class of woody vegetation and out of the class of vegetation with high protein content of high nutritional value as animal forages.

Inoculation, or the introduction of nodule bacteria with the seeding of the soybeans, is not necessarily a practice that will compel the plant to accept the companionship of the bacteria. The latter cannot use cavemen tactics. Rather, the plant and bacteria will unite in their efforts toward getting their necessary nitrogen out of the gaseous supply in the atmosphere only when the soil provides liberally of all the nutrient elements required by both the plant and the bacteria.

Successful soybean growth on soils of declining fertility can not be guaranteed simply by the introduction of particular pedigree microbes. The plant must first be healthy because it is well fed with calcium, phosphorus, magnesium and other soil-contributed elements. Unless it is well nourished by the soil, the inoculating bacteria will not associate with it to give it the one distinguishing character so desirable in legumes, namely, nitrogen fixing capacity.

Inoculation, or the introduction of the bacteria, is no substitute for the high levels of soil fertility that are demanded for successful legume crops.

CHAPTER 10

Purpose of Liming Soil
An Enigma

MORE THAN A QUARTER of a century ago, 400 samples of 21 different soil types of Missouri tested for exchangeable calcium showed a close relationship of the amounts of this insoluble but available plant nutrient to the soil's capacity to give good crops yields. That was also the time when limestone (calcium carbonate, and calcium magnesium carbonate) was applied extensively for the purpose of reducing soil acidity, or raising the numerical value of the pH *i.e.* the degree of acidity of the soil. The pH value as a soil test report was easily obtained by special laboratory equipment. But measuring the exchangeable calcium (or magnesium) was a tedious manipulation. However, the latter related the soil to potential crop production, while the pH was a technical expression, not so readily connected with the nutrition of the crop plants.

At that early date, the evaluation of the soil types with their arrangement in order of decreasing production of crops and livestock and their similar classification as an arrangement into six groups, A, B, C, D, E, F—by the soil surveyors—showed a close agreement with their decreasing amounts of exchangeable calcium by soil test as set forth in the accompanying table. The more productive soils supplied calcium in this exchangeable form of plant roots in quantities three times as great as did the poorer soils. The total quantities so active were large enough, and the differences between soils were great enough, for an accuracy of measurement which left no doubt about it.

Measurements of the clay-humus in the soil made possible the evaluation of the degree of saturation of that part of the soil from which the calcium (and magnesium) are exchanged. Thus, soil testing for calcium

Groups	Soil Types	Exchangeable Calcium, milligram equivalents per 100 gms. soil
A	Marshall	14.80
	Summit	12.64
	Grundy	12.71
B	Knox	11.32
	Pettis	10.86
	Crawford	10.68
	Chariton	10.21
	Eldon	8.99
	Oswego	9.19
C	Putnam	8.89
	Bates	7.86
	Memphis	6.22
	Hagerstown	5.91
	Lindley	8.64
	Union	6.64
D	Cherokee	5.57
	Baxter	5.57
	Gerald	3.82
	Boone	7.59
E	Lebanon	5.51
	Clarksville	4.29

Mo. Agr. Expt. Sta. Bul. 387., pg. 85., 1937. Report for year ending June 30, 1936.

moved itself more closely toward indicating potential nutrition of plants, especially the legumes as producers of proteins. The term "pH" expresses the concentration of hydrogen as an active ion, separated out of any compound. Like the calcium and magnesium, it too is a positively-charged ion. Hence, any of these three can exchange for any other on the clay-humus colloid. Unfortunately, the hydrogen is not a plant nutrient coming from that source, while calcium and magnesium are. So when the hydrogen from cropping, weathering, leaching, etc. replaces the calcium and magnesium, we say the soil becomes "sour" and the crop fails. But the real cause of legume failures is the "going out" of the nutrients, calcium, magnesium, potassium, etc., the presence of which makes the soil non-acid, and not by the "coming in" of the hydrogen by which it is made sour or acid.

When those two exchanges or soil phenomena occurred simultaneously with the legume failure the soil's increased acidity was quickly recognized. We made the error of considering the soil acidity, the hydrogen concentration, the cause of crop failure when it was the fertility deficiency of calcium (and magnesium), or the failing plant nutrition, that was responsible. The validity of this conclusion was experimentally established by preparing a purely hydrogen-saturated clay and then separating lots of it as a series of increasing degrees of saturation by calcium. Half of these were prepared to give a series of increasing calcium saturation with reciprocally decreasing saturation by hydrogen or with decreasing degrees of acidity.

The other half of the lots was a series given barium to just replace the decreasing hydrogen or to approach the neutral condition for all of the lot. This gave increasing saturation by calcium and reciprocally decreasing saturation by the non-nutrient barium. These clays were added to sand in such amounts as to supply constant totals of exchangeable calcium per pot or sand-clay combination and were planted to soybeans. They resulted in literally duplicate series of crop growths according to the differing saturation by calcium that resulted, irrespective of the presence or absence of the acidity as shown in the accompanying illustration. Thus the enigma of the purpose of applying lime was solved long ago when such experiments told us that the benefit from liming the humid soil comes from its nourishment of the crop by calcium, and not from its reduction of the soil acidity by the carbonate accompanying the calcium in the limestone. Seemingly this truth is still much hidden in unopened reports.

CHAPTER 11

Calcium as a Factor in Seed Germination

THAT THE SOIL should be a factor in determining the percentage germination of seeds may seem an overmphasis of the soil's service in plant growth. When the ash content of a plant is approximately only 5% or, as maximum, 10%, then this is a relatively small contribution by the soil. But when growth as a synthesis of carbon-dioxide and water into compounds by means of sun shine energy will occur only after the soil has made its seemingly small contribution, this diminutive offering mounts in its importance. Since the major part of the nutrients from the soil enter the plant in the early phases of its life history, it seemed logical to determine whether variation in soil fertility, particularly of calcium, might not register its effects so early in plant life as even to influence the percentage germination of the seeds of a crop like the tomato, for example, which is not commonly considered a calcophile.

The tomato seeds were planted in ordinary greenhouse flats at increasing rates, starting with 14 seeds per row, or a spacing of 1 inch between the seeds, and increasing to 5, 10, 15, and 20 times this number per consecutive row. The rows and the rates were duplicated in the second of the flats. The soil treatments used consisted of (a) none, (b) calcium chloride, (c) complete fertilizer, and (d) calcium chloride plus complete fertilizer. These treatments were duplicated by duplicate flats.

There trials, each with a growth period of approximately 4 weeks, were carried out in February, March, and May, respectively. The soil treatments were mixed as chemicals and ground with fine quartz sand so as to provide sufficient bulk for uniform distribution by hand in the bottom of the rill. Water was sprinkled on the applied fertilizer, the flats were covered.

Table 1

Plants Produced and Percentage Germination Represented Thereby with Increased Rate of Seeding

Seeds planted per row	February		March		May		Mean % of seeds planted	%
	Plants	%	Plants	%	Plants	%		
14	6.6	47	7.7	55	9.3	66	56	100
70	21.3	30	22.5	32	41.6	59	40	70
140	21.0	15	30.5	21	69.1	49	28	48
210	13.7	6	34.7	16	89.6	42	21	35
280	21.7	7	40.8	14	93.8	33	16	30

Table 2

Percentage Germination as Influenced by Soil Treatments

Seeds planted per row	No treatment		Calcium only		Complete fertilizer		Calcium/ fertilizer % of seeds planted	%
	Plants	%	Plants	%	Plants	%		
14	7.6	54	9.3	66	6.8	48	8.0	57
70	27.9	39	36.5	52	20.8	29	29.1	41
140	35.6	25	51.6	36	28.6	20	45.1	32
210	40.3	19	64.5	30	32.1	15	50.0	23
280	48.1	17	66.7	23	32.6	11	57.1	20

Observations of the early plant appearances were made and the growth with possible disease studied. After 27 to 29 days the counts were made of the plants per row.

When the number of plants produced (table 1) is considered in relation to the number of seeds planted, regardless of soil treatments, a decreasing germination with increased rate of seeding is clearly demonstrated. These data represent a combination of all the soil treatments with 12 cases in each growing period and 36 cases in the mean. The mean is expressed for the plants as percentage of the seeds planted and also as percentage, assuming the plants in the lowest seeding rate as representative of the viable seeds of the lot. The large decrease in number of emerging plants with the increased rate of seeding was observed in the counts of the individual rows as well as in the summation of the data.

These observations raise the question as to the soil condition responsible for the decrease in germination, when careful attention was given to such items as provision of ample moisture, as covering the planted flats with a thin surface layer of quartz sand, and other means of providing optimum conditions for germination. There is an improved germination with the advance in the season, but all three trials suggest that there is some soil factor which may be sufficient for the limited seed numbers but becomes insufficient for their increasing numbers.

That some soil factor, such as a nutrient element, is responsible herein is suggested when the same data are assembled to show the variable germination in relation to the different soil treatments, as presented in table 2.

It is significant that the complete fertilizer applied and watered well into the soil for 3 days in advance of the seeding should give the lowest germination of all the trials. This fertilizer addition may be credited with an injurious effect, since the numbers fell below those for the soil without treatment. When the calcium, which was a chloride and not in an acid-neutralizing carbonate form, was added along with the fertilizer, it served to offset the injury. It improved the germination beyond that in the untreated soil. This improvement was relatively greater as the seeding rate was larger. It was most startling, however, to find that the introduction into the soil of calcium chloride alone gave the highest percentage of plants from the seeds planted.

Such increases suggest a possible significance of calcium in the soil for better seed germination. Its effects can not be ascribed to changes in soil reaction. It must be related to the role of calcium as a nutrient, and gives the calcium of the soil an importance for possible attention in practice in terms of exceedingly small amounts for significant benefits.

CHAPTER 12

Now We Know Lime is a Plant Food—Not Merely a Treatment for Acidity

FOR BOUNTIFUL PRODUCTION in agriculture we must always work with, not against, the stern laws of nature. Sciences are doing much to help in our understanding of nature's ways in the growth of our crops, our livestock and ourselves. But this knowledge still is not complete enough to keep us free from occasional but significant errors.

Such errors most often come about when we try to move too quickly with programs designed to change the habits and thinking of large groups. If we allow time for individuals of the groups to learn and understand basic principles, such errors are not too likely to occur. Then, the new behavior will be the result of changes by each individual—not just because he joined the group. Campaigns dealing with farm production changes may suffer from lack of sufficient understanding at the outset of basic natural forces.

The campaign for liming the soil based on the slogan, "Fight soil acidity" is an illustration. We have added to our understanding of how the soil serves to nourish the plant via its roots. Thus, we ought to be rethinking the wisdom of the idea of fighting soil acidity to the point of getting rid of it—of making the soil "neutral."

Serious disturbances, even disasters, in crop production, followed by irregularities in animal feeds on those crops grown on "neutralized" soils, indicate fighting soil acidity with carbonate of lime in limestone is not in accordance with natural facts of plant creation.

The cry, "Lime the soil for legumes," was well received by the public, followed by such slogans as "Grow legumes to build up the soil." Both of these farm slogans now are being reconsidered for the serious errors delaying activities for better food production. Soil exploitation rather than soil restoration was increased.

While legumes have the ability to fix nitrogen (they can take nitrogen from the free supply in the air as well as the limited supply in the soil) we find they do not necessarily carry out this philanthropic service to the soil. They are not always using atmospheric nitrogen merely because they are growing.

There have been no measurements of nitrogen fixation by legumes growing in the field that are accurate enough to tell us just how much nitrogen is taken from the air by a legume crop. Also, even if a legume takes nitrogen from the air to make plant growth, that nitrogen is made a part of the plant tissue, more in the tops than in the roots. This nitrogen is not made a part of the soil to any extent unless the entire crop is sacrificed on the spot and plowed under. We are now learning that acidity of the soil is not to be blamed when legumes fail to grow on those soils that have become highly acid from the forces of nature. Soils where the rainfall is high, particularly where virgin forests once grew but have been cleared, fail to grow these protein-producing, nitrogen-fixing legumes because these crops do not find enough fertility.

The missing soil nutrients were lost because acidity, or hydrogen, came in to replace them. Decaying or "souring" forest litter made much acid for that effect. The growing trees were setting free acidity or hydrogen from their leaching rainfall. These soils were growing only wood when the pioneers took them over. Shall we expect legumes planted there to make much more than woody tissue even if they grow there? Plants grow because they can put acid out of their roots thru respiration. Plant growth is possible because plants trade that acidity to the soil and take fertility in exchange. If there is acidity present along with plenty of fertility in the soil, then plants grow better than if that fertility is not accompanied by any acidity.

We now are coming to see that had we known more about how plants feed with their roots in the soil, there would have been no "war" on soil acidity. Instead, each of us would have undertaken our separate responsibilities to rebuild our soil first with calcium supplied with limestone. That work might well have started 25 years earlier. Perhaps we would have lime to supply magnesium, too. Had we looked upon increasing soil acidity as nothing more than decreasing soil fertility, we could have believed our soils are declining in supplies of all nutrients, including the trace minerals now so disturbing as to their possible needs.

Only as our understanding of the natural behaviors and natural laws of nature increases, will we farm more effectively on the soil that provides the creative potential for farming. For creation of farm products we need to supply the soil with the fertility for which plants trade their acidity.

CHAPTER 13

Soil Acidity is Beneficial

ONLY RECENTLY HAVE we come to appreciate the services of soil acidity in mobilizing—making available—many of the nutrients in the rocks and minerals of the soil.

When we learned that soils are less productive in giving us legumes and other protein-rich forages, according as they become more acid—either naturally or under our cultivation—we came to the conclusion that soil acidity is the cause of this trouble. We now know that a plant puts acid into the soil in exchange for the nutrients it gets. It is that same acid held on the clay that weathers the rock fragments and serves to pass their nutrients on to the clay, and from there on to the plant. The coming into the soil of excessive acidity is merely the reciprocal of the going out of the fertility. Nature's process of feeding the plants, and thereby the animals and us, is one of putting acidity into the soil from the plant roots in order to break out of the rocks what nutrients they contain for nourishment of all the different life forms.

When we put lime rock on the soil as a fertilizer supplying calcium to our legume crops, we know full well that this rock reacts with the acid-clay of the soil. The acid goes from the clay to the lime rock which, being calcium carbonate, breaks down to give carbonic acid while the calcium is absorbed or taken over by the clay. While the calcium goes on to the clay to be available there for the plants, the carbonic acid decomposes into water and carbon dioxide as gas. Since this gas escapes from the soil, this escape takes away the acid, or, as we say, "it makes the soil neutral." The benefit to the legume crop from the application of this lime rock to the soil does not rest in the removal of this soil acidity. Rather, it rests in the exchanging of calcium as a nutrient to the clay which was holding the acidity or hydrogen, a chemical element that is not of direct nutritional service.

Soil acidity has been breaking potash rock down chemically too. During all these past years the potash feldspars have been undergoing weathering attacks by soil acidity. On this rock the acid clay carries out its weathering effects in the same way as it does for lime rock, except that it trades acid to the feldspar and takes potassium unto itself in exchange. Magnesium rock, as we have it in dolomitic limestone is also broken down by the acid clay. By this same process the clay becomes stocked with magnesium. This is then more readily exchangeable and available to the plant from the clay than it would be if the plant root were in direct contact with the rock fragment itself. By exactly the same mechanism we can expect phosphate rock to be made available for the plant's use. It is in these processes by which the acidity of the soil is beneficial. If the soil contains the two colloids, clay and humus, which can hold acidity, and then if that soil has scattered through it fragments of lime rock, of magnesium rock, of potassium rock, of phosphate rock or in fact of any rock with nutrients, it is the soil acidity that mobilizes to the clay the calcium, the magnesium, the potassium, the phosphorus, or all the other nutrients respectively for rapid use to the plants. This is nature's process of providing plant nutrients on the clay of the soil in available form. By it Nature has stocked our moderately acid soils with fertility. It was that condition of our virgin soils that prompted population to seek new lands in the first place.

CHAPTER 14

Soil Alters Calcium Digestibility in Leafy Greens

THAT THE GREEN LEAFY vegetables of the goosefoot family (spinach, Swiss chard, beet greens, and New Zealand spinach) do not increase the concentration of their calcium according as the soil is more heavily limed— as is true for the leafy vegetables of the mustard family (kale, mustard greens and turnip greens)—has been previously pointed out. Nor do those of the goosefoot family carry as high a concentration of calcium as do any of the mustard family group. The difference in the calcium concentrations between these two families are much more magnified when one considers differences in their nutritional availability of this essential inorganic element. The calcium in the four kinds of goosefoot greens cannot even be digestively utilized in the diet, according to good authorities, because of the large amounts of oxalic acid formed and present in these plants.

This organic compound of plant origin combines with the plant's calcium and also with the magnesium to convert these into insoluble and indigestible oxalates. In sharp contrast, according to these authorities, the calcium, for example, in the mustard greens, turnip tops and the kale is almost completely usable since these of the mustard family are practically free of the oxalates which make the calcium and magnesium indigestible. In some experiments using soils controlled as to both their available calcium and their degree of acidity (pH values) while growing spinach, we made the startling discovery that the spinach grown on the more acid soil had higher concentrations of the inorganic elements, calcium and magnesium, and also of the organic compound, oxalate, than were those found in the spinach grown on the less acid or nearly neutral soil.

But even at these higher concentrations, those amounts of the calcium and the magnesium added together were more than sufficient to neutralize

Carriers of Calcium and Magnesium

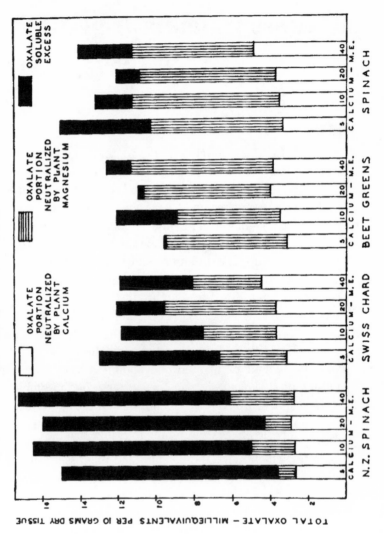

Probable disposition of oxalate in New Zealand spinach, Swiss chard, beet greens, and spinach when grown at variable levels of calcium.

the oxalic acid by forming oxalates and to leave some extra calcium and magnesium in other forms than this indigestible combination of them. The spinach plants on the nearly neutral soil failed to take enough calcium and magnesium from the same soil's supply to offset the oxalic acid produced within the plants. Therefore, they could offer no digestible calcium and magnesium when these greens were put into the diet. Also, on the nearly neutral soils, the application of varied amounts of extra calcium to the soil failed to change the concentrations of calcium within this green leafy vegetable significantly.

When the four goosefoot greens were grown on nearly neutral soils and chemical analyses made of them for their (a) calcium, (b) magnesium, and (c) oxalate, their high concentrations of oxalates were most noticeable. Even though the calcium in the soil was increased through units of 5, 10, 20, and 40, while the magnesium in the soil was held constant, these four leafy greens each produced more than enough oxalic acid to make both the calcium and the magnesium insoluble and indigestible. This is quite different from what would have been the case had the soil been varied in its available calcium while kept at a more acid reaction, which results when calcium in the gypsum rather than in the limestone or carbonate form is used. The chemical results of these greens as carriers of calcium and magnesium in combination with the oxalates when grown on nearly neutral soil under variable calcium supply are shown in the accompanying chart.

In only the best greens was the combination of calcium and magnesium almost enough to overcome the detrimental effect of the oxalic acid in making these two essential elements wholly insoluble and indigestible. These data tell us that not only the amount of calcium in the soil but even the degree of soil acidity comes in to determine whether the green leafy vegetables will give us the mineral elements, calcium and magnesium, in a digestible form. Only slowly are we coming to realize that the condition of the soil, as well as the kind of crops, determine the nutritional value of what we grow and eat.

CHAPTER 15

We Can Grow Legumes
on Acid Soils

LEGUMES ARE ALMOST an indispensable forage for the dairyman. They are high producers of his raw proteins, or the amino acids from which his cows produce the milk proteins. Legumes can use, both from the soil humus and from the atmosphere, the nitrogen that characterizes the chemical composition of these life-carrying substances. But unfortunately legumes are feed crops not grown so universally. We have ascribed their failure to the acidity of the soil. Whether this diagnosis of the trouble is correct may be questioned. It deserves reconsideration in the light of our better understanding of the soil and its interactions with the plants.

Acidity is a common soil condition in many parts of the temperate zone. It occurs where the rainfall gives water enough to go down through and to wash out much of the fertility. In general, if the rainfall is high enough to provide plenty of water during the crop growing season, there will also be enough water to leach the soil of much of its supply of nutrients and to make it acid. Timbered soils of the eastern United States are acid. Those of the eastern edge of the prairie are also sour. Acidity is a natural condition where soils have had rainfall going down through them and where they have been growing much vegetation. Such soils have, therefore, been subjected to a leaching force taking the fertility downward, and to a competitive force of the vegetation with its roots taking the nutrients upward. There they are built into organic combinations of them. Consequently acid soils have a distinct surface soil and subsoil horizons in their profiles. They are naturally low in fertility and have been growing mainly carbonaceous or woody vegetation.

Natural soil acidity is in reality, then, mainly a shortage of fertility in terms of many plant nutrients. This is the situation because the soil has been under cropping and leaching for ages. This was true before we took over to intensify these effects. This, then, is the condition of the soil that prompts the common question. How can we grow mineral-rich, fertility-consuming forages, like the legumes, of good feed values for such a high-powered, protein-producer like the dairy cow?

Applications of limestone, and other compounds carrying the nutrient calcium, to acid soils are known widely to be beneficial soil treatments for legumes and other crops. This was known even to the Romans, who used lime as a fertilizer on their soils. Much later in general, but yet early in our own colonial history, it was reported that Benjamin Franklin used gypsum or land plaster on clover with good improvement of this legume crop. Right here on our own soils the ancient agricultural art of liming the land was practiced for the benefit of better crops as feed. Here the sulfate of lime, or gypsum, which does not take away the acidity of the soil was making better clover. We have forgotten this unusual wisdom about soils among the many bright ideas that came down to us from this colonial sage. We may well go back and look carefully and critically into it now. We need to ask ourselves, Why can't we grow legumes on acid soil when Franklin grew them better by putting on calcium sulfate? This was a soil treatment that not only failed to reduce the soil acidity but even made the soil more sour.

It was the growing agricultural science of the early decades of the twentieth century that brought liming of the soil back as a more general agricultural practice. We cannot say that liming was an art carried over from colonial days. It had been pushed out when fertilizers came into use. Liming the soil has become an extensive practice under the encouragement of an embryo soil-testing service. That service was guided by the belief that the applications, (a) of limestone which is a carbonate of calcium, (b) of hydrated lime which is an alkaline calcium hydroxide, or (c) of quicklime, caustic oxide of calcium, are all beneficial for crop growth because each of these is ammunition in the fight against soil acidity, or against the high concentration of hydrogen in the soil.

This struggle to drive the hydrogen ion, or acidity, out of the soil was aided by the technological advancements giving us instruments and equipments that measured the hydrogen ion to a finer degree than known before. The ease and speed with which soil acidity could be detected and measured encouraged the widespread testing of soils. This activity discovered soil acidity almost everywhere. Through the help of the measuring gadgets we were impressed by the apparent universality of soil acidity. Only a few humid soils were not seriously stocked with acid. We discovered that for acid soil, in general, the productivity was lower as the degree of acidity was higher. From such a discovery we might expect ourselves to conclude— even though it was later found to be the wrong conclusion—that the presence of the large amount of hydrogen ions in the soil was the cause of the poor crops. This conclusion would be expected also from the bigger troubles in growing the proteinaceous, mineral-rich legumes of higher feeding values.

The extensive use of limestone in the corn belt has now multiplied itself into the millions of tons of these natural rock fragments that are annually mixed through the soil. This increased use was prompted by the beliefs (a) that limestone is beneficial because its carbonate removes the acidity of the soil, and (b) that soil is most productive if it is neutral, or when it has no active hydrogen ions in it. Under these beliefs (now known to be poorly founded) we have become belligerent foes of soil acidity. Limestone has become the ammunition for fighting this enemy hidden in the soil. We are just now coming around to a better understanding of how nature grew crops on the acid soils before we did. We are now beginning to understand what limestone really does when it makes better crops.

Only recently have we recognized the fallacious reasoning behind the conclusion that it must be the presence of the acidity in the soil that brings the crop failure when liming lessens the soil acidity and makes better crops at the same time. While the convenience of soil testing gadgets encouraged this erroneous belief about soil acidity as an enemy, it was the diligent study of the physiology of the plants, of the colloidal behavior of the clays growing them, and the chemical analyses of all these, that finally pointed out the errors of such hasty conclusions. It pointed out that soil acidity is not detrimental, but is in reality beneficial.

We now know, of course, that in applying the limestone, which is calcium carbonate, there is possibly some reduction of acidity by the carbonate portion. At the same time there is being applied also some calcium—a nutrient highly deficient in the leached soils—to nourish the calcium-starved crops. This nutritional service comes about both directly and indirectly. We have finally learned that it is this better nourishment of the crop rather than any change in the degree of acidity of the soil that gives us the bigger and better crops. Unwittingly we have been fertilizing the crops with calcium while fighting the soil acidity with the carbonate, the hydroxide, or the oxide of lime.

In spite of our ignorance of how the lime functions, we have benefited by using it. However, an erroneous understanding of what happens to the crop and to the soil when we lime cannot successfully lead us very far into the future. We cannot continue to grow better feeds under the mistaken belief that we do so merely by the removal of the soil acidity through the use of plenty of carbonates on our humid soils. Wise management of the soil to grow nutritious feeds can scarcely be well founded on facts so few and so simple.

Should you decide to demonstrate for yourself the truth of what has been said above, you can apply some soda-lime, or sodium carbonate to the acid soil. This will reduce its acidity. But unfortunately for you if you are a foe of soil acidity this soil treatment will rout the enemy but will still not give successful crops. Merely removing the acidity by a carbonate (of sodium rather than of calcium, in this case) does not guarantee the crop.

As proof that it is the calcium as plant nourishment that is the helpful factor in liming, one can repeat Benjamin Franklin's demonstration and apply calcium sulfate to the soil. One might even apply some "Dow Flake," a calcium chloride. Either of these calcium-carrying compounds will make the soil more acid. But in spite of this fact and because they add calcium, the gypsum and "Dow Flake" will improve the crops on the initially acid soil left so. We are now resurrecting the ancient art used by Benjamin Franklin for whom liming the soil was a matter of fertilizing it with calcium (and sulfur) and not one of fighting soil acidity.

While we were fighting soil acidity we have failed to notice that most of the populations of the world are concentrated on the acid soils. They are not in the humid tropics where the soils are not acid. Nor are they on the arid soils that are alkaline, a reaction opposite to the acid. Soils that are not acid are not necessarily the supporters of many peoples. Yet in fighting soil acidity we labor under the belief that if a soil were limed to the point of driving out all the acidity, such a soil should be highly productive.

We now know that even while a soil may be holding considerable calcium or lime. To a small extent of its exchange capacity, it is also holding nutrients other than calcium. Among these are potassium, magnesium, manganese, and others. But these in total are held in much less quantity and by less force than are either the calcium or the hydrogen, the former a nutrient and the latter a non-nutrient. Should we put on lime or calcium enough to drive all the acidity out of the soil by putting calcium in place of the hydrogen, all the other nutrients would be more readily driven out than would this acid-giving element.

Liming the soil heavily, then, does not necessarily drive out only the acidity. Instead it would also drive out all other fertility. It might load the soil with calcium so completely that it could offer only calcium as plant nourishment. Plants would then starve for other nutrients even though on a neutral soil. Plants on such a non-acid but calcium-saturated soil would be starving for all the same nutrients, except calcium as they do on the acid soils. Making soils neutral by saturating them with calcium does not therefore make them productive. This is the situation of some of the semi-arid soils of our western states. In our struggle against soil acidity we need to remember that neutral soils are not the productive soils. Instead it is the acid by yet fertile ones that feed us and nourish the major portion of the other peoples of the world.

Calcium has been a good fertilizer for legumes on acid soils now for some years. It has been serving directly as a nutrient for the plants. But it has also served indirectly by helping other nutrients get into the plant roots more abundantly. It helps the nitrogen of the acid soil to get into the plant. It helps the phosphorus, the potassium, and other nourishing elements to be taken more readily by the crop. A plant grown for a short time on a lime-rich soil and transplanted to one low in calcium—that is, one that is acid—will take more nutrients from such a soil than will the plant that was starved in its early life for lime. It is because of this behavior of the calcium that a lime soil is soon in need of other nutrients besides the calcium.

We are discovering rapidly that there is need now for potassium on many recently limed but still acid soils. Other soils in similar condition show their serious needs for nitrogen. Lime, of course, may well be the first fertilizer needed. But when once this need is met on these soils that were highly leached long ago, the need for other nutrients may be quickly evident. Perhaps it is these fundamental soil facts that are bringing fertilizers into such prominence in the corn belt today, while only a few years ago limestone was the only soil treatment and the one starting then its extension into the widespread use it has today. Perhaps these are the facts behind the age-old rhyme that told us long ago that "lime and lime without manure, make father rich but son poor."

We now know that instead of saying that acidity has come into our soils we should say the soil fertility has gone out. Legumes which make good feed for milk producing animals must have fertile but yet acid soils from which to make the feed that will be good. Lime is one of the foremost fertilizers in making soils capable of supporting the protein producing crops. For this service to plants, phosphorus is also needed. These are taken out of the soil as the plant trades hydrogen as acid for them. Consequently the highly acid soil is simply one that has become deficient in fertility.

We can grow legume crops on acid soils if we will give them calcium and all the other fertilizers needed by the soil to grow them. Red clover was commonly said to be sensitive to acid soils. Yet liming the millions of acres has not restored this crop to those extensive areas. The high cost of its seed is sufficient testimony of the crop's scarcity today. This crop usually needs potassium, or phosphorus, or possibly other fertility elements on a soil deficient to the point of being naturally very acid. Then, too, when a soil is properly fertilized, red clover will grow even if the soil is highly acid. We now know that the soil acidity is not the problem in growing the legumes. The production of these protein producing crops is a matter of ample soil fertility among which the calcium is only one nutrient. If we provide this one by means of limestone and then add all the other necessary fertilizer nutrients for the soil in question, we can grow legumes of highly nutritious values as feed without removing all of the soil acidity. Growing legumes is a matter of feeding these crops, and not a matter of fighting soil acidity.

Soybeans came in as a "new" legume crop. They were reported to "grow on acid soils." But on such soils they were also reported to be "a hay crop and not a seed crop." We did not realize that if they were not building proteins and other complexes demanding soil fertility to make a seed crop and that consequently they could not be a nutritious hay in these respects. Soybeans need lime, too, if they are to give good feed. They are showing growth troubles when the soils are not well supplied with magnesium. They are also reporting the need for manganese on some soils. Soybeans can be grown on an acid soil that is fertile in more respects than in calcium only.

We need no longer hunt for "acid-tolerant" legumes. Any plant that is well nourished tolerates acidity. It causes the soil to become acid when it takes the fertility from it. The root itself is acid and makes the surrounding soil area acid by the carbonic acid it respires. It is this carbonic acid by which the plant carries on the business of taking calcium, potassium, magnesium, phosphorus, iron, and its whole array of nutrients from the soil. It trades hydrogen or acid for them. Acidity is therefore "natural" for any plant.

Growing legumes is not a problem of getting rid of the acidity of the soil. On the soils where we say acidity is a problem, the problem is one of putting in place of the acidity the list of plant nutrients lost excessively from the soil as it became acid. Legumes that make tons of vegetative mass on so-called "acid" soils do not make the nutrient values or quality of feeds made by those other legumes we say are "failing" on acid soils. We can grow some legumes on naturally acid soils but they will not be the equal in feed value of those on soils once naturally acid soils but given other fertility as well as some calcium in the belief that it was removing acidity. Good feed can be grown on acid soils provided that they are given the fertility required by the plant to manufacture it. Soil acidity is a problem because it means that so much fertility has gone out to let so much hydrogen come in.

CHAPTER 16

Dangerous Grass

SICK SOILS WILL not produce healthy plants. Sick plants will not nourish healthy animals. Sick animals will yield no income. What shall it profit us then, if our frantic search for a foolproof grass to grow on abused soil is successful?

Nationally we have become conservation conscious within recent years. We have come to recognize the threat to civilization from soil erosion. We have embraced the obvious solution, protective covering to heal the scars of wind and water, to hold the remaining surface and fertility.

But suppose we do succeed in getting the sick land back to grass? Suppose we find plants that will exist on it? They will hold the surface, which is desirable, but will they restore the land to useful production? Vegetation that will not support healthy animal life will not solve our problem.

Granting that a sod can be established, what kind will it be—sick or healthy? The query is not concerned with varieties, but with the nutritive content of herbage. Increasing cases of animal malnutrition, animal irregularities, animal diseases have been traced to feeds from the less fertile soils.

Cows sustained on the production of these soils may show symptoms suggesting milk fever in the late winter, even before calving, or before giving milk, and death may occur under similar symptoms much later in the year from an ailment called "grass tetany." Irregularities develop during summer in the gait, particularly of the hind legs, suggesting an attempt by the animal to walk on its toes. A slight rise in the middle of the back and other skeletal deformities may be noticed. Occurrence of these ailments is closely associated with those soil types that are commonly irregular in crop production and which have been leached and exhausted of their basic nutrient elements to such a low content as would misnomer their ailment by the less informative term of "high degree of soil acidity."

Chemical studies have been made of soil and of vegetation it produced that ailing animals consumed. When chemical findings are related to animal case histories, they designate the seat of the trouble as the low level in the soil of the nutrients essential for plants and required in larger amounts by animals. On the more "sour" soils where lime has been badly needed, but was not applied, and where nutrients other than calcium run closely parallel with it in deficiency degree, the pasture herbage has scarcely the equivalent of wheat straw in its content of calcium or lime and phosphorus.

Analyses of herbage which had defaulted in its support of a cow, and which came to the attention of a county agent as an emergency call in the absence of a veterinarian, showed a calcium content of but .27% and a phosphorus composition of only .08%. Ordinary wheat straw has .21% of the former and .12% of the latter.

The deficiency of either calcium or phosphorus might be considered serious, according to these figures. In a certain section of Minnesota, according to the late Prof. C.H. Eckles and his colleagues, the cows showed what has been known as "phosphorus deficiencies" when the phosphorus content of alfalfa fed them dropped to .21%, and that of timothy hay to .11%, and that of prairie hay to .10%. The hay samples submitted by the county agent in Missouri would not prohibit this phosphorus irregularity, if we can believe the Minnesota figures to fit the case located farther south.

The calcium contents of the Minnesota hays provoking the deficiency disease were 1.81% for alfalfa, .39% for timothy hay, and .44% for prairie hay. The Missouri grass, even though it had a sprinkling of lespedeza plants, was lower in calcium than was either the prairie or timothy hay in Minnesota, when one recalls the preceding calcium figure of .27%. Feeding cattle herbage of such composition might well be classed as a case of gross deception. Giving them green pasturage but on a soil failing to stock it to the equivalent of even wheat straw in terms of the most dominant ash constituents needed by the cow, is like bringing on the spring season but feeding a winter ration. Too bad the animals can't prosecute under the law of mislabeled packages.

The animal's response to the "milk fever" treatment of calcium gluconate injected into the bloodstream gives major emphasis to the calcium deficiency. It shows that the soil has not been giving the animal enough calcium, or lime, in her feed to maintain body activities. Under such soil and feed conditions she has been compelled to give up lime, and possibly phosphorus from her own body store to the point of danger to her own life in order to build the bones of the foetus. We may not be sacrificing animals on altars because of religious devotion, but we seem to be sacrificing them to false gods of a false economy that refuses to restore an exhausted soil fertility. Backbones examined after such animals have given their lives to the cause of motherhood against the handicap of existing on the feeds from these base-deficient—particularly calcium-deficient—soils, suggest that these bones have been partially consumed periodically and then rebuilt into deformed shapes. Some have been rebuilt into solid rather than flexible spines in meeting the calcium shortage during pregnancy and rebuilding during non-pregnant or non-nursing times.

Cattle owners of long experience report increasing deficiency cases. An 80-year-old founder of a fine Hereford herd says, "They are coming to be all too common lately." His is a 49-year observation. They come now not as late in the annual breeding cycle as that period marked by the heavy milk flow just after calving. They are common, as early as two months before calf delivery. They come even in young, or growing, steers. The deficiencies in lime in the soil and their effects are so serious that fatalities among fine breeding animals and their offspring are making serious inroads into the animal supply of the country, to say nothing of the farmers' income.

Supplementing the ration with mineral forms, such as limestone and bonemeal, may seem adequate remedy when calcium gluconate is so effective in snatching the "milk fever" animal out of the last stages before death. Before pinning hopes on such supplements, it is well to remember that the very man who started the bonemeal feeding idea, von Gohren, pointed out as early as 1861 that some unfavorable effects might be associated with it. Then, too, whenever soils are so seriously deficient in lime as to reflect it by deficiency diseases in the animals grazing on them, such soils may be expected to be deficient in other basic nutrients of which the shortage is not so simply detected. Crop removal and leaching are not confining their inroads on the soil's supply to that of calcium alone. These other seemingly more subtle deficiencies may still remain in the ration when the lime is supposedly supplied by the mineral supplement.

Sick soils mean sick plants. Sick plants make feed that may be expected to make sick animals. When the plant factory is running short of calcium, the lime content within the plant itself can be expected to be short. Likewise a good number of other items, such as possibly the vitamins, which are manufactured by the healthy plant, may be deficient.

Fertilizing the soil is more than stuffing the plant with minerals. It is a case of balancing the plant diet for better results in the plant factory just as we try to balance the animal ration for better output by the meat or milk factory.

Plant rations are much simpler than animal rations. At most, a dozen to 14 elements are all that can be of concern even when plants are grown in water or without soil. Fortunately, our soils have not gotten so low in fertility that we are immediately concerned with this total number. Limestone and phosphorus treatments to soil are the first requisites in the light of plant and animal needs, because calcium is about 8 times as plentiful in plant ash and 40 times so in the animal body minerals as in the soil. For phosphorus, the corresponding figures are roughly 140 and 400, according to the United States Department of Agriculture. Other nutrients are not put into the plant or animal body in such large concentrations in contrast to that in the soil and the need for them is not serious. Remedying the plant ration by lime and phosphorus additions mainly to the soil will relieve us of remedying the animal ration in many cases, and will be much more simple than tinkering with animal physiology which is infinitely complex.

A simple soil treatment, like liming, can do much for the animal's sake in terms of higher content of minerals and protein in the forage part of the ration. Limestone applied to lespedeza has demonstrated its effects in many places. In one case it increased the lime content almost one-fifth. It was instrumental in helping the plant to rustle enough phosphorus out of the soil to increase the concentration of this nutrient element by one-fifth. It was instrumental in helping the plant to rustle enough phosphorus out of the soil to increase the concentration of this nutrient element by one-fifth. It enabled the plant factory to pack more than one-fourth more protein into each pound of hay, to say nothing of the yield increase per acre in all of these items.

From the cow's standpoint her factory can be more efficient when her feeds are, roughly, one-fourth more concentrated in the items she needs. Other cases—not only of lespedeza—but of alfalfa and non-legumes tell of the same effects by even so simple a soil treatment as liming and suggest the soil as an opening to a simple attack on the animal deficiency problem. Certainly from the standpoint of the farmer, cures effected by soil treatment, through the plant, and to the animals, offer more hope than attempts to diagnose and prescribe for them after they become sick.

Mining our soils of their fertility is bringing us face to face with the simple fact that plant factories are not running as efficiently for feed production as they once did. That wasn't so very long ago. Our farm meat and milk factories are, consequently, also operating on less efficient levels— all our knowledge about better nutrition notwithstanding. Hope lies not so much in diagnostic surveys in the animal factory but more in the simpler approach to treating the animals to more nearly normal nutrition by way of normal feeds grown on fertile soils.

Humans, too, persons subject to hay fever, are vitally concerned in this matter of soil fertility if doubling of case numbers in the last 25 years is an indication. Prolific pollen-producing plants are the only survivors when declining soil fertility supports only widely scattered plants that must crosspollinate over the greater distances between them. We can look for more pollen in the air and more hay fever as soil fertility goes down.

That sick soils will not make healthy animals is particularly significant at this time. We are thinking on a national scale of combating soil erosion by allowing much of the fertility depleted soil to go back to grass. In our desperate search for varieties of plants that will exist on such soils, perhaps we have given too little thought to whether the forage so grown would be put by the cow on her list of dietary delicacies. Perhaps we may well give ear to the voices of the many animals in their unattended deficiency ailments. They are seemingly shouting, "Don't let land merely 'go to grass.' Why don't you use sound methods of grass farming through soil-fertility restorative treatments requisite for good feed production and quicker and better soil cover?" Attention to the evidence of soil deficiencies as given by the dumb animals will react with profit both individually and nationally. Soil treatments also will serve the purposes of erosion control more effectively in the better cover developed more quickly.

CHAPTER 17

Should Farmers Receive Tax Allowance for Soil-Building?

THE 85% OF THIS country's population living in urban areas do not yet feel any obligation to help maintain fertility resources coming to them gratis from people in rural areas. How soon will the country wake up to the obligation owed those who maintain reasonable levels of soil fertility so that the country may be well fed? Carefully lobbied legislation has set up laws, economics and taxation procedures so that this country's urban commercial businesses and industries have capital investments which are self-sustaining.

For example, the owner-investor of a limestone quarry may be allowed a depreciation figure as high as 15% of his income for rock taken from a quarry. And it may be a larger figure for the owner-investor of an oil well. Capital investment in these mineral businesses is soon recovered.

As yet, no economist or taxation authority has suggested the justice of a depletion allowance to the landowner for the maintenance of his soil fertility capital to replace mineral fertility taken from the soil and delivered as food to the urban population without charge. The landowner's investment in soil minerals for good production is gradually being liquidated under the economic thinking—or the lack of it—which contends that the farmer is thereby taking a profit. On the contrary, the landowner throws by installments his financial and the national security into the bargain every time he makes a sale of farm products. Those on the urban receiving end of that transaction get those installments free and flush them into the sea.

Everyone is a party to the crime of soil fertility exploitation but yet are complaining against the rising costs of living. People are slow to see that such shortsightedness in economic, agricultural, and other policies toward the soil's fertility resources are seriously undermining national security. All this is more serious with a growing pressure on the soil's production potential by an increasing population, not to mention the rest of the world calling on this country to share that potential with them. Liming soils deserves consideration as an operation undergirding future food security—particularly foods of high protein content. It has long been known that lime is needed for legumes. Again, people are slow to see that need as one for the production of protein, rather than the tonnage, yield of the crop. By the soil route, lime provides meat, milk and eggs.

Viewed in this light, one cannot escape the question whether people dare expect the farmer to continue liquidating his fertility assets under the false idea of taking a profit and, at the same time, ask him to purchase large amounts of limestone to increase his liquidation rate all the more.

Isn't it about time that a basic agricultural policy, the required machinery of economics and taxation be designed to guarantee the self-perpetuation of the farmer's fertility capital which must feed everyone—both urban and rural?

Shouldn't soil fertility maintenance—and thereby of agricultural industry—be interpreted by the same views in economics and taxation as those prevailing in other industries? This should be true now that fertility rebuilding by limestone and fertilizing the soil is moving itself into the category of soil chemistry for the nutrition of plants, animals, and people. Perhaps this country can bring about self-perpetuation of soil fertility capital under the agricultural business in the rural areas in the same manner as perpetuation prevails for monetary capital under all businesses in urban centers. If that situation is brought about, then rebuilding the fertility of the soil will become big business by meeting major soil needs.

CHAPTER 18

Calcium-Bearing Versus Neutral Fertilizers

OUR INCREASING KNOWLEDGE of nutrition has been compelling us periodically to list newly recognized requirements in the diets of plants, of animals, and of humans. If fertilizers are to be helpful in meeting these newer demands, then their composition must be shaped to improve the plant's synthetic performances and thus to initiate, by way of the soil the improvements in kind and quality of their products to be used for the better nutrition first of animals and finally of humans.

Our knowledge about plant nutrition was long content to list but ten requisite chemical elements, so ably arranged in a simplified memory picture around his own name by the late C.G. Hopkins. Today that list has been extended, at least by four. It may soon be further extended. For animal and human nutrition, the essentials were listed for a long time as proteins, carbohydrates, fats and minerals. Only lately accessories were added, referring not to a single item but to many as this all-inclusive term indicates. With the increasing number of vitamins now recognized under this category, our minds are prepared for an extension of this list, as in the work of H.H. Bunzell of New York, when he finds that wheat germ gives effects on yeast growth beyond those of any, or all, of the vitamins yet listed.

Fertilizer thinking was long tied down to the three ingredient concept. Later it was adjusted to include the micro-nutrient necessities. This was a very easy adjustment when these were already passing into the goods mainly as unavoidable accompaniments or contaminants. Now the soil fertility has declined to the economic danger point, with resultant disturbances in animal and human nutrition manifesting themselves in many deficiency diseases some constructive thinking must be applied to revised fertilizer composition. This is especially important if fertilizer use as a soil treatment is to make crops yield not only more tonnage, but also feed of the quality and of the nutritional effectiveness it must eventually have. On the basis of better plant performance, the fertilizers and their functions may well be given critical examination in the light of (a) the various and the intricate soil processes, and (b) the plant's complicated physiology, as science is rapidly elucidating them. It is from this viewpoint that the question of "acidity" of fertilizers deserves to be viewed. We need to raise the question whether this so called "acidity," is so simple as a mere matter of the physico-chemical condition relative to the hydrogen-ion concentration of the mixture itself, or of the ash resulting from its ignition.

The introduction of the hydrogen electrode as a laboratory tool, brought a greater refinement in measuring the degree of acidity than had previously been possible. But when scientists can see better, or farther, objectively, it does not necessarily follow that they can see more clearly subjectively. Soil scientists seized quickly upon the hydrogen electrode for more critical study of soil acidity. They found that when limestone was applied to the soil for improved legume growth, it also corrected soil acidity. From these observations they drew the conclusion that soil acidity was the enemy of the leguminous nitrogen-fixing, protein-rich forage crops. This conclusion that calcium carbonate can remove, or reduce, soil acidity was objectively correct. But to say that it is the correcting of the soil acidity by the limestone that improves growth of the legume crop, is subjectively incorrect. Such observation demonstrates that nature is consistent, but such reasoning illustrates that human logic may be decidely inconsistent. Reliance on the effect of limestone as calcium carbonate, or as magnesium carbonate, on the acid soils for the neutralizing effects by the carbonate radical rather than for the plant nutrient significance of these two dibasic cations, calcium and magnesium, may be leading us astray in fertilizer thinking. It has been leading our soil thinking astray where it has been diverting our attention from the function of calcium as a fertilizer to that of its carbonate as an antidote for hydrogen presence.

That soil scientists and plant physiologists should have neglected the role of the element calcium and should have given the carbonate premier significance in soil improvement by liming for crops, seems strange. As early as the days of Benjamin Franklin a story of his experiences with gypsum, or land plaster, for clover improvement was widely told. That gypsum, as calcium sulfate, with no acid neutralizing power should benefit red clover points suggestively to the possible importance of the calcium.

It emphasizes calcium all the more when chemical analysis of this crop tell of its lower sulfur but high calcium content, and when young animals demonstrate it as an excellent growth-promoting feed.

It was the observations by farmers that cast doubt on the accuracy of the deduction that liming is beneficial to the crop through acidity removal. Farmers using limestone to get clover on heavy soils with high buffering capacities found crop establishment and improvement where no change in degree of acidity could be shown. They showed that acid soils need calcium to get a clover crop even if the acidity is not corrected. Their suspicion of the inaccuracy of the belief that the degree of soil acidity was the disturbing factor provoked experimental tests to separate the effect of the calcium from that of the carbonate. For this purpose use was made of such compounds as calcium chloride in commercial Dow Flake, and of calcium silicate in the form of ordinary cement. Both of these gave beneficial results in legumes on lime deficient soils. Here, then, the legume growth was improved by applications of calcium that carried no carbonate, and did not reduce the degree of acidity.

Similar confusion apparently prevails about fertilizer acidity and fertilizers are about to undergo universal acidity correction. Again, very fortunately, the economic aspect has come to our rescue unbeknown to us. The cheapest carbonates in the form of calcareous and dolomitic limestones are going to correct the fertilizer acidity. Unwittingly they are providing extra nutrients as calcium and magnesium to deliver the beneficial effects when in our confusion or misunderstanding of the facts, the acid neutralizing value of the carbonate is given the credit. If sodium carbonate were not more costly, and were more convenient, it might have gone in and given disastrous disturbances to our acid neutralizing belief. Its substitution of sodium for calcium would have revealed the wrong interpretation of the value of making fertilizers "neutral."

Up to the present time, fertilizer analyses have paid no attention to available calcium. This nutrient of a fertilizer deserves consideration since in the humid region the increasing calcium deficiency in the soil is roughly the reciprocal of the increasing soil acidity. That liming the soil is beneficial because it delivers calcium to make up this soil shortage rather than because it removes the hydrogen ions was clearly demonstrated by some research using carefully prepared clays of different degrees of acidity. By mixing different amounts of clay with sand, the soybean plants could be given more or less calcium at any degree of acidity or pH. The plants grew better with less acidity. But they also grew better at any degree of acidity as they had access to more clay and to more calcium.

As a more accurate test, a series of clays with increasing amounts of calcium (representing increasing degrees of saturation of the clay by calcium) and accompanied either by decreasing amounts of hydrogen as acidity or of barium as neutrality were used to grow the same crop. The amounts of clay for addition to the sand were chosen so as to deliver the same amount of available calcium in every case. Strange as it may seem, the crop growth followed the degree of calcium saturation. The crop content of calcium did likewise, regardless of whether hydrogen or the degree of acidity was decreasing, or whether all the soils were neutral.

Here the lime addition demonstrated clearly that its beneficial effect was not one of fighting the soil acidity by means of its carbonate addition as a neutralizer, but that it was one of supplying calcium as a plant nutrient. Viewing fertilizers in the same light, we may well raise the question whether it is the neutralizing of their acid that is significant, or whether it isn't the addition of the calcium as an extra nutrient, or possibly calcium as a mobilizer of other nutrients, that makes the so-called "neutral" fertilizers of more value as crop producers.

The increasing degree of calcium saturation of the soil makes the treatment more effective in delivering its available calcium to the crop. According to these studies, as the calcium was put on less clay to saturate it more completely, a larger percentage of the exchangeable calcium moved from the clay into the crop. With the clay carrying 40% saturation, the crop used but 12.3% of the available supply. With 87.5% saturation of the clay the crop got 29.3% of the applied lime. The efficiency of use increased more than twice. The concentrations of calcium in the crop for these two degrees of calcium saturation of the soil were .50% and .76% respectively, or the crop was made about 50% richer in calcium concentrations by what corresponded to drilling the calcium into the soil. In relation to our need for calcium-bearing feeds, this improvement may be significant.

Drilling fertilizers with seedings may at times be detrimental to germination. This effect is reduced, and germination may be improved, by adding calcium chloride which is a salt that has no neutralizing value. This effect has been shown for such non-legume seeds as tomatoes and bluegrass. Whether this effect is one of lessening fungus injury to the seed or one of improved germinating physiology has not been determined. |Nevertheless, increased calcium offerings have been shown to lessen the fungus attack on soybean seedlings in what resembled the more common "damping off" troubles. Even if the exact function of the calcium in the improved seed germination is not understood, its beneficial effect is recognized and its use becoming an adopted practice.

Such results point out that by putting the calcium, as has been done with the other nutrients, into the limited soil volume to saturate a part of it more completely, as is the practice by drilling, there is a much greater efficiency in getting the nutrients into the crop. This is the fundamental reason for drilling, rather than broadcasting, even limestone. Drilling makes the calcium carried by the fertilizer so much more effective than we have been wont to believe and brings calcium up for consideration as a significant nutrient within the fertilizer mixture.

For purposes of illustration let us imagine that the soybeans used in these studies were drilled with a 4-12-4 fertilizer at 200 pounds per acre. Let us suppose they made a ton of hay. According to their analysis they would contain the calcium equivalent of 40 pounds of calcium carbonate. With the gypsum of the fertilizer contributing the calcium equivalent of about 32 pounds of calcium carbonate, and with the neutralizer for the ammonium sulfate acidity adding about 60 pounds, then this drilled fertilizer would be delivering 92 pounds of carbonate. At a 30% efficiency figure found in the experimental studies, this fertilizer treatment would provide almost three-fourths of the calcium required for the ton of the soybean hay. Drilling the "neutral" fertilizers makes their calcium content effective. It suggest that when fertilizers are neutralized by limestone or dolomite, this is simply a case of supplementing the calcium already in the acid fertilizer in order to supply more nearly the amount of calcium badly needed by the crop. It is making for more effectiveness of the calcium, needed by the crop and hidden away in the fertilizer.

That calcium is of service in mobilizing other nutrients into the plant was suggested over 20 years ago by Professor True of Pennsylvania. That it mobilizes soil nitrogen was shown by growing some soybean seedlings for ten days in sand only, and some in sand given calcium carbonate. These were removed, washed and transplanted into an acid soil in order to test the significance of the calcium they could get and take with them in consequence of contact with the carbonate for but ten days of their seedling life. The calcium so gotten carried over to influence their growth. Those plants with calcium made more growth by 50% in the first ten days after transplanting. They excelled in growth for the rest of the time. During this same initial period after transfer, and before they had nodules, they took 20% more nitrogen from the soil. The calcium that was carried within the plants served to mobilize the soil nitrogen into them.

Calcium serves also to mobilize phosphorus, according to studies with both leguminous and non-leguminous pasture crops. Phosphate used with limestone returned three times as much phosphorus in the crop as when phosphate was used singly. A critical study of the data from the outlying fields of Kentucky points out that the crop increases from the use of lime and phosphorus in combination are greater, in general, than the sums of their separate effects.

Calcium is not only instrumental in mobilizing nitrogen and phosphorus into the crop, but it has been demonstrated for soybeans that as its supply in the soil becomes low, the nitrogen, phosphorus and potassium may even move from the plant to the soil. Thus, the plant may contain less of these than was in the seed originally planted. Such movement in the reverse direction has not been shown for calcium. Apparently no growth occurs unless calcium moves into the seed and crop. Experimental results also give some suggestion that the same holds true for magnesium as for calcium and that this element always moves into the crop if growth occurs.

Table 1

Diammonium Phosphate as Fertilizer in Contrast to Gypsum-Bearing Superphosphate and Urea. (Results for Bluegrass Based on No Treatment as 100).

	Forage yield	Nitrogen	Total in harvest Calcium	Phosphorus
No treatment	100	100	100	100
Superphosphate	100	96	86	97
Superphosphate + extra calcium	103	98	96	97
Superphosphate + urea	110	114	119	113
Superphosphate + urea + extra calcium	109	114	112	109
Diammonium phosphate	103	112	86	95
Diammonium phosphate + extra calcium	110	114	109	111

With calcium mobilizing both nitrogen and phosphorus, and with all three of these nutrients associated with protein, which is the basis of growth, calcium may be more significant in growth promotion than direct measurement of calcium contents of crops might lead us to believe. It is some of these seemingly indirect effects that may be responsible for much that we believe is the benefit in making fertilizers neutral by means of calcareous or dolomitic carbonates.

That the calcium in the gypsum of the superphosphate is of fertilizer value has been shown by some work with bluegrass. Superphosphate applied at the rate per acre of 200 pounds of 20 per goods served as the basis for using diammonium phosphate at equivalent rates. The same amount of nitrogen as was contained in this concentrated fertilizer was then applied as urea in combination with superphosphate of which the accompanying gypsum might exert its effects. These different treatments were used for bluegrass on a soil needing nitrogen, phosphorus and lime. Because of this latter requisite, extra calcium was used in amounts to equal that carried by gypsum. This was used in both the sulfate and carbonate forms. The results are given in table 1.

In terms of tonnage produced, the diammonium phosphate was no better than superphosphate coupled with a doubling of its own calcium content as gypsum, or about what one might expect from superphosphate on limed land. The nitrogen of the ammonia in the diammonium phosphate was not used by the plant to increase its growth as forage even though it moved into the crop. When, however, calcium equivalent to that in the gypsum of the superphosphate was added to the diammonium phosphate, then this nitrogen made plant growth, delivered nitrogen, and returned phosphorus in the crop on a par with that by urea in combination with superphosphate.

These facts indicate clearly that the calcium of the gypsum is serving to mobilize the nitrogen of the urea and the phosphorus of the superphosphate into the bluegrass. This was not done when nitrogen and phosphorus in combination as diammonium phosphate were applied in the absence of the calcium. In the light of such effects, calcium will soon take on importance as an ingredient in fertilizer. These data suggest the possible danger in going to the more concentrated nutrient carriers that omit the calcium. They indicate that we may well think of using fertilizers in combination with lime or certainly in terms of the calcium they carry, more than whether they are neutral or acid in reaction.

The significance of calcium for the non-leguminous crop of cotton has been emphasized by the experiment stations of the South. Its service in

Table 2

*Increases in Cotton From 5-8-5 Fertilizer With Different Carriers
of Nitrogen (Louisiana Data).*

Nitrogen carrier	Increase by fertilizer Pounds seed cotton	Increase by "neutralization." Pounds seed cotton
Nitrate of soda	250	
16-20-0 Ammophos	-109	
16-20-0 Ammophos, neutral	-47	62
Cottonseed meal	116	
Cottonseed meal, neutral	196	80
Sulfate of ammonia	-81	
Sulfate of ammonia, neutral	1	82
Urea	23	
Urea, neutral	121	98
Calnitro	147	
Calcium nitrate	165	
Cyanamid	184	

mobilizing phosphorus was announced by F.L. Davis of Louisiana, when, as a result of his studies on available phosphorus in connection with nitrogenous fertilizers, he said, "Calcium containing compounds apparently maintain soil phosphorus at the highest available levels." The data from that station reporting mean cotton yields for the three years 1938–40 in a test of different nitrogen sources in a 5-8-5 at 600 pounds per acre show some interesting effects from the fertilizers made "neutral." The increases in seed cotton in consequence of "neutralization" are given in table 2.

If these small amounts of extra calcium used in neutralizing the fertilizers can give these increases, should not some significance be given to the calcium present in the fertilizer even before it was neutralized? The effects of fertilizer neutralization and those of the calcium-bearing nitrogenous compounds on the cotton, all suggest that emphasis on fertilizers should not go to their acidity but rather to their calcium-bearing aspect even for this crop. When Ammophos reduces the cotton yield in Louisiana, as the data show, this again brings the gypsum aspect to the superphosphate in the mixed fertilizers into importance.

Also, the Alabama Station has called attention to the need for limestone to neutralize fertilizer acidity, which may be as much as 500 pounds of limestone per ton of 5-15-5 fertilizer. Applying 600 pounds of such a fertilizer after it has been neutralized would be equivalent to applying 150 pounds of limestone. Drilling limestone is not common practice for cotton, but drilled as a fertilizer neutralized it may be given benefits much as an application as light as 300 pounds of limestone does when it helps red clover in some soils of the cornbelt. Professor Tidmore points out that "an application of limestone is the most practical method of correcting the acid condition of the soil and supplying calcium."

Much of the variation in cotton response to nitrogen from different sources in a mixed fertilizer may be connected with the variation in calcium content of that fertilizer, according to the suggestion of W. R. Paden of the South Carolina Station. In speaking of their results he says "These data show clearly that no marked difference in yield would be expected from the various sources of nitrogen on limed soil. When the question of soil acidity has been taken care of, one might expect approximately the same yield from the various sources of nitrogen."

L. G. Willis in a study of "the value of gypsum as a supplement to a concentrated fertilizer," particularly for cotton, suggests that the more concentrated fertilizers are deficient in some nutrient. He used limestone and extra gypsum in a search for this shortage. He hesitated to attribute significance to calcium since he says "freshly applied limestone did not correct the deficiency." But he follows with the report that "other observations, however, appear to indicate that exchangeable calcium in these soils is as suitable a corrective as are the neutral calcium salts."

Most of the southern soils need nitrogen and phosphorus. They apparently fit into the category of the soil cited previously, within which the effects of the calcium were separated from those of the phosphate. The Louisiana soils show similar conditions for the concentrated Ammophos and poor crop yields. It is therefore most probable that much of the irregularity in the so-called acidity of the nitrogenous fertilizer is due to a shortage of calcium for the crop's most effective use of the nitrogen and phosphorus as well as for the crop's need of the element calcium itself. These conditions are aggravated more as the superphosphates are concentrated to reduce the accompanying calcium. Calcium deficiency is presenting itself more prominently because the long existent shortages are not being covered by heavier calcium dosages in the lower grade superphosphates.

Neutralizing a soil with calcium carbonate encourages manganese shortage in some crops. But as more limestone is put into a limited amount of surface soil to put more calcium into the plants, then more manganese is taken from the untreated lower soil. Accordingly, the limestone functioning as a carbonate plays a detrimental role, but functioning as a calcium contributor it has a beneficial role in the same crop.

Soils should not be neutral if the products grown thereon are to be rich in calcium in particular, according to research by R.A. Schroeder. His recent work with spinach demonstrates that more calcium and more magnesium moved into this common, mineral-carrying, dietary component when the calcium content of the soil was increased and the soil kept acid at pH 5.2, than when the same calcium fertilization took place and the reaction was changed to nearly neutral, or pH 6.8. The calcium treatment was much more effective in giving calcium returns within the spinach, when grown on acid reaction. Three units of calcium applied on soil at pH 5.2 delivered more calcium in concentration and in total, in the spinach crop, than when 12 units were put on the soil at pH 6.8. It narrowed the potassium-calcium ratio and suggests a composition nearer the proteinaceous, mineral containing vegetation rather than that of vegetation that is mainly woody matter. According to this, a fertilizer can have less calcium and use it more effectively by having acidity present. Perhaps spinach will be more effective as a mineral contributor, or as an antirachitic factor, in our diet when we learn that the effects of calcium as a plant nutrient must be separated from the carbonate effects in acid neutralization, and that very probably even some hydrogen may be required in the soil to mobilize the calcium into the crop most efficiently.

Now that virgin soils are no longer available, we are more cognizant of the fact that we have been farming the organic matter of the soil. The seriousness of this is evident, especially in the South, where the farmer experience still maintains that much of the fertilizer should be in the organic form. These facts remind us that the fertility in the organic matter is tuned with the growing season for delivery of the nutrients at the rates of decay suited to the needs of the growing crop. The use of strictly mineral fertilizers with the seeding does not fit into the picture of plant needs so well. Consequently, the leaching loss from fertilizers is being appreciated. It suggests that fertilizers may be used on grass sods or crops growing heavily enough to take up the fertilizers quickly and to reduce the leaching loss. With more fertilizer used on seed crops, particularly those with legumes mixed through them, the fertilizers will be held back against loss in leaching. Such will be building fertilizer into the organic matter to extend the season of its nutrient delivery when the sod is plowed up and put to a tilled crop. This will spread the fertilizer effect over a longer time, and make it less of a hypodermic one. In fact, it will be a case of fertilizing the crops whose organic matter will have an additional fertilizing effect on other crops following.

Fertilizers have an opportunity for greater service as the plant functions and soil processes are more clearly understood. Their use will increase only as their service becomes greater. No fertilizer manufacturer would want his goods to render other than maximum possible benefit. Attention to other ingredients besides the nitrogen, phosphorus and potassium bids fair to improve fertilizer effects and to extend their service.

The present concern about improving the reaction of fertilizer is testimony that manufactures are eager to make their goods better. When these good intentions are supplemented by more fundamental information from research in plant physiology and soil science, fertilizer improvement will shift from this concern about neutrality to one of concern about calcium content. It may even aim to deliver hydrogen. It may add many other revisions that will be of greater value in making soils more serviceable for better plants, for better animals and better health to humans.

CHAPTER 19

Bugaboo of Soil Acidity Dispelled

SOIL ACIDITY IS A bugaboo that farmers for years have been uselessly fighting. As a matter of fact, acidity may actually be beneficial instead of harmful if proper soil conservation measures are used.

It is not the acidity in soils that is injurious but the shortage of nutrients that are replaced by acidity. Given the proper fertility, plants will turn in their customary or usual performance even in the presence of soil acidity. This acid condition is merely a case of increased shortage of plant food nutrients for which crops suffer.

Experiments with soybeans in which increased soil acidity made both calcium and phosphorus actually more effective than in more neutral soil, improved the feeding value of forage and kept the sand element lower.

Experiments indicate that it is no longer necessary to fight soil acidity, on the contrary, acidity is beneficial if lime or calcium, phosphorus, potash and other plant foods are utilized to restore full fertility and if soils are helped to maintain their needed stores of organic matter by means of sod crops or corresponding recuperative rest periods.

We can now say that acid tolerant legumes have been discovered. But they tolerate acidity only when fertilizer materials are properly supplied in balanced amounts.

In this connection it was pointed out that the three vital plant foods on which crops depends most are: 1—nitrogen, which encourages early and abundant growth, builds protein and develops the fleshy portion of roots; 2—phosphorus, which hastens the ripening of seed and promotes early maturity; and 3—potash, which is the balance wheel, enabling a crop to make better use of the other plant foods, develop resistance to disease and maintain an improved quality.

CHAPTER 20

Lime Soil to Feed Crops— Not to Remove Soil Acidity

NODULES ON ROOTS OF CLOVERS in acid soil far below streaks of limestone drilled with seedings show that legume bacteria do not require lime mixed throughout the soil. Such observations suggest that limestone is needed to feed plants rather than to fight acidity. All acidity does not need to be removed from the entire soil layer in which roots are growing.

Measurements of soil acidity demonstrated that drilling limestone no deeper than a few inches did not change the degree of soil acidity very much. This was even true in soil near the limestone. Yet red clover had numerous nodules on roots at varying depths below streaks of limestone in the soil. Those evidences of action by nitrogen-fixing bacteria were in soil areas of decidely acid nature with pH values as low as 4.5. It can scarcely be believed that bacteria were dragged down there by advancing roots. Very likely they were down there before-hand but went into action only when roots came along that had been properly nourished by contact with limestone calcium or magnesium in upper soil layers.

This nutrition served to make the symbiotic connection between roots and these particular bacteria possible. This evidence needs only to be seen to doubt the validity of the belief that soils must be neutral, or have all acidity removed before red and sweet clovers will grow, he continues.

In some other trials using sweet clover, a supposedly "acid-sensitive" legume, applications of mill-run, ten-mesh limestone at rates of 300 and 600 pounds per acre served to establish this legume better than the same application of pulverized or highly active limestone.

While none of the soil under these treatments showed measurable changes in degree of acidity, or pH, sweet clover roots were still getting enough calcium to nourish the crop from coarser particles that lasted longer in clay. Roots were not so nourished where pulverized limestone was used. Speedy reaction and absorption of pulverized limestone made this soil fraction too much of a competitor to be matched by roots as a force taking up limestone calcium.

Apparently a few coarser limestone particles scattered through the soil to break down slowly and to feed the legume in those few focal points were all that was required. It was not necessary to drive out all soil acidity.

Much has been learned about clay and its capacity to adsorb and exchange calcium and magnesium. Also, it is known that plant roots have similar capacities taken by hydrogen—that is, acidity. From these facts it is known that legumes can grow on soils that are by no means neutral and free of acidity. Even when clay carries a set of nutrient ions well balanced for a particular crop, some heavier soils will still grow good legume crops when as much as 20% of the soil's exchange capacity is taken by acidity or hydrogen.

The pH of the soil does not need to be brought up to 7.0. There is no need to get rid of all soil acidity for growing nitrogen-fixing, protein-producing, mineral-rich forages. Lime is required. But this serves to feed them by its contents of necessary calcium and magnesium, rather than to fight soil acidity by carbonates.

CHAPTER 21

Lime-Rich Soils Give Size and Vigor to French Stock

WHEN ANYONE SPEAKS ABOUT the agriculture of France, most of us think immediately of big horses and oxen with good muscles and heavy bones. Yet, when anyone speaks about French farm people, it is not uncommon for us to hear these farmers of a more mature agriculture and producers of fine live-stock referred to with seeming reflection as "peasant" farmers.

Perhaps the man of the land over there may not have been formally educated in the science of farming; but, when it comes to understanding the art of agriculture, he surely must have long known the relation of his soils to the nutrition of his animals in order to have grown them to such size, style, vigor and vitality. This seems all the more true when we learn that he feeds them mainly on grasses and home-grown feeds. Apparently we must grant that even this "peasant" farmer knows live stock production "from the ground up."

That this older agriculture is built from the ground up in the fullest sense of those words was the belief that prompted my study of soils in France as an accompanying vocation while teaching soils to our soldiers at Biarritz American University. After a careful survey of the geology of France, there followed some travel over her main soil regions primarily in Army trucks and jeeps. The study, collection and analyses of soil samples in relation to crops were undertaken with the help of Captain C. E. Ferguson, originally with U. S. Soil Conservation Service. The net result was the conviction that, in assigning causes for the big live stock in this older country, one must give foremost place to fertility of the soil.

Here is a soil that serves in growing animals as well as—or possible better than—it does in fattening them. Here is an agricultural foundation, based upon generous stocks of lime and phosphorus, which builds bone from nutritious, mineral-rich forages and also produces proteinacious crops which builds muscle, possibly more than it provides big yields of starchy crops with fattening values.

Almost anywhere that one selects a soil in cultivation and puts a sample to chemical test, one is impressed with the soil's liberal supply of lime. In this calcareous nature of the soil one can see the reason why alfalfa (spoken of as a "lucerne"), clovers and other legumes are so common in their crop rotation schemes. One can also understand why most farmers answer no to a query as to whether limestone is used for crop improvement.

The geology of France helps explain the extensive areas of calcareous soils. Many of the broad stream valleys, with low or very gradual grades leading out from them—where most of the farm regions are located, are residual soils from limestone, from calcareous shales and from other secondary rocks with high contents of lime. Even geological erosion, and unobserved sheet erosion from top soil under cultivation are pushing the development of a new soil downward in the profile apparently fast enough to compensate for these losses. The farmer is seemingly making some new soil in the bottom of furrows just about as fast as he is wearing off the old soil at the top.

Then, too, this country is located fairly well north. It lies between the latitudes of about 42½° N and 51° N—equivalent to stretching out between Detroit and the tip of James Bay, or from Sioux City, Iowa, to Winnipeg, Canada, in our hemisphere. As a peninsular land, however, it does not have wide fluctuations in weather. It does not have very cold winters or very hot summers. It does not have short, alternating hot and cold or wet and dry spells. Instead, its seasonal changes are gradual. Its rains are drizzles rather than "gulley-washers." The water goes into the soil more that it runs off. Every rain has a high percentage of penetration and thereby a high potentiality in benefit to the growing crop. This is pronounced under the low evaporation at this northern latitude. So that, even though annual rainfall is not much more than 30 inches, it serves very efficiently especially for the shallower rooted crops such as grass.

France also has a distribution of rainfall and temperature which is known as "Mediterranean climate." These heavier rainfalls last during a very short season while the lighter rains are regular during the rest of the year. The soils, therefore, do not have enough water going through them to wash or leach out the lime excessively. Yet they are kept wet enough that cultivation breaks down soil minerals and rock fragments. Thus, the soils give up mineral fertility to balance the removal by growing crops, in keeping with the fertility-conserving kind of agriculture that is so common in these older countries.

Such combination of country and climate provide a good set of conditions, namely, plenty of mineral fertility and not so much rain. But when that rain comes it makes a grass which one can say—much as we do of our short grass country— that "every mouthful counts" in terms of animal growth. Here there are feeds for growth more than for fattening, since the plants have the fertility to compel them to do more than just catch fresh air, water and sunshine to give a starchy product and fattening values. It has the contributions from the soil that are needed to build bone and brawn in big animals.

Where lime has not been leached out, then other elements of soil fertility also remain. It is well to remember that calcium serves to mobilize other nutrients into the crop. Even though these others are, at times, not so plentifully present, yet they serve efficiently because they are associated with the lime.

Fortunately for France, many of her limestones are rich in fossils. These skeletons of animal life in the ancient seas represent considerable phosphorus. In testing what would be considered almost a sandy or even a gravelly soil one is often surprised to find it high both in lime and phosphate. This is the fertility combination which represents nearly complete chemical constituents of the skeletons of farm animals—a combination that is so essential for growing leguminous feeds that produce young animals so efficiently.

The farmer of France has for years practiced feeding his animals on homegrown feeds. Because these crops from fertile soil are highly nutritive, he does not have to search for supplements to bolster bulky roughage feeds. For generations he has clung to the principles of the old art of agriculture for which science has only recently given us a better understanding. We have gained a fuller appreciation from such experiments as those carried out, for example, by the work of Professor Weaver at University of Missouri.

Professor Weaver pastured different lots of hogs, each on a different crop. It was significant to note that alfalfa, regularly admitted as needing a fertile soil, made 592 pounds of pork per acre. Soybeans, claimed by some to be a crop which can be grown on a lime-deficient soil where alfalfa fails, produced only 175 pounds of pork per acre. Likewise, for each bushel of grain supplements fed while the hogs were on pastures, the alfalfa has a pork-producing value of 192 pounds while that from soybeans dropped as low as 67 pounds.

In short, only about one-third as much pork was obtained from the crop which is said to grow on soils of much lower fertility than that required for alfalfa. It means that, after all it is fertile soil which makes live stock. The farmer of France has long been growing good animals largely because of the fertility of his soil, which has been well maintained in terms of lime and phosphate. Although there naturally, fertility has been carefully conserved by the wise and consistent use of manure.

It may be that the farmers in these older countries have been not so much the leaders as they were the followers in this whole matter. It may be that allowed the animal's choice to take the agriculture to the more fertile and more lasting soils. In these older agricultures, originally nomadic, it is quite possible that the flocks and herds, more than their owners, led the way to particular soils where the plow came later to bring a permanent agriculture. It may have been the choice of good natural herbages by the animals, or the biochemical assay of the soil fertility by live stock, that led pasturing animals initially and arable agriculture later to the fertile soils and kept them off those not so productive.

Regardless of factors leading to the initial selection of agricultural lands, whether by man or by flocks and herds, the lime rich and relatively phosphatic soils have contributed much to the agriculture of France. It will be well, too for France if that fact is not forgotten as she comes out of the present political turmoil and economic shake-up in Europe and begins to make plans for her future. There are many suggestions that in the days to come she may be depending upon her lime-rich soils in a still larger way for feeding not, only live stock but her people as well.

CHAPTER 22

Lime Your Soils For Better Crops

THE SCIENCE OF THE SOIL has done much for our better understanding of how the soil and the plant roots interact to make the crops grow. From better understanding, some principles have resulted for better guidance of our farm practices.

Liming the soil is one of those practices improved through science. We formerly encouraged liming as a struggle against soil acidity. It is now practiced to put calcium into the soil for nutritional service to the crops. It helps them in their synthesis of proteins and other complex compounds of higher food values to man and beast.

Calcium plays its role as a small part of the material of construction. It is recognized more readily in the ash. In animals and man, calcium is recognized easily as bone. In all life it is far more important than merely a part of the final structure. It serves as the tool in many life processes. It is a necessary tool for fashioning the different proteins that only plants can fabricate from the elements. It seems to be associated with the processes by which livestock assembles these plant proteins into choice animal products of great nutritional value. We have long been liming for legumes and we have connected livestock with legumes. But we have been late in recognizing this basic principle of the interaction between the calcium of the soil and the roots of the crops. As a matter of fact it is the working principle of this food creation assembly line.

Calcium serves, in the growth of plants, to mobilize other essential chemical elements into the plant more speedily. It puts a higher content of the ash elements into the forage. It is always associated with the crops that we say are better feed for young animals. It is associated more with feeds for growth and reproduction than with those for fattening only. It is associated with the soil's microbial processes that build up soil nitrogen. It is also effective in making green manure and other organic matter decay more rapidly and release their fertility for crop production. All life, from the lowly microbe to man himself, is dependent on a good supply of available calcium in the soil.

Liming the soil is one of the contributions to the better nourishment of all that grows on our farms. This soil treatment must, however, be judiciously connected with other treatments. It must not, therefore, be used excessively. If wisely used, this farm practice—as it is now undergirded by the science of the soil—will bring about better understanding and use of the other necessary soil treatments. This better knowledge should conserve not only the body of the soil, but also its fertility or internal strength by which all life must be fed.

CHAPTER 23

Physiological Importance of Calcium in Legume Inoculation

THAT CALCIUM SHOULD BE an important factor in the nodulation of legumes on acid, or sour, soils is suggested by the varying results in nodulation obtained on these soils. This is indicated especially in the soils of northeastern Missouri and southern Illinois, where the many or even frequent and repeated failures of inoculation with pure cultures have been found to occur on certain predominating acid soil types; while improved inoculation results when these soils are supplied, either previous to or at the time of planting, with limestone, acid phosphate, or other calcium-bearing materials.

Data presented by Hellriegel and Wilfarth, in their original article, establishing the relation between legume root nodules and nitrogen fixation, show a stimulating effect of calcium upon nodulation and growth of serradella. Recently Alway, in comparing the effectiveness of soil transfer with that of pure cultures as inoculation for alfalfa on lime-deficient, sandy soils, found that when the land had not been limed the soil transfer method was far more effective for the first seeding. Excessive increases in the amount of culture did not make this method as effective as soil transfer. On land limed well in advance of seeding, however, the inoculations by soil transfer and by the pure culture method were of equal efficacy. This seems to indicate an inability of the organisms to establish themselves quickly in a lime-deficient soil habitat.

Fellers, in a summary of his work on the factors affecting nodulation of soy beans, states: "The bacterial infection of roots does not take place readily on acid soils even when the root infecting organisms are plentiful in the soil." Bryan, in a study of the effect of acid soil reactions on nodulation of soy beans, found that in general the hydrogen-ion relations for the organism tend to be the same as those for the host plant. He secured a maximum nodulation at pH 6.5, and none below pH 4.9, although the critical hydrogen-ion concentration for the organisms in solution cultures was found to be pH 3.5–3.9.

Truog ventured the theory that the effect of soil reaction on the activity of the bacteria within the nodule is indirect, since the environment of the bacteria when in the nodule must be that of the plant tissue. Karraker, in examining this viewpoint, found that the root system of a single alfalfa plant, divided between a lime-deficient and a limed soil, gave differences in nodule formation corresponding to those obtained on different plants growing wholly within these different soils. He concluded that the effect of soil reaction on nodule formation must be one of localized character in the plant, a direct effect of soil pH on the bacteria in the nodules, or an antecedent effect of the soil acidity on the bacteria, while they are existing non-symbiotically in the soil.

Scanlan concluded that hydrogen-ion concentration has no direct effect upon inoculation, and analogous inoculation resulted from the use of limestone and calcium acetate where the former lessened the hydrogen-ion concentration while the latter had no effect upon it.

Falk thinks that neutralization of the acid is not the only effect of certain valuable salts, this being indicated by the fact that magnesium carbonate and phosphate improve bacterial growth more effectively than calcium carbonate. Machida demonstrated that calcium salts and not magnesium salts are effective in protecting bacteria against lethal agencies. This work was substantiated by Chambers and Rezinkoff, studying the protoplasm of *Amoeba proteus*.

Winslow and Falk found that concentrations of 0.4 per cent of sodium chloride alone, or of 0.2 per cent of calcium chloride alone, exerted marked lethal effects upon the growth of a typical colon Bacillus, *B. communis*, while, a mixture of these two, in the ratio of one Ca-ion to five Na-ions and in concentrations as high as 5 per cent of the salt, was actually beneficial in its effect upon the growth of the organism. Hotchkiss made a survey of the effects of cations upon the bacterial growth of *B. coli*, and found that calcium chloride in a 0.5 molar concentration limited growth completely, but stimulated growth in a 0.05 molar concentration. Scanlan found that one part of calcium chloride to 1,500 parts of solution was the optimum concentration for stimulating growth and longevity of *B. radicicola*.

Investigations to date give numerous observations on the effects of limed and acid soils on nodulation of legumes, with almost as many theories as to the operating causes. These conditions emphasize the need for a fuller understanding of the fundamental facts controlling the responses in nodule production by legumes and their bacteria on soils of varying degrees of soil acidity or base deficiency.

Experimentation

The work here reported bears testimony to some of the preceding viewpoints. Results analogous to those of Karraker were obtained in working with soy beans on an acid Putnam silt loam. Seedlings were grown in sterile sand for 10–14 days, when the tap roots were cut off just below the lateral roots, which had developed in good numbers and to a length of about 1 inch. These seedlings were placed over a water-tight partition in a container with one-half of the root system carefully planted into an acid soil (pH 5.14) on one side, and the other half into the same soil after it had been thoroughly mixed with calcium carbonate at the rate of 8,000 pounds per two million of soil. Liberal quantities of a suspension of inoculating bacteria were added as the soil was filled into the pans around the root system. Five seedlings with their lateral roots so divided were set into each container. In addition, ten seedlings, with their tap roots likewise cut off, were planted into the container, five on the side of the acid soil and five on the side of the limed soil. Water was maintained at the optimum by daily surface applications.

Although there was a high mortality of plants in consequence of tap root pruning and replanting, those that lived grew very satisfactorily. At the end of 5 weeks they were carefully taken up and the nodules counted. The nodule counts of the plants with divided roots and checks are summarized in table 1. The results show an increase of 208 per cent in the number of nodules formed on the portion of the roots growing in the calcium soil as compared with those formed on the portion in the untreated soil. The difference of 181.1 per cent in nodulation by the check plants, grown wholly within one kind of soil, is approximately the same ratio. The comparison of the degrees of inoculation of the divided root plants and the checks is made on this basis rather than on the actual plant units, because the average nodulation of either portion of the root of the divided root plants represents but one-half of the normal nodulation of the plants.

Table 1

Nodulation of Plants Grown with Part of Root System in Calcium-Treated Soil and Part in Untreated Soil (pH 5.14)

| | Plants with divided roots | | | Check plants | | | |
| | | Nodule production | | Calcium-treated soil | | Untreated soil | |
Treatment	No. of plants	Roots in calcium-treated soil	Roots in untreated soil	No. of plants	No. of nodules	No. of plants	No. of nodules
Uninoculated...	4	0	0	6	0	5	0
Inoculated...	23	160	77	28	494	31	302
Average per plant...	......	6.95	3.34	......	17.64	......	9.74
Percentage increase...	......	208	......	......	181.1	......	......

The reliability of these data is questionable on account of, first, the small number of plants on which the test was completed, and second, the unequal development of the two parts of the divided root systems.

The results obtained for soy beans agree well with those for alfalfa by Karraker. They indicate that, if the effect of the calcium is a physiological one through the plant, this effect is local in character, and the calcium is certainly not translocated to all the roots of the plant for equal effectiveness in improving inoculation; or, that the depressed nodulation in this acid soil is due to an effect of the soil conditions upon the bacteria before they have infected the roots of the host plant.

A test of the stimulating effect of calcium upon nodulation of soy beans on an already well inoculated soil emphasized further the possible physiological effect of this element. The soil used had a pH of 5.5, and was well stocked with the soy bean organism in consequence of well inoculated crops of soy beans on three previous seasons.

Enough of this soil was mixed with calcium carbonate at the rate of 8,000 pounds per two million to fill thirty pots, while a like number were filled with untreated soil, and each of the sixty pots was planted with five sterile, sprouted soy beans. After cautious culture for five weeks, when the

Table 2

*Nodule Numbers as Influenced by Calcium Carbonate on Soil Growing Soy Beans Previously**

Soil treatment	Pots	Plants	Total	Range per pot	Average per pot	Average per plant	Increase per cent
None...	30	130	1659	10–142	55.3	12.0	
Calcium carbonate...	30	133	5353	64–380	178.4	40.2	336.8

Header group: **Nodule Numbers** spans Total, Range per pot, Average per pot, Average per plant, Increase per cent.

* Silt loam soil pH 5.5.

plants showed a uniform healthy growth with slight superiority in color, size, and appearance in the case of those given calcium carbonate, counts of the nodules were made as given in table 2. The results show an increase of 336 per cent in the numbers of nodules as a result of liming, in spite of the fact that the soil was already well inoculated with the organisms. This agrees with Fellers' observation, and while it demonstrates the correlation of nodulation of legumes on acid soils with the acidity, it does not establish the relation of cause and effect between them.

In order to differentiate more closely between the effect of soil reaction upon nodulation and the importance of calcium to nodulation, a study of the effect of calcium, as calcium chloride, on the viability of *B. radicicola* was made. For this a rather well isolated soil, mainly of residual formation from limestone, was collected from a timbered area. It was decidedly acid (pH 5.4), and sterile with reference to the soy bean organism. Sixty pots (3.5 inches in diameter) of this soil were set up, planted to soy beans, and given thorough inoculation with cultures of bacteria. One-half of these pots were given the additional treatment of a solution supplying 88 mg. of calcium chloride per pot, the calcium equivalent of 2,000 pounds of calcium carbonate per two million of soil. Eight additional pots without inoculation or calcium treatment were used as checks. The nodule counts were made after growth of five weeks.

Not a nodule had formed on a single plant in the untreated soils, and but three single nodules on as many plants in the calcium-treated soil, although a good growth of plants was obtained in all the pots. In order to test the soil for the presence of the organism, sixteen pots of each of the treated and

Table 3

Nodule Numbers of Soy Beans as Influenced by
Calcium Chloride Treatment on Soil

	Treatment	Pots	Plants	Sterile plants	Inoculated plants	Total nodules
Inoculated first planting	None...	30	130	130	0	0
	Calcium chloride...	30	133	130	3	3
Uninoculated second planting	None...	16	72	69	3	3
	Calcium chloride...	16	80	0	80	146

untreated soil were immediately replanted with sprouted beans. No further inoculation or treatment was added. Again after five weeks of growth these were taken up and the nodules counted as before. The data are summarized in table 3.

The results of this trial emphasized the difficulty of establishing the soy bean organism within this soil by a single inoculation, and demonstrated that even though the organism did not exist in the untreated soil, it continued its existence in the calcium-treated soil despite no significant change in the soil reaction. This indicates, in substantiation of Scanlan's findings, that the response by the organism must be due to effects by the calcium.

Since calcium seemed to favor nodulation, an attempt was made to determine whether or not this influence comes in consequence of its direct effect on the soil conditions, or of an indirect effect through the plant. Quartz sand was treated with hydrochloric acid for 3 hours, washed with tap water and then with distilled water until the test for chlorides was negative. The sand was dried, and heated at 3° C. for 48 hours for drying and for sterilization. Part of the sand was treated with calcium carbonate at the rate of ten thousand pounds per two million pounds of sand.

Sterilized soy beans, the progeny from a single plant, were germinated for 24 hours, planted in both the limed and unlimed sand, and then grown for 10 days. Seedlings from both the calcium-bearing and the calcium-deficient sands were washed free of adhering particles and transplanted into the respective halves of each of two flats of well prepared soils. One of these soils was a lime-deficient field soil and the other a neutral garden soil, both of which had grown well-inoculated soy beans during the three preceding seasons. Excellent growth resulted in both flats, and after

Table 4

Nodule Production by Soy Beans in Neutral and Acid Soils as Influenced by Calcium in Transplanted Seedlings

| Kind of soil | pH | Seedling Treatment | No. of Plants | Nodule numbers | | Calcium content (Mg. Ca) | | |
				Range per plant	Average per plant	Seedlings Per 100	Electrodialysable per 10 gm. W-free Soil	Seeds Per 100
Neutral	7.8	None	60	12–77	36.6	17.07	24.07	6.85
		Calcium	67	9–67	38.9	30.14		
Acid	5.5	None	69	1–7	3.4	17.07	11.78	6.85
		Calcium	79	2–25	15.1	30.14		

5 weeks the plants were removed and counts made of the nodules, with the results given in table 4.

On the lime-deficient soil the calcium-starved plants developed few nodules. In marked contrast to this, there were almost five times as many nodules within this soil in consequence of allowing the seedlings to grow in calcium-bearing sand and to transplant their needed calcium to the lime-deficient soil. On the neutral soil no differences in nodulation occurred as a result of either treatment to the seedlings.

In order to gain some additional information, the following chemical determinations were made: the calcium content of the bean seeds, of the 10-day old seedlings grown on the calcium-deficient sand, and of those grown on calcium-bearing sand, according to a modification of McCrudden's method; the total dialysable base of both soils, by Bradfield's method; and the total dialysable calcium in these soils by the same method. The summary of these analytical data is given also in table 4, with the omission of total dialysable base.

From the complete data in table 4 it will be seen that the soil on which good nodulation occurred, regardless of seedling treatment, had a pH of 7.8 and gave 24.07 mg. electro-dialysable calcium per 10 gm. of soil; while the soil which gave good inoculation only on calcium-treated seedlings had a pH of 5.5 and 11.78 mg. of electro-dialysable calcium per 10 gm. of soil.

The increased nodulation of the higher calcium-containing seedlings on the calcium-deficient soil demonstrates that the presence of calcium in the plant increases nodulation of soy beans on such a soil. On the other hand, the lack of difference in nodulation of the seedlings on the more calcium-sufficient soil indicates that either the presence of calcium in the plant does not affect nodulation on such a soil, or that if it does, the calcium-starved plants take calcium from the soil soon enough to offset the measurable effect in difference in nodulation.

The increase in calcium content of the seedlings grown on the acid-extracted sand over the calcium content of the bean seeds was due to the calcium that was carried back into the acid-extracted sand by the tap water with which the sand was washed. Although the calcium content of the seedlings grown on this extracted sand was more than expected from the analysis of the seeds, the actual amount contained was but little more than half that of the seedlings grown in the calcium-bearing sand. Improved methods on this point will probably intensify the results obtained.

Part V

After finding that the presence of calcium within the plant increased the nodulation of soy beans on an acid lime-deficient soil, a microchemical study of the seedlings was made to locate, if possible, any histological differences in the calcium-starved and calcium-fed seedlings. Parts from both stems and roots of each of these were collected at the age of 10 days, and prepared by the usual method for sectioning in paraffin. Microphotographs of cross-sections of the stem taken near the plant crown are reproduced in figs. 1–4. These photographs are representative sections from more than forty slides. The differences shown in the figures were the same throughout the slides. The cell walls of the calcium-starved seedlings failed to retain their shape, and apparently gave way before the microtome blade, while the cells of the calcium-fed plants stood up under the treatment and gave distinctly better sections.

These differences were innate to the material, since the comparative sections of calcium-starved and calcium-fed seedlings were cut at the same time, and on the same microtome. The materials were fixed and processed as separate samples, but in duplicate of the same lot, so that variation in laboratory technique was reduced to a minimum. The usual macroscopic, or external differences in stems and roots in consequence of liberal and deficient calcium supply were noted before those of microscopic nature were studied. Miss Day emphasized the former for *Pisum sativum* in recent

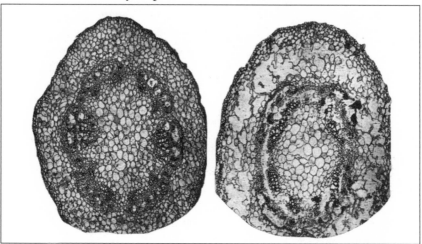

Figs. 1, 2.—Cross-section of stems of calcium-starved and calcium-bearing soy bean seedlings (10 days old): fig. 1, calcium-bearing, fig. 2, calcium-starved; X170.

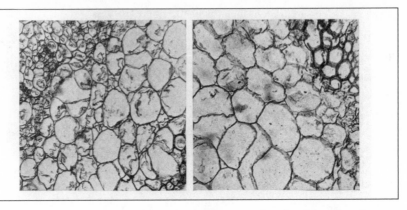

Figs. 3, 4.—Cross-section of stems of calcium-starved and calcium-bearing soy bean seedlings (10 days old): fig. 3, calcium-bearing, fig. 4, calcium-starved; X750.

work, but she reported no significant differences in anatomical structure in these plant parts.

Both microchemical and staining methods for demonstrating calcium and pectate in micro-sections were employed in an attempt to discover any differences in the cell walls. Material from 10-day old seedlings is so minute in structure, however, that as yet it has been impossible to record micro-photographically and differences noted. Further work on this phase is being done, and it is expected that this observed histological difference between calcium-starved and calcium-fed soy bean seedlings can be intensified and substantiated by using seedlings more nearly deficient in calcium through growth on sand leached free of calcium with acid and distilled water, and by using seedlings of greater age to intensify their differences.

Summary

1. An experimental study was made of the effect of calcium on nodulation of soy beans on certain acid soils, with the hope of contributing to the knowledge of the role calcium plays in inoculation.

2. The divided root system of soy beans, grown in acid soil on one side and calcium-treated soil on the other, gave differences in nodule production to as great an extent as those produced when plants were grown wholly within these same soils. This indicates (1) that calcium plays some physiological role in favoring nodulation; and (2) that its effects are local or restricted in increasing the number

of root infections, at least within the periods of time used in this experiment.

3. The addition of lime carbonate to an acid soil of pH 5.4, and already infected with legume organisms, gave a very marked increase in nodule production. It suggests that the effect of liming is not necessarily one of keeping alive the bacteria applied as inoculation, since in this case liming increased the number of nodules by organisms originally present in the soil. Evidently the lime carbonate exerted a physiological effect on the plants, and possibly on the organisms, to bring on the greater nodule production.

4. The addition of small amounts of calcium chloride to an acid soil (pH 5.5) increased the viability of the legume organism, *B. radicicola*, of soy beans, applied to the soil by pure cultures, and stimulated nodulation of the host plant.

5. Calcium taken up by the plant in its early growth influenced nodulation, since there was a difference in the nodulation of 10-day old calcium-starved and calcium-bearing seedlings when replanted to an already well inoculated lime-deficient soil of pH 5.4.

6. This functioning of calcium within or through the plant to produce increased nodulation may have a fundamental histological or physiological basis in the plant, since running parallel with the effect on nodulation by calcium given the seedlings, there is a distinct difference in the plant cell wall structure suggested by differences in ease of obtaining micro-sections of the 10-day old calcium-starved and calcium-bearing soy bean seedlings.

CHAPTER 24

Calcium and Soil-Borne Nutrients

CALCIUM PLAYS WHAT might be termed the *leadership* role amongst the nutrient ions not only as to their entrance into the plants but also as to their combination into the proteinaceous compounds around which cell multiplication and life itself center.

As the protein concentration of forages rises, there is also an increase in the calcium concentration. Also there is accumulation of evidence that with the increase in protein there goes an increase in vitamins.

Legume demand

Legumes, the more nutritious of the forages, have long been known for their demand for calcium and high content of protein. They are also high in other minerals, so that calcium in the plants seems to synthesize the soil-borne nutrients into the organic combinations though it does not itself appear as part of the final products.

Potassium, quite unlike calcium, is more directly effective in the compounding of air and water into carbohydrates, and like calcium does not itself appear in them. Potassium is effective in making bulk or tonnage, of forage.

Potent proteins

Calcium is effective in bringing higher concentration of proteins, and other essential nutrients within that bulk. According as the active calcium dominates the supplies of nutrients in the soil, so proteinaceousness—and with it a high content of growth minerals—characterize the vegetation produced on the soil.

As potassium dominates, there is plenty of plant bulk but its composition is highly carbonaceous or it is dominantly woody.

Ecological array

Here is a general principle that is helpful in understanding the ecological array of vegetation. According to it, the vegetation is highly proteinaceous and mineral-rich on our prairies in the soil regions of lower rainfall or those retaining a high mineral content with calcium prominent. Contrariwise, vegetation is mainly wood, or like the forest, on the more leached soils with lower mineral content but with potassium naturally dominant.

Soil studies

This ecological picture served as a stimulus for some soil studies of the chemical activities of potassium and calcium when present on the clay in different ratios.

Prof. C. E. Marshall of the University of Missouri, has designed electrodes and membranes for measuring the ionic activity of calcium and potassium in the same way as hydrogen ion activities are measured.

Conclusions

His studies demonstrate clearly that the ionic activities in a mixture of elements are not independent of each other, as is true in mixtures of gases. Rather they are complimentary in some combinations, or opposing in others.

Considering calcium and potassium in combination, the latter gains ascendency in relative activities as the ratios between the calcium and the potassium become narrower.

Thus, as calcium is more nearly weathered out of the soil, potassium becomes relatively more active in moving into the plant.

Here is the physico-chemical soil situation that provokes the protein-carbohydrate relation—which in turn represents the "grow" foods versus "go" food situation, so prominently basic in our hidden hungers.

CHAPTER 25

Nutritional Role of Calcium in Plants—Prominent in the Non-Legume Crops, Sugar Beets

STUDIES, USING THE SUGAR BEET as a non-leguminous crop in the Imperial and San Joaquin Valleys of California, have shown by soil tests, measured crop yields, and the storage of the disaccharide sugar in the root, that calcium is a plant nutrient deficient in these desert soils.

It was demonstrated by trials over three years that the drilling in seed contact of a natural gypsiferous mineral, known in commerce as "mineralag", gave decided improvement in the crops as increasing stands and root yields on the neutral and alkaline soils under cooperative supervision of the Holly Sugar Corporation of tests by Geyser Minerals Corp., Denver, Colorado.

It was established that these desert soils with organic matter contents of barely one per cent, or less, a pH of 8.0 and higher, and of excesses of other cations above standard percentages saturation of exchange capacities, the slight variations in applications of nitrogenous, phosphatic and mixed fertilizers in conjunction with calcium, can represent imbalanced plant nutrition as shown by reduced concentrations of the disaccharide sugar in the beet root. The absence, in near total, of both the soil organic matter and the hydrogen cation, or acidity, show clearly how badly unbuffered these soils are to be 'physiologically shocked' by more 'salt' applications in fertilizers.

Accordingly, when so poorly buffered, the excesses of the other cations, namely, magnesium (possibly the most disturbing), potassium and sodium beyond adsorption potentials to be active as salts, are serious disturbers to any attempt to balance plant nutrition for higher, or controlled sugar concentrations, along with higher beet yields.

These studies recognize the need to consider the balance of the cationic fertility as a factor pointing to the concentration of the disaccharide sugar as well as to the tonnage yields of roots. These studies point to the need to consider the quality, first, along with the quantity of the crop as guides for wisest soil management.

Introduction

Liming the soil for improved agricultural production of crops, especially the legumes, was a practice, even with the Romans, before the Christian Era. The belief, that liming was beneficial for legumes because it counteracted an acid condition of the soil, was introduced as late as the first or second decade of the twentieth century. That became a more firmly established idea when the chemists told us about concentrations of the hydrogen ions, measured more accurately by the delicate dye indicators and, soon thereafter, by the hydrogen (glass) electrode, and specially designed machines with dial indicators reporting hydrogen ion concentration (activities) on a logarithmic scale.

But with more knowledge through research about plant nutrition, it soon seemed more logical to consider that in case of improved legume crop growth from liming the soil, it is the nutrient calcium, not the alkalinity, that is operating as the cause. Such a view emphasizes the properly balanced nutrition of the plant, especially as concerns the four essential cationic nutrients, calcium, magnesium, potassium and sodium, as soil-borne factors in healthy plant growth and survival, more than the reduction, of the ionic, acidic hydrogen of the soil as the environment of the plant roots, later discovered as a beneficial one.

One would be expected to envision nutrition certainly more essential, and acidity not so damaging when the plant's uptake of nutrient cations occurs because its root environment, or rhizosphere, is made acid by its own respired waste, namely, carbon dioxide, which, in water, makes the acid encircling the root with ionic hydrogen actively exchanging itself to the surrounding colloidal clay-humus, which offers adsorbed or available cations like calcium, magnesium, potassium, sodium, and others, to be exchanged for it (another cation) to the root as nutrition and growth. When acidity of the soil has been resulting in plant nourishment during all the past ages of the plant's evolution, one can scarcely indict soil acidity as damaging, except as it represents nutrient exhaustion, and thereby plant starvation—an inimical soil environment, a priori, for healthy plant growth.

This belief in supposed damage to legume crops by soil acidity was emphasized in connection with their production of nitrogen-fixing root nodules in which the Rhizobium microbes enabled those plants, on soils of higher saturation by exchangeable calcium, to elaborate atmospheric nitrogen into the plant proteins required for good healthy growth. The accumulated studies concerning calcium required as such nutrition of legume plants for their symbiotic soil microbes, have now come to raise the question whether the soil-borne, nutrient cation, calcium, in balance with other cations does not play a similar and highly beneficial, physiological role in non-legumes. Some studies during the three years, 1965–1967 inclusive, with sugar beets in the desert soils of the Imperial and San Joaquin Valleys of California have suggested the validity of such a theoretical consideration.

Historical and Previous Research

Research studies about legume inoculation to determine how early in the life of the soybean it becomes nodulated under the influence of various cationic nutrients in quartz sand, demonstrated calcium much more stimulative than either magnesium or potassium in early germination and better growth of the plants.

In another study, soybean seeds were started in two sets of watered quartz sand as growth medium to one of which pulverized, calcareous limestone had been added, and to the other only water. Then ten days after planting, the two sets of plants were separately transplanted into the same kind of soil, with low saturation by calcium of its exchange capacity and allowed to grow there for sixty days. The plants given the calcium through early root contact with carbonate of calcium; (a) had carried along 30.14 mg of calcium per hundred seedlings, the smaller plants given no calcium at the planting carried but 17.07 mg; (b) had nodule numbers ranging from 36.6 to 38.9 while those without initially applied calcium had 3.4 to 15.0; (c) had heights of plants of 12 cm in contrast to the other set but 7.0 cm. in height; all as facts testifying to the effectiveness of early uptake of calcium in establishing the young plants for better growth and survival.

The importance of the higher degree of saturation of the soil's capacity for colloidal adsorption of the essential cations and their later entry into the plant root as balanced plant nutrition, emphasized itself in a study of the inoculation of soybeans as seemingly related to the degree of soil acidity. Germinated seeds were placed in quartz sand as skeleton medium carrying electrodialyzed acid, colloidal clay with an initial pH of 3.35 and titrated with calcium hydroxide to provide calcium-hydrogen clays of the chosen degrees of acidity; and reciprocally degrees of saturation by calcium; namely, a pH (water) series of 4.0, 4.5, 5.0, 5.5, 6.0, and 6.5. These clays were then taken in such amounts as needed to supply a specified, constant amount of calcium per plant in each of the above six clays of degrees of acidity, or controlled pH. There were three duplicate pH, or varied acidity, series of them. One of the three series had 0.05 me of total exchangeable calcium per plant; another series had 0.10 me; and the third one had 0.20 me of calcium per plant. In the three series of the increasing pH values, each of the six represented increasing degrees of saturation of the clay's exchange capacity, but each series had a constant total quantity of exchangeable calcium offered each plant. These three represented roughly 'low', 'medium', and 'high' levels of total calcium through a series of calcium saturations of the soil's adsorption capacity of 17, 31, 45, 59, 73, and 87 per cent, accompanied by the reciprocal percentage (on basis of 100) concentration by the hydrogen cation.

Nodule production, as index of healthy plant nutrition, was limited to the *two* highest pH values and also to the higher values of saturation by calcium in the 'low' total calcium; and to the *three* highest pH values as the two higher total calcium values offered to the roots. Each pH series, from the most to the least acid soil, was an exhibition of increased or improved crop growth as pH values (increase percentages saturation) went higher, or degrees of acidity became less. (See Table A).

But, more significant was the fact that of the lower pH values the plant roots still managed to take some of the calcium from the clay which should have been made more acidic thereby. But yet, contrary to these expectations, the clays had been raised in their pH values, indicating cations moving from the growing plants to the soil, or a case of the acid-clay colloid robbing the plants of cations during their growth period. At the higher pH values, or higher degrees of calcium saturation of the clay, larger amounts of calcium were taken off the clay by the plants to lower its pH and make the clay more acid. (See Fig. 1).

Chemical analyses of the crops and tests of those clays for nitrogen, phosphorus and potassium after crop growth, showed that all three of those elements (two anions and one cation) moved to the clay from the plants to give crops (tops and roots combined) with less of each of those three elements than were initially in the planted seed.

Table A

Nodulation and Growth of Soybeans (first crop) as Influenced by the Calcium and by the pH of Calcium-Clay Soils.

Plant characters		Calcium per plant me/plant	pH at outset (first crop)					
			4.0	4.5	5.0	5.5	6.0	6.5
Nodules 50 plants		0.05	0	0	0	0	7	14
		0.10	0	0	0	8	28	40
		0.20	0	0	0	60	69	127
Height, cm		0.05	11	26	28	31	36	36
		0.10	9.5	27	34	42	44	45
		0.20	8	25	40	45	48	52
Weight of 50 plants in grams	Tops	0.05	4.8	6.3	6.8	7.0	7.9	7.6
		0.10	4.2	6.3	7.3	8.9	9.5	8.7
		0.20	4.6	6.0	8.7	9.2	9.4	9.9
	Roots	0.05	1.5	2.5	2.0	2.0	4.0	3.6
		0.10	1.7	2.2	2.1	4.3	4.3	4.2
		0.20	1.0	1.7	2.5			

We had grown plants which were holding on to their calcium, but were losing other cationic nutrients back to the soil. The startling facts were (a) the suggestion that the calcium, in particular, was not readily taken away from the plant by the clay of such high hydrogen saturation and, reciprocally, of such low calcium saturation; and (b) that nodulation did not occur at all the higher chosen percentages of calcium saturation. The losses from the plant back to the soil occurred in seventeen of the eighteen pans in the three series. It required a percentage saturation of the highest listed above to bring about what would seem like legume plants able to move nutrients in normally expected amounts into themselves from the supplies adsorbed on the clay.

That the lowest percentage of saturation, by calcium, of the soil's exchange capacity for legume growth and nitrogen fixation (in soils of low

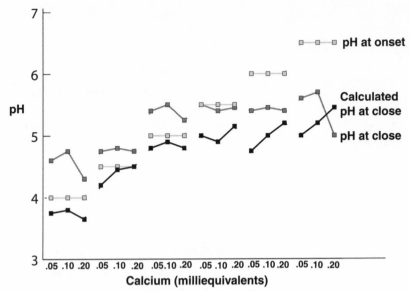

Fig. 1. *Changes in pH of calcium clay soils in consequence of soybean growth (first series).*

organic matter)* lies near but above sixty, was duplicated in another study.

Other studies and experiences from soil tests have suggested similar standard values for other nutrient cations at the following ranges of percentages saturation as balanced nutrition from the soil; magnesium, 7–15% (possibly 10–20); potassium, 2–5%; and sodium 0.5–3%. With calcium at a figure so much higher among the four cations, it is evident that small excesses in the saturations of any of the latter three would quickly represent imbalances in the plant diet from the soil by them in relation to the calcium, when its high percentage saturation required would so often be too low.

In these citations of past experiments and experience, the calcium uptake in the very early plant life of seed germination and sprouting of the rootlet with such lasting effects on plant growth, suggests that, in practice, the calcium should be applied in contact with the seed at planting. The lasting effects suggest that the root growth carries calcium, and the favorable effects

In the preparation of the colloidal clay from the Putnam Silt Loam as a plant growth medium on which the concept of plant nutrition as a balanced cationic ration is based, its final chemical analysis showed that it carried but little organic matter. But even after treating it with 30% hydrogen peroxide at 100°C for 24 hr it still contained 1.50% carbon and 0.15% nitrogen. Hence, the technique of using colloidal clay must be considered using a soil highly devoid of humus, save as that might be a part of the clay molecule.

of that, along with the root's extension of itself, when nodulation results in the deep, or distant and even inimical, untreated soil horizons. Dare we envision the root hair as a calcium-membrane of which the seemingly 'selective absorptions and exclusions' of nutrient elements manifested only when cell-wall's normal calcium saturations, activities and effects are exhibited only according as the surrounding clay, too, has a relatively high calcium saturation and the exchange services of which to the root-hair are not offset by competition of its excessive saturations by magnesium, potassium and sodium?

Membrane studies under observations by means of the electron microscope by Preston exhibit cell-wall structures made up of parallel fibrils of closely-laid cellulose, bound by cross-fibrils of calcium at regular spacings with their filtering functions, seemingly, dependent on this calcium arrangement. Dare we not believe this calcium arrangement and its functions in the root-hair membrane are modified according to the varied degrees of calcium saturation of the soil's colloidal clay-humus enshrouding the roots and thereby also to that clay's degrees of saturations by magnesium, potassium and sodium as disturbers? Can these latter high saturations not be particularly significant in desert soils where cations, other than calcium, are so recognized, and more so than we imagine by our agricultural experience and studies on only acid, humid soils?

Plan of Testing the Theories

The sugar beets seemed to offer themselves as a unique, nonlegume crop for testing the validity of the theoretical considerations prompting this study, since their seeds are borne as clusters in a glomerule, or brood-seed. That simple, natural fact would permit measuring the increased field stands of beets from planting the clusters treated with a natural gypsiferous mineral, in contrast to similarly treated and measured stands and yields of beets from planting the single seeds from clusters broken and the seeds covered as preparation for precision-spaced plantings. Such procedures would allow the use of sugar beets from seeds, treated and untreated by calcium, as a physiological test by stand counts and crop yields, of the soil's offerings of, and needs for, this nutrient element in the early life of these non-legume seedlings.

Also the yields of the sugar beet on field dimensions, harvested carefully and measured accurately as tonnages per acre when the freshly harvested crop goes directly from the field to the sugar mill to make the data collection an integral part of gathering the crops commercially for simultaneously measured quantities and qualities resulting from calcium treatments of the soil growing the sugar beets; all seemed to offer an inviting experimental test of the theoretical considerations on such an extensive field scale.

The soil treatments and crop tests were made in the desert area of the Imperial and San Joaquin Valleys of California, by applications of the partially granular commercial product known by the trade name of 'Mineralag.'

The field trials extended over the years 1965–1967, inclusive, in both arid valleys in close proximity of the mills of the Holly Sugar Corporation by whose cooperation through their agronomist and other interested scientists, the tests were carried out.*

Results

Stand counts. Imperial Valley. Planting 1965. Harvest 1966.

In making the stand counts, usually some area of the adjoining two field plots under test was selected, say, one hundred paces, 275 feet, from one or the other ends of the field, to eliminate irregularities occasioned by flooding, back-up, or washout by irrigation or any other accidental disturbance. At this point two strings, 25 feet apart, were stretched across the plot and all the young beet plants counted per row between them. These row counts of 25 feet each were repeated in other areas of the plots to arrive at an average number of plants, or mean, for 20 to 48 such row lengths.

In connection with the 1965 planting, for the 1966 harvest, only four of the total of seven growers' tests were subjected to stand counts, of the treated and the untreated plants. In the Table No. 1 giving the data of stand counts, there are given additional data, namely; (a) acres of test plot area; (b) rates mineralag applications, pounds per acre, (c) placement of it; (d) total row-length counted; (e) average numbers of plants per 25 feet row length treated and (f) untreated; and (g) increase as percent of plants per row due to the single mineralag treatment at planting.

It is significant to note from the data that the single seeds of sugar beets, planted in 1965 by the various placements (a) on listed and/or pre-shaped bed; and (b) on top of planted seed row, showed the minimum increase in stand of 8.62 per cent, and the maximum of 18.51 per cent. Those occurred when the associated additional soil treatments were nearly a constant, to

---

Mineralag is a natural resource, a ground rock fertilizer and soil additive of volcanic, hydrothermal alteration and mineral deposition (Colorado, e.g. Sec. 9–10; T47N; R11E) of mainly calcium sulfate consisting of a collective balance of primary, secondary and micronutrient (trace) elements for plants, with other unique physical, chemical and biological assets.

Table 1

Stand Counts, Imperial Valley, Planting 1965, Harvest 1966

Grower's contract number	Acres in test plots	Mineralag application lbs/A**	Placement	Total length counted (feet)	Number of Plants per 25 Ft. Section		Increase by mineralag (percent)
					Treated	Untreated	
112	11.0302* 5.5151	475	On planted row	500	94.50	87.00	+ 8.62
E. 109	6.1746 6.1746	414	On preshaped bed	600	72.00	64.75	+ 11.19
252	5.454 5.454	1012	Before listing				
W. 109	6.106 6.106	419	On preshaped bed	600	95.25	80.37	+ 18.51
35	2.651 2.651	346	On listed bed				
539	7.552 7.552	180	On listed preshaped bed	1200	82.95	76.25	+ 8.78
30	12.1952 12.1952	209	On planted row				

*The upper figures represents plot treated mineralag, the lower figures, the untreated ones.

**In addition to mineralag, the plots were given also nitrogen at 200–250 lbs per acre of ammonia, or the equivalent, and also 200–250 lbs per acre of ammonium phosphate, 11–48–0.

include nitrogen (most commonly anhydrous ammonia) and ammonium phosphate at closely constant rates, but none of which carried applications of calcium.

Such data giving those increases in the numbers of plants from single seeds planted, leave no doubt but that these non-legume crops of sugar beets needed calcium sadly on those heavy, desert soils, if the potential crop stand was to be obtained from the seeds planted and normal to beets on fertility-balanced soils.

They also point to the small application of the calcium carrier needed, even when not in direct contact with the planted seed, to increase the germination of the seed numbers, planted at the customary rate of six pounds per acre.

Those data were the early suggestions that the excessive saturations of the soil's exchange capacities by the cations of magnesium, potassium and sodium in contrast to the deficient saturations by calcium and no saturation by hydrogen, or acidity—shown by the soil test—made the chances for the calcium cation as competitor for entrance into the plant root-hairs all too low for them to manage the nutrient intake as we believe is common when ample calcium is taken by the crop during the early growth of the seedlings.

The high stand counts of 95 plants per 25 feet of row suggested an excessive rate of planting to limit each beet to less than a 4 inch diameter as row space, to say nothing of soil volume per beet too severely limited for ample calcium nutrition in a soil so hostile and not what would suggest a balanced one, especially with respect to sufficient calcium.

Harvests of sugar beets. Imperial Valley. 1966.

There were seven test areas of sugar beets, including untreated soil and such treated with mineralag (a gypsiferous material), planted in the fall of the preceding year with stand counts taken and harvested in 1966 in the Imperial Valley. The resulting harvest data are given in Table No. 2 as tonnage increases per acre due to treatment over the yields per acre for the companion area given no mineralag. Also, the increases of yields are given as percentages increase and monetary earnings per acre over those from no such treatment.

Along with those data, there are also given such of several soil fertility factors revealed by soil tests, (a) the soil's total exchange capacity; (b) the calcium deficiency as percentage relative to the desired degree of calcium saturation; (c) the excesses of magnesium; (d) of potassium; (e) of sodium; and the imbalance of cations (exclusive of sodium) against

Table 2

Increases in Yields of Sugar Beets 1966 and Related Soil Test Data, Imperial Valley 1966

Grower's contract number	Increase per acre			Soil test data					
	Tons	Per cent	Earnings $	Exchange capacity me/100 g***	Calcium deficiency %	Magnesium excess %	Potassium excess %	Sodium excess %	Imbalance (sodium excluded), %
112	{ −0.6492 26.3821*	−2.46	−2.19	44.00	18.0	71	122	166	211
East 109	{ +0.3530 18.6360	1.89	16.22	45.50	18.0	74	102	164	194
252	{ +0.7526 16.2767	4.62	−5.11**	37.00	6.9	42	79	122	128
West 109	{ +0.7616 17.3771	4.38	7.04	49.00	19.0	75	44	172	136
35	{ +0.7767 16.4328	4.72	4.43	51.00	25.0	74	60	274	159
539	{ +0.9871 25.4973	3.87	31.79	37.50	11.0	44	60	235	115
30	{ +2.1714 20.3325	10.67	27.77	47.50	23.0	70	103	240	196

* The lower figure represents the yield of the untreated plot (given no mineralag) while the upper figure is the increase in tonnage per acre by that soil treatment.

** The reduction in percentage of sugar in the beets in connection with heavy application of nitrogen and also of mineralag (discussed in the text) points to cation need for 'balanced' plant nutrition, especially in case of soils low in organic matter.

*** These high exchange capacities, and other test data, point out (a) these very 'heavy' clay soils; their alkalinity, or high pH, with all, save one, at 8.0 or above and (c) their low organic matter content, all below 1.00% save one, contract number 112.

calcium, calculated as the addition of percentage figure for calcium as deficiency, and for magnesium and potassium as their excess, or a total quantitative evaluation for these three prominent nutrient cations, commonly held on the exchange capacity of the soil's colloid.

Against these hindrances of the desert soil's imbalanced cationic array, it is quite surprising to find the application of calcium in mineralag increasing not only the stand counts cited in the first of the preceding two tables, but it is of more significant note that the early entrance of calcium into the seedlings and its nutritional effects carry through the growing season to give increases as tonnage of the harvested beets in six of the seven trials. With only one of the tests giving a decrease in crop harvest, the increases of it as percentage over no treatment in the six, in the order listed, ranged from 1.89 to 10.69, with a mean of 5.03 per cent.

That calcium as an alkaline earth, moved into the plants early for such lasting seasonal effects, represents significance when that was competition against the combined excess of potassium, an alkali, and of magnesium, another alkaline earth, all of them combined to be more than 100 per cent as excesses. Then, when the pH figures of all these soils were 7.9 and above, it is all the more expectable that not very much calcium would be 'available' from such soils to the roots of the sugar beet, at least not for long after the calcium was applied and the soil's equilibrium state had become established. Then, too, with the organic matter contents of these soils scarcely up to 1.0 per cent, there would be little microbial dynamics as seasonal deceay making the nutrient cations active.

Certainly, when their test data are viewed, these soils represent themselves deficient in mobility of calcium into any plant roots. Accordingly, calcium emphasizes itself prominent as a needed nutritional element, not only for legumes but here for a non-legume, when for sugar beets its fresh application in less than 500 pounds per acre with the seeding does so much in both increasing the stand count and in carrying forward its growth-stimulating effects through the growing season to give increases as much as a mean of five per cent in the harvest of this biennial root crop.

There is suggested, in these data, one item of caution against excessive application of the calcium carrier on the sugar beet, illustrated by the grower contract No. 252 when the fertilizations associated with mineralag applied 238 pounds of the element nitrogen and simultaneously the mineralag application was 1012 pounds per acre equivalent of 185.8 pounds calcium in this 1966 harvest.

While there was a yield increase of .7526 tons per acre, or 4.62 per cent over the check plot, yet there was a decrease of $5.11, or loss, per acre between the two plots because of the extra calcium or excessive nitrogen.

Since calcium is physiologically effective in the plant's synthesis of proteins in opposition, or antagonism, to potassium's activities in sugar, or carbohydrate, synthesis, there is the suggestion that the high rate of calcium application was an excess to disturb sugar production and to reduce the financial returns even when the yield as tonnage was favorable by nearly five per cent.

Stand counts. Imperial Valley. 1966.

The resulting data from the stand counts and yields from the initial phase of this study 1965–1966 gave the suggestion that the application of the calcium carrier for the sugar beets might be more effective if placed in closer contact—and possibly at higher application rates—with the planted seeds. Accordingly, such was the theoretical consideration tested in all the plantings of the plots in 1966 for the stand counts in the Imperial Valley and the measured yields as increased by the single soil treatment of mineralag for the harvests in both the Imperial and the San Joaquin Valleys in 1967. No stand counts were taken in the San Joaquin Valley due to the single seed, precision planting used there in 1966.

The same procedures for the stand counts in the Imperial Valley, 1966 were followed as were used there the preceding year. The data for the latter are assembled in Table No. 3 in arrangement duplicating that of the first Table No. 1.

In the 1966 plantings for the 1967 harvest in the Imperial Valley, the applications of the mineralag were made directly on the seed while planting, except in the case of the Contract Number 312, where it was a sidedressing. The rates of application ranged from a low of 54 to a high of 210 pounds per acre. The additional fertilizations carried no significant amount of calcium, when 200 to 300 pounds per acre of 11–48–0 were applied in most all cases, and additional nitrogen, from 75 pounds to heavy applications in the several forms of this element commercially available and encouraged for direct application in connections with crop plantings.

In all nine cases of stand counts in 1966 for the 1967 harvest, there were increased stands ranging from 1–59 per cent, due to the applied calcium carrier of two hundred pounds and less per acre directly on the seed while planting. Since for both the 1966 and 1967 harvests in the Imperial

Table 3

Stand Counts, Imperial Valley, Planting 1966, Harvest 1967

Grower's contract number	Acreage in test plots	Mineralag application lbs/acre**	Placement	Total length counted	Number of Plants per 25 ft row		Increase by mineralag (per cent)
					Treated	Untreated	
371	5.52*	54	On seeding	700	62.3	61.6	1.0
312	0.992	160	side-dress	600	148.4	124.7	18.0
332	5.30	105	On seeding	600	148.2	118.2	25.3
(Burson) 716	3.716	172	On seeding	600	74.6	69.0	8.1
'Y' 307	3.224	200	On seeding	400	68.9	62.7	9.9
'X' 307	3.224	124	On seeding	400	62.4	57.8	7.9
Jordan 530	5.89	210	On seeding	700	84.7	53.3	59.1***
Jordan 531	11.78	125	On seeding row	700	100.8	94.2	6.9
373	2.88	107	On seeding	600	100.3	90.3	11.0

*Treated and Untreated plots by mineralag were of same dimensions, hence only one acreage figure is recorded.

** Additional soil treatments, much similar to those reported in Table 1 were again used including generous applications of nitrogen and up to 400 lbs/a of 11—48—0. The plant spacings in the row varied from $\frac{3}{4}$" to 3".

***Mineralag served as an anticrusting agent in connection with heavy rains just after planting. Nematode infestations were also present.

Valley, the single seeds were planted, so prepared by breaking the seed clusters, and in some cases coating the seeds for more precision in spacing the plants in the row, the effect of the treatment on improved germination spells out an improved physiological response shown as increased plant stand, and not one hidden in the planting of seed clusters. This fact suggests that the beets' roots must retain this extra calcium well into the growing season to improve also the root's uptake (or exclusion) by the calcium-laden root hair of other nutrient elements, possibly out of balance in the soil as normal plant nutrition.

A startling observation, made soon after seeding the 1966–67 beet crop, deserves mention in connection with the heavy rains on the freshly planted seeds on September 15, 16, 18, and October 3 and 4. Such rains usually give crust formation of those soils, prohibiting seedling emergence and crop survival. Mineralag treatments gave a stand increase of 59.1 per cent over no treatment by the stand counts. Instead of crustation, there was excellent granulation of the surface soil layer containing the shallow-planting of the beet seeds. Some questions arise here as to the efficiency of applied (distilled) water by the sprinkler system of irrigation in contrast to salt-laden water delivered by furrow irrigation. Some questions arise also as to possibly more effective calcium uptake by the plant in its early life and possibly improved adsorption of this cation on the clay in competition with the excessive magnesium and others in the cationic array there, by such kind of salt-free water as sprinkler treatment.

Harvests of sugar beets, Imperial Valley, 1967

There were nine test areas of sugar beets, managed for the 1967 harvest data, much as was done for the 1966 harvest in the same area. The data for 1967 are given in Table No. 4 in arrangement similar to that for the yields of 1966.

Again the soil factors, as measured by soil test, are tabulated with the crop yields, and offer their suggestions that calcium should be considered the major deficiency in nutrition of planted seed, especially in soils of such heavy texture, so devoid of organic matter and carrying so much excess of the cationic salts.

Harvest of sugar beets, San Joaquin Valley, 1967

Sugar beets were planted also in San Joaquin Valley for 1967 harvests on six test areas, ranging in test plot sizes from 2.56 to 6.64 acres, duplicated

Table 4

Increases in Yields of Sugar Beets and Related Soil Test Data. Imperial Valley 1967

Grower's contract number	Tons	Earnings $	Exchange** capacities me/100 g	Calcium*** deficiency %	Magnesium excess %	Potassium excess %	Imbalance (sodium excluded), %	Sodium excess %
272	−1.0925 21.1170*	−18.14	37.0	16.1	63.6	13.6	93.3	270
371	−0.8531 29.1250	−12.62	38.0	9.6	30.2	56.4	96.2	425
312	−0.2645 21.6586	−4.39	40.0	13.6	54.8	0	68.4	304
332	−0.1727 21.2839	−2.89	40.0	11.1	53.7	44.6	109.4	200
'Y' 307	−0.0559 23.7484	−0.92	40.5	10.9	61.5	77.9	150.3	135
'X' 307	−0.1149 24.2965	1.91	36.0	10.0	51.5	33.3	94.8	250
716	0.8977 34.5618	15.35	41.0	9.1	62.4	9.0	80.5	141

530	1.9663 23.3254	32.54	47.5	17.4	70.5	68.4	156.3	222
373	2.0486 29.4739	34.03	25.0	−11.1	16.0	−58.0	−52.1	70

*The lower figure represents the yield of the untreated plot (given no mineralag) while the upper figure is the increase in tonnage per acre by that treatment.

**Exchange capacities are given as milligram-equivalents per 100 g dry soil. Most of them are high values to indicate 'heavy', clay soils, save Reese Ranches sample, approaching a silt loam. These high cationic exchange capacities were not due to soil humus or organic matter ranged by soil tests from 0.1 to 1.3 percent.

***Of the four cations calcium was deficient in all but one case, viz Contract 373. The other cations, magnesium, potassium and sodium are all excesses except again for contract 373 pointing to the soil as responsible for the order of arrangement of improved yields and earnings.

for treated and untreated soil trials, representing a total each of 26.99 acres in this arid valley of California. Precision plantings of single but coated seeds, in larger spacings, ranging from two to eight inches within the row were used, with the calcium carrier applied in direct seed contact at planting. No stand counts were taken. The yield data related to the soil factors, by soil tests, are assembled much as in preceding style, in Table 5 for the six test areas.

The yields of sugar beets indicate clearly that these soils did not carry such excessive salts as was true of Imperial Valley soils. The column of 'imbalance' indicates similarly by its lower percentage values, which suggest four soil areas of ample or near ample calcium, by soil saturation values as two negative and two of zero deficiencies, or near ample soil calcium supplies. Similarly, two cases show negative excess of potassium, or represent deficiencies rather than excess of this salt in relative degree of soil saturation, hence the 'imbalance' values as calculated were of lower percentages than were found for the soils of Imperial Valley. Accordingly this arid soil is less inimical by both soil test data and sugar beet crop-yield test results than the soils of Imperial Valley.

That the calcium deficiency, in its mobilization into the sugar beet, a non-legume crop, is the major problem for growing crops in such soils is verified by the response of the sugar beet by yields to the mineralag application at rates per acre no larger than 93 to 166 pounds. All six tests were positive with yield increases from 0.87 to 34.0 per cent, because of possibly the less inimical soil, but very likely also because of larger plant spacings in row planting to escape excessive crowding of plants and cutting down potential soil fertility supply per plant.

Attention is directed to the two separate 254 tests, namely B-1 and A-2; the former a heavier silt loam of 27.0 me exchange capacity, and the latter a sandy soil that with of but 8.0 me. The beets on the sandy soil were observed to have a 'heavy' infestation of nematodes while the silt loam had but a 'light' one. One expects lesser infestation in soils of heavier clay, a fact reported in the earliest California studies of this pest on citrus. In these cases it is significant to note that the soil factors showed the sandier soil the less hostile as an alkaline one, but yet the application of the mineralag calcium carrier gave a larger improvement in tonnage yield (over 30 per cent) above the untreated soil with but 5.0546 tons per acre to suggest that given extra calcium, the sugar beet built improved self-defense against this plant pest.

Table 5

Increases in Yields of Sugar Beets, San Joaquin Valley, 1967, and Related Soil Tests

Grower's contract number	Increases per acre		Soil test data					
	Tons	Earnings $	Exchange capacities me/100 g	Calcium deficiency %	Magnesium excess %	Potassium excess %	Imbalance (sodium excluded), %	Sodium excess %
B–1 254	0.1440 16.4002*	1.93	27.0	0	50	56.9	106	0
232	1.0148 10.9954	13.60	38.0	10.8	60.6	–6.0	71	217
286	1.1847 35.2871	15.88	30.0	–13.3	14.0	11.0	38	33
A–2 254	1.7344 5.0546	23.06	8.0	–21.6	8.8	–68.1	92	0
241	2.6747 31.6001	35.84	40.0	10.8	9.5	71.4	91	505
282	6.7389** 29.7388	90.31	34.5	0	12.1	14.2	26	94

* The lower figure represents the yield of the untreated plot (given no mineralag) while the upper figure is the increase in tonnage per acre by that soil treatment.

** The seed spacings in the row of this sixth grower were 8"; the fifth grower 4"; growers No. 2 and 3 were 3"; and for growers No. 1 and 4, 2".

Chemical Analysis of the Sugar Beets Grown on Untreated and Treated Soils

Since the extra calcium offered to the beet plant by the soil treatment gave extra tonnage harvests per acre, some ash analysis were made of the dry matter of beet samples from the Contract Number 307, Lot 'Y' in 1967 to get suggestions as to which elements represented increased or decreased effects by the calcium treatments on possibly the plant root hair activity as one of either increased uptake or exclusion as effects modifying the plant's chemical composition. The beet samples were collected and prepared with meticulous care, washed, sectioned to use one-eighth of each of twenty beets, quickly frozen, to represent the lot for ash analysis of the dry matter, from both treated and untreated test plots.

The results of the analysis are given in Table No. 6 for six major nutrient elements as percentages; and for six micronutrient elements as parts per million, with indicated increase or decrease as the modification of the

Table 6

Chemical Analysis of the Treated and Untreated Sugar Beets

Elements	Grown on treated soil (per cent)	Grown on untreated soil (per cent)	Increase, or decrease by Mineralag soil treatments (per cent)	Change (per cent)
Calcium	0.399%	0.379%	Increase	5
Magnesium	0.351%	0.351%	None	0
Potassium	1.059%	1.395%	Decrease	24
Sodium	0.275%	0.263%	Increase	4
Phosphorus	0.086%	0.092%	Decrease	6
Sulfur	0.026%	0.051%	Decrease	49
Iron	799.7 ppm	465.2 ppm	Increase	72
Manganese	42.8 ppm	33.8 ppm	Increase	26
Copper	11.8 ppm	10.4 ppm	Increase	17
Cobalt	0.1 ppm	Nil ppm	Increase	00
Molybdenum	0.5 ppm	0.3 ppm	Increase	60
Zinc	21.6 ppm	27.2 ppm	Decrease	20

sugar beet's chemical composition by the gypsiferous soil treatments. No determinations were made of the nitrogen, carbon or volatile and organic combinations expected to be modified compositions because of the generous nitrogen fertilizations, and those affected by calcium, which combination is a factor in protein synthesis and, thereby, possible reduction of the beet's concentrations of stored sugar. The respective sugar percentages of each of the beet harvests are not reported in tabulations, but are indicated in some instances of shifts in the earnings by the soil treatments. Those dollar values are given along with the percentages increase in the yields per acre by the soil treatment.

As to the shifts in the beet's chemical composition connected with the dozen elements measured, it is significant to note, first, that the addition of the calcium sulfate to a soil, already high in sulfur, served to reduce the sulfur concentration in the beets by nearly fifty per cent. This suggests a physiological effect by the application of the cation, calcium, rather than of the anion, sulfate. The increase in the amount of calcium within the beet by but 5.2 per cent, according to the table, was effective in bringing about (a) neither reduction nor increase in the seemingly excessive magnesium; (b) a reduction of potassium by 24.0 per cent, and only a very slight increase in sodium, as the changes among the cations in their prominent imbalance. There was a slight reduction in the beet's concentration of phosphorus, indicated by test so excessively present in the soil; but there was a decided reduction of the sulfur in the beets considering these two major anions.

Among the trace elements, it is significant to note the relative increase of iron concentration in the beets by 70 per cent; (b) an increase in manganese by over 25 per cent; (c) also increases of copper, cobalt and molybdenium; but (d) a decrease in the beet's concentration of zinc.

These are decided changes in the chemical composition brought about in the beet as the 'seed' plant of a biennial plant cycle, when there was but such a small change by the limited soil treatment in the plant's concentration of calcium. Accordingly, the calcium suggests for itself the physiological roles as tools, or controls, rather than as materials in plant construction. Dare we not envision its role possibly as membranous control within the root hair, or other activities, requiring little change in the supply or concentration of calcium while functioning to control many elements entering the plant from the soil, some as increases and some as decreases in the plant's uptake?

If the increased growth of a 'seed' plant, like the biennial sugar beet, and the associated changes in its chemical compositions in connection with seed treatment by calcium are considered as gains in the struggle of the species to survive in a given environment, then the absence of any shifts in magnesium concentration might be interpreted as if this element, as another alkaline earth chemically so closely similar to calcium in its biodynamics, is unaffected in its movement into the beet by the small alteration of this root's calcium content occasioned by the small applications of calcium. These two alkaline earths, apparently, cannot be considered 'antagonistic'. But for potassium, the beet's better growth registered a reduction of, or a 'defense' against, the high potassium saturation of the soil. Such defense against the soil's excessive sodium was weak, and likewise against the excess of the anion, phosphorus; but against the other anion, sulfur, there was a strong defense shown by a reduction of 50 per cent of it in the beet's dry matter, even if calcium was applied as the sulfate.

Amongst the trace elements, five of the six increased their concentrations in the beet's dry matter to suggest these shifts as advantages in survival, or as hindrances in deficiency unless the calcium was added to the soil. That same line of reasoning would apply to the zinc as an excess, or hindrance, in the soil in contrast to deficiencies or low availabilities in the soil of the preceding five in the set tested.

Discussion

The series of soil fertility tests under the sugar beet crop exhibits the problem of balancing most effectively the soil's nutrient availability with respect to both the crop yield as tonnage and the concentration of sugar in the beet root. The reduction within the latter of the mono-in relation to the di-saccharide is a challenging criterion for more successful soil fertility management. The effects of the higher supplies of available calcium taken into the beet when heavy applications of nitrogen fertilizers were simultaneously made suggest reduction in concentration of the sugar. That was clearly shown by the monetary earnings, sometimes as reductions in spite of increased tonnages yielded. None of those data are recited in detail in these studies, however economically important they become since the tonnage yield, multiplied by the percentage of disaccharide sugar determines the pay check for the crop at the sugar mill.

The excessive degrees of the soil's saturation of its exchange capacity by magnesium in these desert soils, and the beet root's manifestation of little, or no, control of magnesium uptake in relation to its increased uptake of calcium—shown by chemical analysis of the root's dry matter—suggest the magnesium, an alkaline earth, as the one most serious disturber in the plant's uptake of, and functions by, calcium, another very similar alkaline earth.

The excess of magnesium saturation on the soil colloid, even enough to leave extra salt, bringing plant behavior equivalent to a calcium deficiency, has come into prominence in recent years under wider observation of the nutritional help from drilling gypsiferous, natural minerals for crops, both legumes and non-legumes other than the sugar beet. This has been the case, especially in areas of high concentrations of magnesium in the drainage water of the United States, as has been indicated accordingly by the map of such magnesium (over 20 ppm) drawn by S. B. Detweiler, from the Data of Geochemistry, F. W. Clarke. More critical study should offer more information.

In considering the major plant nutrient cations, viz: hydrogen, calcium, magnesium, potassium; sodium and others, in that order of their decreasing energy of adsorption which holds them exchangeably on the clay-humus colloid in the surface horizon of the soil profile, dare we not envision such a particular energy situation giving also the same order of the cations as decrease in their biochemo-dynamics in soil development, and in nourishment for evolution of the plant and microbe species on the earth's surface in what is called "The Living Soil"?

In the humid soils, hydrogen takes on its tremendous biochemical importance at the ionic concentration of carbonic acid by which it weathers rock, leaches out salts, and leaves the clay residue with its unique colloidal capacities holding, against leaching, the array of nutrient cations exchanged therefrom by root-respiration's carbonic-acid hydrogen emphasizing the clay's requisite highest saturation by calcium and its connection with protein synthesis and nitrogen fixation. The other cations follow in order of lesser amounts and lesser chemo-dynamics on the clay as more nearly naturally balanced, and available plant nutrition.

The moderate degree of acidity of humid and semihumid soils, near pH 6.0 with their calcium reserves, makes them most productive for plant's synthesis of protein-rich tissues; their liberal reproduction; and their specific compounds for immunity and self-protection against diseases and pests. Calcium within the root-reach in the profile and its application on the soil surface as liming material of humid soils have lacked our appreciation of its importance as a plant nutrient. The cation, hydrogen, has suffered similarly under its consideration as the arch-enemy in soil acidity. This confusion, covered by the term 'soil acidity' so widely, has prevented their recognition of calcium and hydrogen as major cations supporting nutrition of the entire biotic pyramid. The hydrogen, root-made by its respiration, has been the mobilizing agent, via its high adsorption energy, of the other essential cations from the clay-humus colloid into the plant roots by exchange phenomena. Soil acidity has been nutritionally beneficial, in the presence of ample reserves of calcium first, and all other cations following in order to give these two, major cations energywise, their foremost nutritional importance in both legumes and non-legumes.

But in the neutral or alkaline, arid soils, there are no measurable hydrogen ions adsorbed on the clay, and there is too little soil organic matter under microbial decay to maintain active hydrogen equal to the benefits from carbonic acid. Accordingly, dare we not envision calcium, the second prominent cation in the order cited, coming into prominence in evolution and survival of the plant species via early plant functions suggested by help in germination and seemingly early control of nutrient intake as well as exclusions by which the plant's nutrition may have been naturally managed for survival? The manifestations by calcium's nutritional roles in the sugar beet, as the equivalent of a 'seed' state in its biennial cycle, seem to transcend highly any similar roles we might associate with the cations magnesium, or potassium. Those manifestations suggest themselves as reasons for the higher degrees of saturation by calcium of the soil's exchange capacity, especially for only connection with processes like protein synthesis and nitrogen fixation, and more so for calcium's reported requisite role by presence for the amino acid synthesis brought about by the electrical spark's discharge in the gaseous combination, duplicating the earth's primitive atmosphere by which such phenomenon probably gave origin to primitive living substances.

CHAPTER 26

Agricultural Limestone—For the Sake of More than Its Calcium

THE USE OF LIMESTONE on the soil is an agricultural practice as old as the Romans and the centuries B.C. But the concept of how and why its application on humid soils can modify them enough to grow better legumes and other crops of higher protein contents and nutritional values, is still recent and incomplete. A more adequate understanding of how calcium carbonate, *i.e.*, limestone, a calcium salt of carbonic acid, functions in growing better crops is still challenging the research thinking of students in soil fertility and plant nutrition.

Liming the soil has long been a wise practice—but for the wrong reasons. It has long been the belief that this cheaper carbonate serves because this part of the compound overcomes the condition called "soil acidity" by neutralizing or removing the soil acid, *i.e.*, hydrogen. This explanation, though not in accord with the natural facts, has persisted since the time of Edmund Ruffin (1794–1865), a Virginia farmer, who was probably the first one to call attention to what is commonly considered "soil acidity" in upland, mineral soils of the humid climates.

The belief that soil acidity is bad for plants because of the presence in the soil of ionic and therefore highly active hydrogen was reinforced and widely disseminated as a result of the demonstrations by H. J. Wheeler (1861–1945) of Rhode Island, who showed that many upland soils are distinctly acid in chemical reaction and will grow better crops when limed. This was the beginning of the wise practice of using limestone as a fertilizer to build up the sustaining mineral fertility of the soil. It was also the beginning of the propagandization of the erroneous explanations of how it functions, when it was claimed that limestone serves because it reduces the degree of, or removes completely, the acidity or active, ionic hydrogen of the soil.

The persistence for almost a century of this erroneous explanation illustrates our reluctance to study the facts of Nature. It illustrates, also, our readiness to accept without scrutiny what some one reports as truth. The failure to see so-called "acid soils" as a case of *fertility deficiency in terms of calcium and magnesium,* while making acid the scapegoat and fighting it by applying the carbonate part of the limestone as ammunition, has its modern parallel. We made the microbe the scapegoat in disease, rather than seeing the invasion of the body by almost any micro-organism as the symptom of nutritional deficiencies, and maintaining our body's own protection against them. Such is the slow rate at which we come to understand Nature's mysteries, Her causes and Her effects.

In both the arts of managing agriculture and of maintaining health, there is still much that is empiricism, or mere practice to get results, regardless of our unfamiliarity with the natural laws underlying agriculture and health. Yet in an age of science, while making an effort to organize our knowledge and to comprehend causes and effects, we dare not propose to work with Nature in food production of high nutritional value unless we learn how and why the natural processes function through the soils and crops in that activity.

Colloid chemistry interpreted soil acidity as fertility deficiencies. We learned lately that limestone functions, not because its carbonate part neutralizes or removes the acidity or hydrogen from the soil, but rather because it fertilizes the soil with calcium and magnesium. This concept came to us when colloid chemistry became a part of the larger science of chemistry. By the help from that segment of this science, the clay of the soil was recognized as a silicate colloid with many negative electrical charges. It was found to be performing according to its enormous surface for adsorbing and exchanging the many positively charged atoms, or ions, like hydrogen, calcium, magnesium, copper, zinc, and the host of others, including both the essential and the non-essential for the nutrition of plants and animals.

By experimenting with clay in accordance with the natural laws outlined by colloid chemistry, *i.e.*, by adsorbing on clay varied amounts of both calcium and hydrogen in which plants were grown, differences in plant growth served to separate the effects of the calcium on the clay from the effects of the hydrogen held there. Since both calcium and hydrogen, the former a nutrient and the latter a non-nutrient, are positively charged and held by the clay, they were experimentally put there as increasing concentrations of calcium associated with reciprocally decreasing concentrations of hydrogen or acidity, in one plant series. (See illustration, upper series.)

In another plant series the same concentrations of calcium were used, but associated with decreasing concentrations of potassium, thus excluding nearly all the hydrogen, or all the acidity. (See illustration, middle series.)

Likewise, in place of hydrogen, positive elements, or cations, like magnesium, barium, and even the organic molecule methylene blue (illustration, lower series) were reciprocally associated with the varied concentrations of calcium, each in other plant series. None of the soils were acid in these other-than-hydrogen series. Yet the increases in the growth of the plants in each series followed increasing concentrations of calcium supplied on the clay in the sand-clay soil. The plant behaviors on these nearly neutral soils duplicated the growths of the series in which the increasing concentrations of calcium in association with decreasing hydrogen concentrations represented decreasing degrees of soil acidity. This occurred when the amount of total exchangeable calcium in the many sand-clay soils was kept constant.

This experimental work demonstrated clearly that deficiency of calcium as a plant nutrient was the trouble with the so-called "acid" clay, rather than the presence there of hydrogen, since the nearly neutral soils duplicated the plant growth given by soils of decreasing acidity and reciprocally increasing calcium saturation. Thus, regardless of whether the soil acidity in the plant series was lowered by the successive units, or whether all the soils were almost entirely neutral and all of the same degree of soil acidity, plant growth responded to concentrations of exchangeable calcium on the clay and not to concentrations of hydrogen, or the degree of acidity (pH) present.

As a consequence of these demonstrations of plant behavior, the practice of liming soil is now viewed as an attempt to put the nutrient elements calcium and magnesium on the colloidal clay part of the soil in their proper ratios to all other positively charged atoms, or ions, held by the clay for exchange to the plant root as nutrition. Liming is no longer a fight on acidity, or hydrogen, in the soil. In fact, calcium and magnesium move into the plant more efficiently if there is some hydrogen present on the clay, and is present even in certain ratios to calcium, magnesium, and to other nutrient ions of positive electrical charge.

Liming the soil is mainly an application of fertilizing materials. It is not a case of using a *starter fertilizer*, but one of building up the *sustaining fertility* for many years to come. When for better growth of plants, calcium is put on the clay to take as much as 75 percent of its adsorbing capacities, when magnesium is put there to represent about 7.5 percent, and when the potassium supply there amounts to about 3 percent, these three nutrient ions, comprising about 85 percent of the clay's capacity, will leave little chance for much hydrogen ion, or acidity, of similar positive charge on the clay.

Consequently, liming soil is a practice of loading the clay so highly with fertility elements that the partial removal of hydrogen (or its partial displacement from the clay by those elements) is merely a reciprocal result. When the entrance on to the clay of the fertility, and not the exit therefrom of the acidity, is the major cause of improvement in the crop growth, we may well direct some attention to the possible need for some hydrogen to be always present in the soil. The presence of hydrogen on the soil naturally has always been the case for humid soils. There we have regularly had maximum plant production in the presence of soil acidity. Let us consider the possible benefits from some hydrogen in the soil. Experimental studies suggest that hydrogen, a non-nutrient cation, serves beneficially for activation of nutrient cations when hydrogen occupies about 10 percent of the clay's capacity; calcium, 75 percent; magnesium, 7.5 percent; and potassium, 3 percent. Accordingly, any single one of the cations adsorbed on the clay seems to behave according to the company it keeps, whether that be nutrient or nonnutrient, including even hydrogen, which was so long erroneously considered injurious.

Shall we lime for the sake of carbonic acid as well as for calcium? When the application of lime as calcium carbonate loads the clay with calcium, it also is replacing hydrogen from there to unite with the carbonate part of limestone, and liming soil is likewise a case of treating carbonate with an acid soil and thereby producing carbonic acid in the soil. Let us give some consideration, then, to the possible significance of the carbonate part of limestone, or carbonic acid resulting from liming as an active factor in bettering soil for plant growth, since now we know that acidity makes many ions more active for entrance into the plant roots. Dare we emphasize only the smaller, active cations of positive charge like hydrogen, calcium, magnesium, potassium, sodium, etc., held on the large, sluggish clay anion of negative charge, and disregard other anions like bicarbonate, nitrate, chloride, sulphur, phosphate and even all the organic anions, as well as these inorganic ones?

Now that we have emphasized these cations on the clay because they replace hydrogen (or because they are what we thought of as "bases" for neutralizing acid), we have forgotten that either calcium or magnesium in limestone is speedily effective and safe in large doses only when it is applied as a carbonate. Calcium reacts differently when put on soil as sulphate, in gypsum, or in phosphates. Since soil liming as an ancient art brought our thinking of it slowly around to become scientific about its

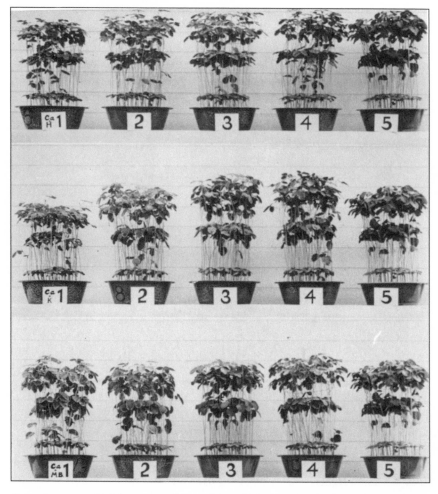

Less clay, more highly saturated by calcium (left to right), but of such amounts of clay in the sand to supply constant totals of exchangeable calcium per crop, show better growth (left to right, upper series) where acidity decreases accordingly, and likewise where there is no acidity (middle series).

Where varied calcium saturation is associated with the organic compound methylene blue on the clay, the crops do not vary with calcium saturation but are uniform with the constant total exchangeable calcium in the soil (lower series).

services in applying calcium, and thereby helped us to appreciate the services from other cations, we may well inquire about the services of liming for its application of the carbonate anion; we may likewise consider the services from anions other than carbonate, as used in other fertilizers.

In virgin soils the negatively charged bicarbonate anion is the most universal one by which positively charged cations in rock minerals are broken out to become active. Carbonic acid is Nature's most universal acid and mineral-dissolving reagent. It puts most of the cations into active form. Resulting as it does within the moisture around the microbe or the plant root into which the waste carbon dioxide is respired by these life forms, they are regularly enshrouded, then, with active hydrogen in company with the carbonate anion. This hydrogen can then be exchanged by the root or

Fresh organic matter added to the soil ahead of the grass seedings stimulated better early growth as pot tests demonstrated for orchard grass, timothy, and brome grass (left to right, by pairs).

288—rye soil, rye under—plus chopped Irish potatoes
218—rye soil, rye under—plus green turnips and tops
599—rye grass soil, rye grass under—plus chopped oranges
519—rye soil, rye under—plus chopped green turnips and tops
548—alfalfa soil, alfalfa under—plus chopped Irish potatoes
598—rye grass soil, rye grass under—plus chopped oranges
(Courtesy of Chas. J. Schnabel)

the microbe to the clay surrounding it, from which it takes ionical active nutrients like potassium, calcium, magnesium, and others.

It is by this continued exchange of hydrogen from root to clay and by crop removal of the nutrients taken from the clay that soils become acid naturally. The acid soil then in turn decomposes the rock reserve minerals, among them limestone. Thus, since carbonic acid is the great reagent for processing the original rock substances by which growth of crops can take place, we can see the good in the carbonate part of limestone when we lime the soil, and soil acidity serves to process this stone to give carbonic acid as well as to stock the clay with calcium and magnesium.

One needs only to recall that neither calcium sulphate, *i.e.*, gypsum, nor calcium chloride, *i.e.*, Dowflake, can be used on the soil in equal amounts with the same degree of safety as calcium carbonate. If the proper ratios of nutrient cations—calcium, magnesium, potassium—and the non-nutrient hydrogen held by the clay are a significant matter for better plant nutrition, it seems logical to raise the question for research whether the less adsorbed anions, nutrients like nitrate, chloride, sulphate, and phosphate, or supposed non-nutrients like bicarbonate, for example, must not also be present in proper ratios as the mates of cations, if their combined interactions and effects are to result in proper plant nutrition and crop production.

Liming the soil, as it supplies carbonate and liberates carbonic acid, Nature's most universal anion, would suggest that we have been more fortunate in our use of limestone as a form of "sustaining fertility" than we yet appreciate. Perhaps Nature has been caring for us in spite of our ignorance of these natural performances, rather than because of our knowledge of them.

Limestone helps put more organic matter into soil. While carbonic acid given off by limestone in acid soils may be considered an inorganic acid, its carbon is nevertheless of organic origin. This acid behaves like other organic acids in that it does not give highly active acidity. We appreciate this fact when we taste acetic acid, an organic acid, in vinegar.

Carbonic acid has neither a highly stable nor a highly soluble acidity, as we learn by drinking carbonated waters. It does not activate its hydrogen completely, and therefore it has much of its total content inactive or un-ionized. It decomposes, producing carbonic dioxide, which escapes into the atmosphere. It also produces water, which when left in the soil, shows no acidity. This is quite different from what happens when calcium chloride is put into soil. That compound is calcium salt of muriatic or hydrochloric acid. It is highly active, does not decompose readily, and is highly soluble.

There may be more good fortune for crop nutrition than we appreciate in the fact that calcium, magnesium, and potassium, which compose most of the nutrient cation supply on the clay, take to the bicarbonate forms of compounds so readily. Were they in the soil only as chlorides, rather than the bicarbonates, it is certain that in such large supplies they might be injurious to plant nutrition. Heavy applications of muriate, *i.e.*, chloride of potassium as fertilizer are reported to show these disturbing results. Damage is most serious on soils which are low in organic matter, and therefore where there is less carbonic acid from organic decay, which would produce carbonic acid in larger and regular quantities to offset the detrimental effects of chlorides and other anions. Chloride in small quantities (much like trace elements) is a necessity for plant nutrition, but in large amounts it seems a more serious disturber than is commonly appreciated.

While we believe calcium to be more effective in the presence of organic matter and carbonic acid, we need to remind ourselves that, reciprocally, organic matter has built itself up to higher concentrations throughout greater depths of the soil where the supply of calcium has been high. It is calcium that helps grow leguminous crops; and the nitrogen of legumes, taken from the atmosphere, holds carbon. We also know that, when they are applied on soils of high organic matter contents, can the concentrated salts in fertilizers be used with least disturbance from the "salting effects" which the chloride of calcium, for example, exhibits so highly in contrast to the carbonate compound of that element.

It is interesting that the amounts of highly concentrated fertilizers used have increased recently only in that area of the United States where soils are still high in organic matter. The amounts used have decreased on soil of low organic matter. The organic part of the soil has been the "shock absorber" for the "salt" danger from chlorides, nitrates, and sulphates of sodium, ammonium, and potassium, or those combinations of more active, monovalent elements commonly used in fertilizers.

These facts present the question whether carbonic acid serves to lower the activity of and thereby lessen the possible injury from these cations, *i.e.*, sodium, ammonium, and potassium, by combining with them, and also to lessen the injurious activities of the anions, *i.e.*, chlorides, nitrates and sulphates, by diluting them with itself, a less active anion. Perhaps such theoretical thinking should be considered, since liming is effective on those soils lower in organic matter and is required there to enhance the efficiency of many other fertilizers, with resulting nutritional effects we cannot yet comprehend, much less explain.

On Sanborn Field at the Missouri Experiment Station, one plot has been in continuous wheat cropping under a heavy fertilizer treatment which applied the equivalent of nitrogen, phosphorus, and potassium removed in the grain and straw of a 40-bushel crop since 1888. This heavy application of salts with the seeding was without injurious effects for about 30 years. But during the last 35 years, or since the organic matter has been seriously lowered through such treatment and has not been built up by the return of any crop residues, it has been necessary to divide this heavy fertilizer treatment into two and more applications to escape injury to the seeding from these applied salts.

Before commercial nitrogen fertilizers were so extensively available, we were building organic matter and nitrogen into the soil by growing protein-rich and mineral-rich legume crops. Unfortunately for the rebuilding of the soil's supply of organic matter, legume crops were such good and seriously-needed feeds, that they did not find their way into the soil to build up much organic matter there. Now that commercial nitrogen is going into non-leguminous crops, which do not require soils highly stocked with calcium, it is believed that nitrogen is building proteins by pushing higher the nitrogen content of grasses and producing the equivalent of legumes grown by liming and fertilizing for them.

In this belief we forget that in measuring the total nitrogen in the crop and in multiplying this value by 6.25 to call the result "protein," we are not measuring proteins complete enough in their required constituent amino acids for nutrition of our animals. We are getting a value of "crude" proteins; that includes other forms of nitrogen than those in the amino form of the protein. Those others include nitrogen in the organic-ring combinations, in ammonia, and even in nitrates.

The drought of 1954 put enough of this form of nitrate into corn stalks to be over half the total nitrogen commonly contained in them. This form of nitrogen was concentrated highly enough to kill livestock that consumed the fodder. This experience serves to tell us that grasses, like corn, grown readily without attention to soil liming, even if they have high nitrogen (and thereby high "crude" protein) contents, are not giving us the feed values we get when we lime the soil and grow legumes for feed. Quality knows no substitutes.

We should recall that the soils well stocked with organic matter (because they were also well stocked with lime and other fertility) supported legumes, and protein-rich, mineral-rich grasses grew naturally there, to feed the bison; and they are still growing to feed much of our livestock today.

Similar soils are still standing up under heavy cultivation and heavy fertilization. The soil as fullest nutrition is still much of an unknown in terms of the organic matter we grow. Little research is in progress to learn what the vegetation we produce is doing for organic matter in the soil, to serve as nutrition for the microbes there, and as nutrition for succeeding crops in terms of the organic compounds their roots take up to improve the feed and food values of crops.

Limestone on humid soils helps crops help themselves. Soils which are well stocked with both lime and organic matter will mobilize both the inorganic and organic items of fertility into crop growth more effectively. Studies using the colloidal clay technique by which the supply of exchangeable nutrients in sand-clay substrata for growing test crops can be accurately controlled, have shown that the concentration of calcium on the clay must hold high the activity of this element if the root is to take nutrients from the soil into the plant generously, rather than allow nutrients like nitrogen, phosphorus, and potassium to go from the plant back into the soil.

With a low degree of calcium saturation in the soil, there was plant growth, but less nitrogen, phosphorus, and potassium were found in the total plant than was originally in the planted seed. It has also been shown that, as the calcium in the soil was present in an increasing ratio to other fertility elements, many of the latter were mobilized into the plant to an accordingly higher percentage taken from the soil's supply and to a greater total and a greater concentration in the crop.

The fact that the help given the plant root allows the root to help itself the more, suggests that it is so enabled when the help given makes more protein in the plant and therefore in the root. In experiments with legumes, some of the plants were inoculated with nodule-producing bacteria, while others were not so treated, but were kept from the chance to get nitrogen from either the atmosphere or the special soil growing them. The nodulated plants of higher protein concentration moved a higher percentage of the fertility supplies off the soil and into the crop. Inoculated legumes removed more fertility off the clay. They exhausted the soil fertility to a lower level; but they made plants more mineral-rich and more protein-rich.

Protein production in the plant helps it because the higher concentration of the protein-colloid in the root takes more ions of fertility from the clay colloid in the soil. Thus, giving the legume some calcium to help it in making more protein within itself, aids in making more of the other fertility elements in the soil available.

When the different amounts of calcium on the clay are associated with differing amounts of other nutrient elements, the influence exerted by each on the other for the amounts moving into the plant vary widely. The amount of any inorganic ion going into the plant depends much on "the company it keeps" with other ions on the clay. When those "other ions" are organic ones, the inorganic ones are influenced to get into the plants in proportion to the amounts on the clay. This is particularly true of calcium, which moves into the crop according to the total calcium, rather than its percent of saturation on the clay. (See the *Less clay, more highly saturated by calcium* illustration earlier in this chapter.)

Only recently have we learned that the roots of plants take up organic compounds within which inorganic elements are combined. This means that these inorganics are taken into plants when, in the absence of the organic compounds, they are suffering deficiencies of these particular inorganic essentials. This has been demonstrated by some organic compounds especially synthesized in the laboratory. These synthetic organics moved into the plant simultaneously with the inorganic elements, and resulted in the plant's growth. Whether the improvement was due to one, the other, or both is not fully understood.

This reaction of linking an inorganic element into an organic compound with resultant beneficial effect in plant nutrition is known as "chelation". In an experiment the root system of a plant may be divided between two containers, in one of which the inorganic ion is failing to be taken up by that half of the root system of the plant, demonstrating that failure by plant symptoms. The chelating organic compound may be applied to the other container, or to the remaining half of the root system, and it will go through that into the first half of the root system. The previously inactive, inorganic ion will be mobilized into the roots and bring about the removal of the deficiency symptoms. Extracts of decaying organic matter have demonstrated that they may serve as natural chelating agents, or mobilizers.

These facts suggest not only that organic compounds resulting from decay of previous crop residues are taken up by the roots for plant nutrition—as we know it for mushrooms, for example—but that decaying organic matter as a chelating agent may be the means of making inorganic elements of soil fertility serve more effectively in plant nutrition.

Thus, when the cold soil of winter is warmed in the spring to start the processes of organic matter decay, those chemically dynamic processes are not only liberating carbonic acid to exercise its possible benefits as an anion in the soil, but also discharging carbon dioxide into the atmosphere, concentrating it in the air layers just above the soil around the plants as possible helps for increased photosynthesis. One scarcely appreciates the large amounts of organic matter decomposed in highly fertile soil, and the large amounts of carbon dioxide liberated by the soil, for example, under a high-yielding corn crop. As a simple comparison one may liken the soil dynamics of organic matter combustion in mid-summer in a 40-acre corn field to the coal fires under a 40-hp. steam boiler.

Organic matter decay also provides organic compounds which nourish plants in much the same manner as mushrooms live mainly on the organic fertility from the composted layer of manure in the bottom, but are nourished by the mineral fertility from the layer of "casing" soil on the top of the mushroom bed. Then, too, this organic decay is also a chelating process enshrouding less active inorganic fertility elements, like iron, and compensating for their inactivity when left in purely inorganic forms. These conversions within the soil require lime for the microbes, and it brings them about to meet the requirements for their life processes, just as lime is needed in plant life processes.

Limestone leads all soil treatments. Lime, as calcium carbonate, puts this major nutrient cation on the clay of the soil. It is the mobilizer of many nutrients, both cations and anions, into the plant. It supports the production of proteins by which plant roots are more effective in taking the adsorbed inorganic fertility from the clay. It is also an essential in the growth of organic matter in the soil and in the microbial transformations there which provide organic nutrients for crops and organic chelators of the less active inorganic fertility ions.

Now that we have learned that limestone on our soils helps because of its calcium, we need to determine whether it may also help because of its provision of carbonic acid, and because of its significance in growing an organic matter of higher values in feeding the succeeding crops, as well as in feeding livestock and ourselves.

CHAPTER 27

Soil Acidity as Calcium (Fertility) Deficiency

FOR ALL TOO MANY YEARS our concept of the soil conditions called "soil acidity," and of the relation of these to plant nutrition, has been one which originated in the greenhouses and chemical laboratories dealing with solutions, and one mentally transplanted to the soil. It carried the belief that soil acidity *per se* is detrimental to plants. It provoked the conclusion of the converse, namely, that neutrality, therefore, must be beneficial. Such was the concept that gained wide popular acceptance, and unleashed in agricultural practice the extensive war on soil acidity with the carbonate of calcium as the ammunition for its annihilation.

Now that we have (*a*) found the hydrogen ion in potentially large numbers as a common cation part of the clay molecule, (*b*) measured this highly active element ionized from there in varying degrees to give different pH values, and (*c*) recognized its origin abundantly in the respiratory processes of the soil microbes and of the plant roots themselves, a newer concept is replacing this older one. We now consider those conditions called "soil acidity" as fertility deficiencies, of which calcium (and magnesium) is a prominent one.

We are coming to see the active hydrogen—even if it is not a plant nutrient when coming via the soil—as the major force in the many chemo-dynamics of the soil through which plant nutrition results. The activities of this ion are the major force in bringing about (*a*) the decomposition of the mineral reserves in the silt separates for increased availability of their nutrient contents, (*b*) the formation of the clay separate as a result of the mineral breakdown, (*c*) the adsorption on the clay of many essential nutrient ions made active as a consequence of that mineral decomposition, and (*d*) the exchange of these from the clay-organic-colloid to the microbes and the plant roots for nutritional services to these living forms.

When the world's population has located itself mainly on what is considered the "acid" soils; and when life is scant on those of alkaline reaction, even those of much less degree of this opposite to the acid; it seems high time to re-examine the simple chemical solution concept of acidity-neutrality-alkalinity, considered as bad-good-bad condition, respectively, for plant nutrition. This reconsideration seems especially necessary when these reaction differences, as only such with no other accompanying differences, are transplanted into the soil. It is, therefore, proposed here to defend the thesis (a) that an acid reaction of most soils is not a hindrance, but rather a help, to plant nutrition via the provision of the essential nutrient ions, (b) that it is only under significant hydrogen ion activity that the processes of mineral breakdown, clay formation and fertility delivery can be carried on, and (c) that the respiration of plant roots and microbes generates active hydrogen to maintain the flow of nutrient cations from the soil's rocks and minerals in the assembly line of agricultural production.

Soil acidity is not a hindrance when fertility is present

At the outset, let us accept the widely experienced and correctly interpreted observation, namely, that in Nature there are less and less of the more nutritious herbages, especially the legumes serving for growing young livestock and for multiplying its numbers, according as the natural degree of soil acidity goes higher. Let us also note that in waging the fight on soil acidity, it was probably more good fortune than wisdom when the carbonates of calcium and magnesium rather than of sodium or other alkaline and alkaline earths were chosen for soil treatments to drive the hydrogen out. After the years of growing concern about soil acidity, there is gradually dawning the broader concept, namely, that the increasing degree of acidity is merely the reciprocal of the real trouble, namely, the decreasing store of the soil fertility. While the earlier concept of soil acidity as the hydrogen's damage may now be slowly going into the discard, it has served, nevertheless, as the means by which the later one evolved, and, with it, our concept of at least some of the mechanisms—including the hydrogen as a part in them—by which the soil, rather than a solution within it, serves to deliver its fertility and to nourish the plants.

It was the modified Comber method of testing soils for the degree of acidity (the thiocyanate method) which served early to point out that liming a soil is helpful in growing clovers and other legumes because it applies the plant nutrient calcium and not because it applies carbonate for bringing about a reduction of the degree of acidity. Two fields, failing to grow clover, on the same farm were tested for their degree of acidity and were found highly acid. Two tons per acre of ten-mesh, agricultural limestone, were applied on each of them in the autumn ahead of the wheat seeding. The clover seeding followed the next spring with an excellent stubble crop of this legume as the result the next autumn. The soil test, repeated at that season, showed the soil nearly neutral for the one upland field of silt loam. The test, however, for the bottomland, a clay soil, showed still the same degree of acidity after liming and clover establishment as that which prevailed before the soil treatment. Here the clover had resulted from the same kind of liming which removed the acidity in the one field of upland soil with its low exchange or buffering capacity, but which brought about no change in reaction in the other field of bottomland soil with a high exchange or high buffering capacity. Here was some of the first evidence that it is an erroneous explanation of the effects of liming the soil, when we say that this practice is beneficial because it reduces the degree of acidity or lowers the pH value. Here was evidence that the presence of acidity is not a hindrance to clover growing if the fertility (calcium) is present.

As a test of this error in reasoning, a field of "acid" soil was put to soybeans—a supposedly acid-tolerant legume—by using calcium chloride, calcium nitrate, and calcium hydroxide as successive treatments applied through one side of the fertilizer attachment of the drill at seeding. Each of these treatments applied calcium. Regardless of whether the soil was made more acid in case of the first two, or reduced in its acidity in the case of the last one, of these treatments, the soybean plants grew larger, were greener, gave better nodulation and nitrogen-fixing, and brought about more stable nature of the plant tissues under microtomic sectioning wherever any one of these calcium-carrying salts was applied.

As additional test of the physiological effects of the lime because of the calcium going through the plant rather than the carbonate through the soil for acid neutralization, some finely pulverized limestone was drilled with clover seedings of inoculated seeds on acid soils. Clover was well established by drilling limestone with the seeds. Nodule production occurred on the roots in the soil at significant depths below, and distances from, the location of limestone in the drill row. Determinations of the pH around the nodules at these depths found this as low as 5.0. Here were legume root growth and excellent nodulation on all roots in soils of

Applications of calcium chloride, calcium nitrate, and calcium hydroxide (right to left) gave improved growth and nitrogen fixation by soybeans on this "acid" soil, irrespective of the resulting increase in its acidity by the first two and the decrease of it by the third of these treatments.

high degree of acidity as the result of merely growing some of the roots in contact with calcium in limited soil volumes or in only a few focal points. If lime is required for nodulation, this certainly occurred not where the acidity of the soil around the nodule was neutralized, but where the nodule-producing bacteria met a root of nutritional contents for mutual benefits, to which the calcium, taken by the plant roots in some other part of the soil made its contributions.

Separation of the lime's effects as a nutrient from those as neutralizer of acid makes the soil's exchange capacity a major factor in fertility

By means of electrodialized colloidal clay, which is a hydrogen-saturated clay at a pH of 3.6 when free of cations other than hydrogen, it is possible to titrate this to any desired degree of calcium (or other cation) saturation, or to any pH figure between 3.6 and 7.0 with all the cations adsorbed and none in solution. Since the amount of clay in the suspension can be controlled, then by taking a given volume of known concentration of clay to be mixed with sand, any given amount of exchangeable calcium (or other cation) can be so offered per plant. One can, then, choose the degree of acidity, or pH and keep it under control, and independently of that can also control the amount of supplied calcium by merely putting into the sand more or less of the clay of the chosen pH. By means of this colloidal clay technique, nitrogen fixation and other physiological processes of plants have been studied to segregate the various effects of the hydrogen ion on plant nutrition.

It was by means of this technique that the exchange capacity of the soil demonstrated its significance in the effects on the soil and the plants when liming to fertilize with calcium or to fertilize with any other nutrient element. For example, by putting into given constant amounts of sand, increasing amounts of clay of any chosen pH, or thereby a clay of any chosen degree of calcium saturation, this gives an increase in the exchange capacity of this artificial soil and by that means the amounts of calcium (or other nutrients) offered the plants can be increased while the pH remains a constant. Thus, the pH is eliminated and is consequently not mistaken as a measure of the amounts of calcium (or of other nutrients and hydrogen) offered to the plants growing in the given soil volume. By this it is demonstrated that the pH cannot be construed as of any value in determining the amount of lime to be supplied either as nutrition or as neutralization of soil acidity. This points out, then, that a knowledge of

Increasing the amount of calcium offered the plants by increasing the colloidal clay (pH 4.4) in the quarts sand (left to right) in the glass containers made the difference between poor and good growths and between attacks by a fungus and immunity to it.

the soil's exchange capacity is necessary if the degree of hydrogen saturation is to be quantitatively interpreted as total hydrogen and conversely as totals of the cations other than hydrogen exchangeable from the soil. The exchange capacity of the soil becomes the important property when quantitatively interpreting soil tests of exchangeable ions.

By means of this colloidal clay technique, permitting varied control of the pH of the clay as well as varied control of the amounts of calcium or other cations on the clay, studies of plant nutrition in relation to the hydrogen ion have been extensively carried out. When a series of the clays was prepared to include the pH values going from 4.0 to 6.5 by increments of .5 pH, and the amounts of each of these six clays were taken so as to give .05 milligram equivalents of calcium per soybean plant, the plant growth was poor at the four pH values of 5.5 and lower, but it was good at the two pH values of 6.0 and higher. When twice as much of each of these clays was put into the sand to offer .10 milligram equivalents of calcium per plant, the corresponding pH values differentiating between poor and good plant growth as above were 5.0 and 5.5, respectively. But when four times as much clay was put into the sand offering .20 milligram equivalents for root contact, the dividing pH figures between poor and good plant growth were 4.5 and 5.0.

Thus, had one seen the plant growth of only the first series, it would have been logical to report that the soybean plant is "disturbed by," or "sensitive to," a pH of 5.5, and "requires" a pH of 6.0. Had one seen only the second series, it would have seemed logical to refute these reported figures and to contend that this plant species is disturbed by a pH of 5.0, but not by the required one of 5.5. Then similarly had one seen only the third series, the contradiction of both preceding sets of figures given above would have been expectable, and the claims anticipated that soybeans are not disturbed seriously by soil acidity until the degree of it becomes as severe as pH 4.5. Here would have been apparent grounds for claiming that the soybean is an "acid-tolerant" crop. However, in this third series, which exhibited higher "tolerance" of a degree of acidity by ten times more than that "tolerated" in the first series, this "tolerance" was brought about by merely quadrupling the exchange capacity in the constant volume of sand-clay soil. Increasing the nutrition as calcium by four times was the counteraction or the antidote for an increase of degree of acidity, or hydrogen-ion concentration, by ten times.

Equally as interesting as this preceding observation of what has erroneously been called "toleration" of acidity by plants, were the changes

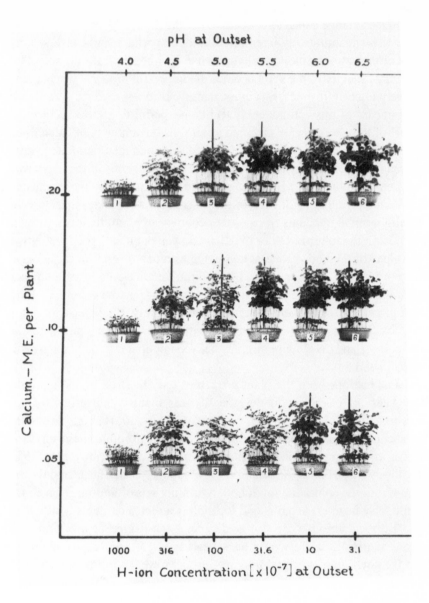

Decreasing degrees of acidity (increasing degree of saturation of the clay by calcium) were offered the soybeans (pH, left to right, 4.0; 4.5; 5.0; 5.5; 6.0; 6.5). There was an increasing amount of calcium offered as a constant per horizontal row by putting more clay into the sand-clay medium in going from the lower to the upper one, viz.: .05; .10; and .20 milligram equivalents per plant.

Plants lose fertility back to acid (infertile) soils or gain it from these according to their degree of saturation.

in the reactions, or pH values, of these colloidal clays as a result of growing the soybean crop for a time extending scarcely from planting to the blooming stage. The measurements of the pH values of all the sand-clay mixtures after they had grown the crop showed a shift of the reaction toward neutrality from the initial pH values of 4.0, 4.5, and 5.0, and a shift toward more acidity from the initial pH values of 5.5, 6.0, and 6.5. These shifts were greater in the last three cases according as the initial value was higher. As a consequence, the pH in these soils resulting finally from the crop's growth in them was almost the same, namely, near 5.5, for all the different sand-clay mixtures that originally were pH 5.0, 5.5, 6.0, and 6.5. The first of these resulted from a decrease, and the last three from an increase in the degree of acidity. Here the plant growth modified and determined the degree of acidity of the soil, and not vice versa.

Chemical analyses of the crops, in comparison with those of the seed, showed that they had all taken calcium from the clay-sand mixture in consequence of their growth. The amounts taken were about the same for all those cases of pH 4.0, 4.5, and 5.0. If this calcium removal represented an exchange of it to the plant for hydrogen from the roots, this hydrogen added to the clay should have lowered its pH figure below the initial values, and to about the same amount for all these three of them. The amounts of calcium taken from the soil, however, by the soybeans growing at pH values 5.5, 6.0, and 6.5 increased with these increasing pH values. This was not in agreement with, but was more than the equivalence represented by, the increasing degree of acidity of the soil resulting from the crop growth. In only one case was the increasing degree of acidity equal to or slightly more than the increasing degree of calcium removal. In only one case was there a suggestion that the hydrogen going from the root to the soil was replacing nearly exactly the calcium taken from there by the root. The extra cations, besides the hydrogen, going in the reverse from the root to the soil in exchange for the calcium were shown in later studies to include potassium and nitrogen, since in respect to these two elements, the total crop (tops and roots) contained less than was in the planted seed.

Here, then, there was an interchange of cations, including hydrogen and others from the roots to the clay as well as from the clay to the roots. The final hay crop contained less nitrogen, potassium, and phosphorus than was in the planted seed. As for the calcium, this was found moving only in one direction, namely, from the clay to the roots, when the plants were growing or even barely surviving. Calcium was moving into the plants in larger total amounts at any given pH of the soil when the exchange capacity of that soil was pushed higher by increasing the clay in the sand-clay soil. Calcium was taken both in larger totals from, and at larger percentages of, the same exchangeable supply offered, according as there were increasing degrees of saturation of the clay by that calcium, or with higher pH values, only when these were 5.5 and above. Thus, the delivery of calcium from the soil to the crop was more efficient in terms of the applied calcium according as the soil was more highly saturated by it, or of higher pH values above this figure of pH 5.5 for this particular clay. This suggests that the efficient use of a given amount of lime calls for its application so as to give highly saturated, limited soil volumes rather than an infinite distribution throughout the soil of the entire root zone. Drilling the lime well down into the soil for root contact and for fertilizing effects is suggested as better practice than mixing it throughout the entire soil body for effects in acid neutralization.

Relative degree of saturation of the colloid by the different ions, and this of each in relation to the others, influences their activities in plant nutrition

Because the degree of saturation of the colloidal complex by calcium exhibited its significance in the efficiencies with which the constant amount of exchangeable calcium was passed to the plants, studies of the increasing degree of calcium saturation with reciprocally decreasing degrees of saturation of other cations were undertaken, using constant amounts of exchangeable calcium offered to the soybean crops grown by means of the colloidal clay technique. In the first trial, the percentages of calcium saturation were 40, 60, 75, 87.5, and 97 reciprocally combined *(a)* in one series with hydrogen, *(b)* in another with magnesium, and *(c)* in another with barium. In the hydrogen series, this increasing degree of calcium saturation represented a corresponding decreasing degree of hydrogen saturation or decreasing degree of acidity as increasing pH values, namely, 5.10, 5.50, 5.90, 6.45, and 6.85, respectively. In the other two series this increasing calcium saturation represented no ranges in degree of acidity, since all the clays were made nearly neutral by means of cations other than hydrogen, namely, *(a)* magnesium, a nutrient, and *(b)* barium, a non-nutrient, and both similar to calcium in many of their properties.

The plant growth increased nearly 50%; the nodule production increased by more than 50%; and the calcium uptake increased by more than 100%, as a result of the increase in calcium saturation, regardless of whether there was at the outset a range in the degree of acidity in the series or whether all the soils were nearly neutral. Since the increasing efficiency of calcium, as measured by the increase of plant growth, of numbers of nodules, and of calcium taken from the same exchangeable amount in the soil, resulted from the increasing degree of saturation of the colloid by it, regardless of whether the soils were of differing degrees of acidity or all nearly neutral, there can scarcely be much disturbing significance, either hindrance or help, ascribed to the hydrogen ion as an acidity factor when these other active inorganic cations of fertility or non-fertility values are associated with it.

As a comparison of the behaviour of calcium when associated with the highly active hydrogen in contrast to its behaviour when associated with a much less active or less ionized cation, the large, positively charged ion of methylene blue was adsorbed on the clay with the calcium as the reciprocal to it in its increasing degrees of saturation of the clay colloid. There were three series, similar to the preceding ones, as regards the constant amounts of total exchangeable calcium as increasing percentage saturations, but this combined with decreasing percentage saturations of *(a)* hydrogen in one series, *(b)* potassium in another, and *(c)* methylene blue in still another.

In the first two series, the plant growth increased by nearly 50%, the nodulation by the same degree, and the uptake of calcium by almost 100%, according to the increasing calcium saturation and the reciprocally decreasing saturation of these other two accompanying active, inorganic ions, one of which made the soils in the series decreasingly acid and the other made all of them nearly neutral. But in the third series, where the reciprocally decreasing saturation was the result of the inactive, large, organic ion of methylene blue, also making all the soils in the series neutral, the constant amounts of exchangeable calcium, regardless of the differing degrees of saturation by it, gave nearly constant weights of crops, constant numbers of nodules, and delivery of calcium suggesting larger amounts as the saturation degree of the colloid by it was smaller. All these results from the calcium in this series were nearly the equal of the maxima in all the other series for it, regardless of whether accompanied by hydrogen, magnesium, potassium, or barium.

In these two trials with the six plant series, there was again demonstrated the increase in the degree of acidity of the soil resulting from the crop growth. This demonstrates the fact that the removal of fertility from the clay in the clay-quartz medium increases the hydrogen presence there or increases the degree of its acidity. For the two series in which the decreasing hydrogen saturation of the clay, or the increasing pH values,

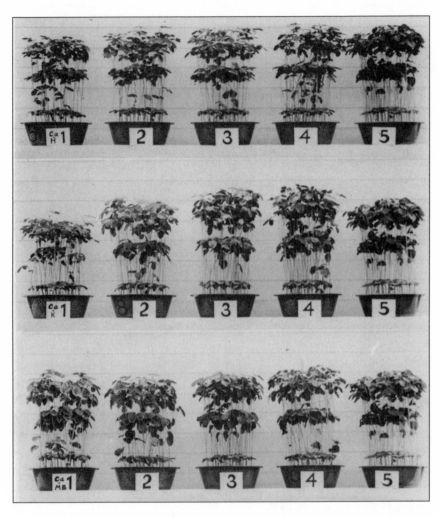

Increasing calcium saturation (40, 60, 75, 87.5 and 97 percent, left to right) of the clay colloid in the clay-sand soil offering the same amount of exchangeable calcium per plant, gave increasing plant growth accordingly when the inorganic hydrogen and potassium were the accompanying ions. But the saturation degree was without effect and the plant growth reflected the constant amount of exchangeable calcium when methylene blue was the accompanying ion.

accompanied the increasing degree of calcium saturation, the growth of the crop for the six weeks lowered the initial pH values by the following amounts, .20, .20, .60, 1.10, and 1.65 respectively for the units of decreasing hydrogen saturation. In the three neutral series, made so with decreasing degrees of saturation by (a) magnesium, (b) barium, and (c) potassium accompanying the increasing calcium saturation, the pH values were lowered as a result of the crop growth by amounts varying from 1.10 to 1.60. In the case of the series with methylene blue, here, too, the crop growth made the soils more acid by pH amounts as much as 1.30 to 1.60. By the growth of a single crop for six weeks on these soils that were initially neutral, the degree of acidity was increased by amounts approaching even a hundred times. Acidity can scarcely be much hindrance when the very crop growth itself increases the degree of acidity to such magnitudes.

Hydrogen, or acidity, helps in mobilizing other cations (possibly anious) from the soil colloid into the plant roots

The association of the active calcium with the inactive methylene blue molecule reported above, presented the concept that the activities of any adsorbed ion resulting in its entrance into the plant are determined not only *per se*, that is, by its chemo-dynamics, but also according as these are modified by the activities of other ions by which it is accompanied. From these results there arose the concept that not only the activity of the hydrogen ion deserves measurement by its glass electrode, but that plant nutrition in terms of calcium will be better understood when the calcium activity can be measured by a similar electrode, or if we can have a pCa as an activity measurement for calcium, and similar measurements for other ions just as we have pH for activity of the hydrogen ion.

As a partial measure of the influence on the calcium activity by some of the cations associated with this element in the suite of ions on the colloidal complex of the soil, some calculations were made of the efficiency with which the exchangeable calcium on the colloidal clay was moved into the soybean plants in some studies (a) using increasing degrees of saturation of a constant amount of clay by calcium and thereby offering increasing amounts to the crop, and (b) using increasing degrees of saturation on decreasing amounts of clay to offer constant amounts of calcium to the crop. In both studies the calcium was associated with (a) decreasing hydrogen and thereby decreasing degree of acidity, and (b) decreasing barium and thereby with all soils nearly neutral.

When the decreasing hydrogen was associated with the increasing saturation of the clay by calcium in both of these cases, the exchangeable calcium moved into the soybean crop with a higher efficiency than when barium was the accompanying ion as is shown in table 1. Here is the suggestion that as the hydrogen is adsorbed on the colloid and comes into the suite of ions held there, it may serve to push off or make more active, the other cations on the clay. Thus, the presence of hydrogen of no nutritional service itself, and too long considered a detriment, becomes a benefit in that it mobilizes the other cations of fertility value into the plant more efficiently.

That the active hydrogen ion on the colloidal clay serves to move larger shares of the other cations (nutrient ions) from the colloidal complex into the plant root was clearly demonstrated by growing spinach on two five-pot series of similar soils, one of which series was acid at pH 5.2, and the other was nearly neutral at pH 6.8. The amounts of the separate nutrient ions put on the clay as chlorides to make the acid series and as oxides and hydroxides to make the neutral one, were duplicates throughout the series

Table 1

Degree of saturation by			In plants %		Total mgms.		Efficiency	
Cal-cium	Hydro-gen (acid)	Barium (neutral)	(acid)	(neutral)	(acid)	(neutral)	(acid)	(neutral)
Increasing saturation with amount of clay constant								
40	60	60	.507	.386	25.2	23.9	12.6	11.9
60	40	40	.651	.594	44.8	38.0	22.4	19.0
75	25	25	.702	.672	50.9	47.0	25.4	23.5
87.5	12.5	12.5	.764	.707	57.1	56.2	28.5	28.1
Increasing saturation with amount of exchangeable calcium constant								
25	75	75	.27	.29	40.27	1.20	40.2	31.2
50	50	50	.55	.31	85.54	45.54	40.7	22.7
75	25	25	.71	.66	122.40	104.84	40.8	34.9

Table 1. The increasing degree of saturation of the soil colloid by calcium was more efficient in moving calcium into the soybean plants when hydrogen (acid) rather than barium (neutral) was the reciprocal of the calcium.

except for the calcium. This was put on as increasing amounts from 0 to 12 milligram equivalents by increments of three.

The spinach crop grown on the acid series showed a general yield increase with more calcium applied. More significant, however, were the much higher totals and higher concentrations of the soilborne, inorganic nutrient elements, namely, calcium, magnesium, strontium and manganese, for this crop on the acid series than for that on the initially neutral soil. Also, as a result of both the increasing amounts of calcium added and the increasingly higher degree of saturation by calcium of the colloidal clay, there were increasing totals, and increasing concentrations of these elements in this vegetable crop, which was not the case for it when growing on the soil initially neutral. On all soils, the amounts of phosphorus and potassium did not show such clear correlations. They followed more nearly the crop yields.

The oxalate contents of the spinach, by combination with which calcium and magnesium become highly insoluble, and thereby indigestible, as a synthetic product of the plant's processes were even more interesting than the uptake of the six inorganic elements contributed from the soil. The oxalate contents of the plants from the acid soil were higher than of those from the neutral soil. Also, they increased with the increments of calcium on the former, but not on the latter soil. However, when matched against the equivalents of the crop's contents of calcium and magnesium combined, the oxalate there in case of the acid soils was less than required to make both of these alkaline earths insoluble. On the neutral soil it was more than enough. Here was evidence that the acidity of the soil is a help, and not a hindrance, not only in the transportation of the inorganic elements from the soil into the crop plants, but also in the plants' synthetic creations through which the soil fertility serves first in plant nutrition and then later in the nutrition of animals and man.

Soil acidity serves to process the applied minerals as well as those natural in the silt and thereby to restock the clay with active fertility

In our mechanical analyses of soils, the three separates, namely, sand, silt and clay have not been emphasized for their differing potential contributions to fertility according to the humid or arid climates they represent. When the clay is the colloidal, dynamic separate which takes up, and gives off, nutrient cations but offers none of significance by its own chemical decompositions; and when the exchangeable supply of fertility in the soils of low exchange capacity is exhausted so quickly by a few successive crops; we must look to the silt and sand separates as the source from which the fertility store on the colloidal clay is regularly renewed.

For that renewal, the sand separate can offer little because of its large particle size and limited total surface for acid-clay contact. Its insolubility and hardness, by virtue of which it naturally remained as large particles, testify to its high potential in quartz as its mineral component and thereby little or no fertility value. The silt separate may well be expected to offer more to the clay because of smaller particle size or more surface for contact. Silt is of the size sufficiently smaller to be windblown. It is brought to the humid regions from the dry, unweathered areas by that means. By virtue of such origin it is more apt to be an extensive collection of minerals other-than-quartz containing more nearly all the elements of fertility. It is the silt loam soils in the semi-humid areas, or under moderate degrees of soil development, which have grown the legumes naturally and have given us the protein food supplies most abundantly.

By mixing specially prepared silt minerals with a colloidal clay suspension of controlled degree of acidity, or by putting the moist silts into a collodion tube and immersing this into the acid colloidal clay, it has been demonstrated that the acidity of the clay serves like any other acid to decompose the silt minerals. The active hydrogen from the clay passed through the membrane. It decomposed the minerals, while the cations so released passed in the opposite direction, were adsorbed on the clay, and from there were taken up by the plant roots with plant growth according to the differing degrees of development the silts had undergone.

Thus, the acid clay is offering its active hydrogen as an agency decomposing the silt minerals, releasing cations from these reserve supplies, and developing more clay thereby. It suggests that our productive soils have been those with the proper mineral mixtures in their silts as reserves of fertility rather than silts as merely fortunate physical makeup for easy tillage. It suggests also more significance in windblown soils of the semi-humid areas for the fertility value of their origin in arid regions than we have been wont to believe.

That soil acidity should serve for decomposition of the soil's reserve minerals and for making their fertility contents available for plant use, should be no new concept, when we realize that liming the soil is that very same process. Particle sizes, of ten-mesh and smaller, of limestone applied on the soil are calcareous minerals being processed there by means of soil acidity. They are being so processed in order to make their calcium or magnesium contents available as fertility at various focal points throughout the soil rather than to change degree of acidity of the entire soil volume. The former, as a kind of heterogeneity and not the latter as a distinct homogeneity, appears as the more logical concept of the soil as continued source of plant nutrition. All too long, however, has liming the soil been viewed not in terms of the soil acid as a means of processing this application of a calcium (magnesium) fertilizer, but rather in terms of this carbonate carrier as a means of neutralizing the soil acid. Liming is merely an illustration of how agriculture is an industrial chemical industry using mainly soil acids to provide the raw, starting materials for its creative business.

Summary

In summary, then, it now seems evident that our research efforts on soil acidity for these many years would have been more fruitful and earlier for agricultural production if that research had been guided by the concept that the increasing degree of soil acidity is disturbing to our protein-producing crops because this soil condition represents not a disturbance by the increasing hydrogen, but by the decreasing fertility within the suite of ions adsorbed on the clay among which suite, in a productive soil, calcium occupies the major part. This concept visualizes the hydrogen ion, originating around the soil microbe and around the plant root because of their respirations excreting carbon dioxide, as the cation which they offer to the clay colloid through contact exchange for its stock of nutrient cations. A high degree of hydrogen saturation of the clay, then, is the result of the high concentration of this ion being built up around the microbial or root hair cells as well, when it can no longer be exchanged for other cations in the environment. A high degree of hydrogen saturation of the clay, then, is simply a high degree of fertility deficiency both there and in its immediate environment, including the silt and sand separates. That there is an increasing degree of hydrogen concentration built up around the root as the fertility in its environment decreases has been demonstrated by the research of Dr. E. R. Graham and W. L. Baker.

It is simple to conceive, then, that the higher hydrogen concentrations built up on the clay by plant root activities of plant growth serve as the acid reagent for reserve mineral breakdown and nutrient cation exchange from there to the clay for the hydrogen from it. In this concept, the plant root is merely treating the soil with the acid generated by the root's own respiration; this acid then flows from the root to the clay; and, under higher concentrations resulting there, flows on to the mineral reserves (present naturally or applied as limestone, rock phosphate, etc). As a result of this acid treatment of the soil by the growing plant roots and the microbes, the fertility reserves are "made available" or they are moved out from their mineral crystalline forms into the active ionic conditions to make their way, under their own power of ionic activity and ionic exchanges in the opposite direction going from the mineral reserves to the clay, and to the plant roots for plant nutrition.

Thus, since the forms of life finding their nourishment in the soil do so by trading the hydrogen for it, it should be no other disturbance to our thinking when a soil is highly loaded with acidity than to tell us that when this occurs the soil has given up its fertility to microbial and plant crops for it. Soil acidity, then, is the regular natural result of crop production, and its accumulation is merely the result of our failure to restock the mineral reserves (of which limestone is only one) by which that acidity would neutralize itself in keeping more fertility flowing out from these restored resources and along the assembly lines of agricultural production.

Interlude

An interlude seems to be indicated if we are to register all the points so subtly unveiled by William A. Albrecht. Students of Albrecht found, soon enough, that excessive calcium will cause magnesium, phosphate and minor element deficiency. This assuredly means vegetables without digestive calcium. In general, it means plants with imbalanced hormone and enzyme systems; ergo poor health, the magnet for bacterial, fungal and insect attack.

High magnesium and low calcium permit organic residue to decay into alcohol, a sterilant to bacteria. It may also prevent normal dry down and nutritional ripening of any growing crop. It may cement clay soil tightly together; thereby creating a crust that can easily exclude oxygen and water retention and proper insoak and capillary return during dry spells. It is no accident that such soils produce abundant weed crops. Lessons even Albrecht learned standing on the shoulders of giants have become current coin in the literature of eco-agriculture. Albrecht's student papers figure, of course. So does a swayback shelf of books published since his death.

Because the folklore of "lime and lime some more" hangs on even in academic circles, Albrecht felt compelled to issue a clear and succinct explanation whenever he spoke and often as a constituent part of his papers.

If basic soil meant little or nothing, the principles of base exchange and cation exchange capacity meant everything, not only for calcium—the general subject of this volume—but also for magnesium, sodium, potassium, etc. The key word is milliequivalent, generally written as meq. It represents the amount of colloidal energy needed to absorb and make secure to the soil's colloidal mass calculated amounts of positively charged cations or base metal elemental nutrients. Each of these nutrients has its own atomic weight. The old handbook Albrecht used for his post-professional correspondence course compared the different values of nutrient elements to the differences encountered in weighing out grain—corn, wheat, soybeans, alfalfa seed all having different weights per bushel, give or take from the average.

As the saying has it, comparing a bushel of shelled corn at 55 pounds compares to a bushel of barley at 48 pounds the way an apple compares to an orange.

One meq of base exchange capacity was Albrecht's practical unit representing the colloidal energy needed to adsorb—note the spelling of the word—and hold 400 pounds of calcium to the top seven inches of an acre of soil.

Obviously, the base exchange capacity of soils varies. Pure sand has no meq reading. As clay, organic matter and a humus fraction settle in the sand, substructure picks up exchange capacity. That is why a sandy soil will exhibit only, say, an exchange capacity in the five or six range. A soil enriched with organic matter and talcum-fine clay can easily run up a 40 meq number. Assuming the absurdity that a soil exchange capacity be entirely satisfied with calcium, then a six meq soil would adsorb, hold and exchange 400 × 6, or 2,400 pounds of calcium. A soil with a 30 meq reading could adsorb, hold and exchange 400 × 30, or 12,000 pounds of calcium.

These different capacity levels pour ridicule on many liming recommendations. Using pH to compute liming applications with no reference to the base exchange expressed as milliequivalents for a four or five meq soil has been compared by Brookside Laboratories to using a five horsepower motor to run a sewing machine. This is the mandate for a soil audit, a computation of existing calcium in the soil, and an equally astute calculation of room for more, taking the necessity for other nutrients into consideration.

All of Albrecht's papers must be read with this equation in mind.

–Charles Walters, Editor

CHAPTER 28

Interrelationships of Calcium, Nitrogen, and Phosphorus in Vegetable Crops

COINCIDENT WITH THE RAPID advances being made in soil science, an increasing interest has been shown in the soil mechanisms as they control plant nutrition, growth, and crop production. One of the most influential factors involved is that of the interaction of nutrients. The equilibrium among ions in the soil and the culture solution has lately been designated as "nutrient-element balance." Emphasis has been placed on the interrelations of essential plant nutrients, on "antagonisms" between specific cations, and on the possible application of such relationships to fertilizer practices in the field.

In the nineteenth century Wolff noticed that with barley the greatest growth occurred in "complete" nutrient cultures. Excess potassium depressed yields. It was observed, however, that the depression in growth could be overcome by the addition of another nutrient. He noted also that sodium amendments offset the effects of excess potash. Lagatu and Maume recorded a decrease in the yield of grapes when potassium was omitted from an otherwise balanced fertilizer application. Thomas substantiated the work of Lagatu and Maume, and his data further emphasized the importance of proper balance in fertilizer applications with reference to absorption.

Associated with nutrient balance are the frequently demonstrated cationic antagonisms. Hoagland, Lundegärdh, and Richards summarized the interactions existing in the absorption of potassium, calcium, magnesium, and sodium. Possible ways in which one element in nutrition may substitute for another are outlined by Cooper. A decrease in plant growth and an accentuation of mineral element deficiency symptoms by unbalanced soil cations have also been demonstrated by many investigators. The concept that a lack of balance may be more harmful to plant growth than a deficiency of two or more nutrients has been suggested. The reports of Davidson and Blake, and of Waugh, Cullinan, and Scott, and recently those of BROWN on nutrient balance in the peach bear this out. Phillips, Smith, and Hepler reached a similar conclusion with the tomato plant.

During the past six years at the Missouri Agricultural Experiment Station, the importance of nutrient balance in obtaining maximum response to fertilizer treatment has been repeatedly observed in nutritional studies with vegetables. This report deals with the yields of some vegetable crops as influenced by the balance of calcium, nitrogen, and phosphorus when the plants were grown in cultures of beidellite clay. This is a naturally occurring clay of which most of its readily available nutrient ions have been removed by leaching and H adsorption during continuous weathering.

Methods

Spinach, Swiss chard, lettuce, tampala, and tomato plants were grown under controlled greenhouse conditions in glazed gallon crocks using colloidal clay cultures for nutrient media. Variable fertility levels were achieved by titrating the exchangeable ions, in the desired amounts and ratios, onto the original acid clay subsoil or B-horizon of Putnam silt loam, which has an exchange capacity of 28 milliequivalents per 100 grams, 12 of which are hydrogen. Of the remaining 16 milliequivalents of adsorbed nutrients, 12 are calcium and the remaining 4 are composed of smaller quantities of potassium and minor nutrient elements. Although these nutrient cations occupy a considerable portion of the total exchange capacity of the native subsoil, numerous biological tests have demonstrated its contribution of nitrogen and phosphorus to be nil, while practically none of the calcium and potassium is available for plant growth. Various nutrients, held on the clay in exchangeable form, may be provided for plants in any desired ratios and quantities simply by replacing the hydrogen on the clay with selected cations and by using the proper amount of prepared clay in the nutrient substrate. The pH values of the resulting media approximated 6.5. Stability of the clay and its naturally high content of replaceable hydrogen make its use, by simple additions of cations as exchanges for its hydrogen, very convenient for balanced nutrient studies.

The usual procedure followed in setting up the colloidal clay cultures was the preparation of a series of clay aliquots to which were added 5, 10, 20, and 40 milliequivalents of nitrogen in the form of ammonium nitrate. To each of these levels of nitrogen there was added calcium, as calcium acetate, in variable amounts to provide 0, 5, 10, 20, and 40 m.e. of calcium. This provided, then, twenty soil treatments giving four levels of nitrogen, each of which had combined with it five variable amounts of calcium as additions to the supply native in the initial clay. To each of

Table 1

Nutrients Added to Clay to Provide Variable Levels of Calcium and Nitrogen

Treatment	Milliequivalents per Plant						Clay per Plant
	Ca	N	P	K	Mg	S	
	m.e.	*m.e.*	*m.e.*	*m.e.*	*m.e.*	*m.e.*	*gm.*
1	40	40	20	20	6	6	717
2	40	20	20	20	6	6	633
3	40	10	20	20	6	6	592
4	40	5	20	20	6	6	571
5	20	40	20	20	6	6	550
6	20	20	20	20	6	6	467
7	20	10	20	20	6	6	425
8	20	5	20	20	6	6	404
9	10	40	20	20	6	6	467
10	10	20	20	20	6	6	383
11	10	10	20	20	6	6	342
12	10	5	20	20	6	6	321
13	5	40	20	20	6	6	425
14	5	20	20	20	6	6	342
15	5	10	20	20	6	6	300
16	5	5	20	20	6	6	279
17	0	40	20	20	6	6	383
18	0	20	20	20	6	6	300
19	0	10	20	20	6	6	258
20	0	5	20	20	6	6	238

these individual treatments were added other nutrients in constant quantities. The additions consisted of 20 m.e. each of potassium and phosphorus and 6 m.e. each of magnesium and sulphate (table 1). Growth responses indicated that sufficient quantities of all trace elements are supplied by the native clay subsoil employed as an adsorptive media, the absolute amounts varying, of course, directly with the quantity of clay used. Effects of the variable quantities of colloid in the several treatments, since they might influence diversely the physical properties of the growing media, were reduced to a minimum by blending the clay with large quantities of pure sand or other chemically inert material. Single treatments were replicated at least three times, but usually ten times. Variations in plant growth within individual treatments were extremely small, resulting from the degree of control exercised upon the chemical as well as the physical properties of the substrate.

In the more extensive studies involving variable levels of nitrogen, calcium, and phosphorus, aliquots of clay with ammonium nitrate and calcium acetate added in quantities to secure the desired ratios were prepared. Variable phosphorus levels were achieved without altering other nutrient levels, simply by adjusting the quantities of monobasic and dibasic potassium phosphates. Additional potassium, when needed, was supplied as the acetate. Control of nutrient levels was thus achieved with all nutrients other than nitrogen, calcium, and phosphorus constant for all treatments (table 2). The amount of subsoil clay required to provide the exact exchange capacity for the added nutrients in each treatment was determined beforehand in terms of the known qualities of the clay. Putnam subsoil material was then mixed under moisture with the particular nutrients and homogeneously blended with either pure white quartz sand or "Zonolite."[1] Plants grown in the resulting mixtures were harvested and yields expressed in terms of fresh weights of the tops.

Results

The yields, expressed as fresh weights of spinach (Bloomsdale Long Standing), Swiss chard (Lucullus), and head lettuce (Iceberg), grown at variable levels of calcium and nitrogen with all other nutrient constant in all treatments, are given (table 3). It is noteworthy that the lowest production occurred in spinach and chard when the highest level of calcium (40 m.e.) was combined with the lowest nitrogen level (5 m.e.) in treatment 4.

[1] *A type of vermiculite widely used as an insulating material.*

Table 2

Amounts of Nutrient Salts (M.E.) and Clay Used in Providing Three Levels Each of Nitrogen, Calcium, and Phosphorus in 27 Possible Ratios

Treatment	Variables			Salts Used to Provide Desired Milliequivalents of Ions												Clay per Plant
	N	Ca	P	$NH_4–NO_4$		$K(H_2)–PO_4$		$K_2(H)–PO_4$		Ca–Ac		K–Ac		$Mg–SO_4$		
	m.e.	m.e.	m.e.	m.e.	m.e.	m.e.	m.e.	m.e.	m.e.	m.e.	m.e.	m.e.	m.e.	m.e.	m.e.	gm.
1	90	90	90	45	45	15	45	30	45	90	90	.....	.....	10	10	1583
2	90	90	45	45	45	.....	.....	30	45	90	90	15	15	10	10	1583
3	90	90	15	45	45	.....	.....	10	15	90	90	35	35	10	10	1583
4	90	45	90	45	45	15	45	30	45	45	45	.....	.....	10	10	1167
5	90	45	45	45	45	.....	.....	30	45	45	45	15	15	10	10	1167
6	90	45	15	45	45	.....	.....	10	15	45	45	35	35	10	10	1167
7	90	15	90	45	45	15	45	30	45	15	15	.....	.....	10	10	958
8	90	15	45	45	45	.....	.....	30	45	15	15	15	15	10	10	958
9	90	15	15	45	45	.....	.....	10	15	15	15	35	35	10	10	958
10	45	90	90	$22\frac{1}{2}$	$22\frac{1}{2}$	15	45	30	45	90	90	.....	.....	10	10	1396
11	45	90	45	$22\frac{1}{2}$	$22\frac{1}{2}$	.....	.....	30	45	90	90	15	15	10	10	1396

Continued

Table 2 (continued)

Amounts of Nutrient Salts (M.E.) and Clay Used in Providing Three Levels Each of Nitrogen, Calcium, and Phosphorus in 27 Possible Ratios

Treatment	Variables			Salts Used to Provide Desired Milliequivalents of Ions						Clay per Plant
	N	Ca	P	NH₄–NO₄	K(H₂)–PO₄	K₂(H)–PO₄	Ca–Ac	K–Ac	Mg–SO₄	
12	45	90	15	22½ 22½	⋯ ⋯	15 10	90 90	35 35	10 10	1396
13	45	45	90	22½ 22½	45 15	45 30	45 45	⋯ ⋯	10 10	1021
14	45	45	45	22½ 22½	⋯ ⋯	45 30	45 45	15 15	10 10	1021
15	45	45	15	22½ 22½	⋯ ⋯	15 10	45 45	35 35	10 10	1021
16	45	15	90	22½ 22½	45 15	45 30	15 15	⋯ ⋯	10 10	771
17	45	15	45	22½ 22½	⋯ ⋯	45 30	15 15	15 15	10 10	771
18	45	15	15	22½ 22½	⋯ ⋯	15 10	15 15	35 35	10 10	771
19	15	90	90	7½ 7½	45 15	45 30	90 90	⋯ ⋯	10 10	1271
20	15	90	45	7½ 7½	⋯ ⋯	45 30	90 90	15 15	10 10	1271
21	15	90	15	7½ 7½	⋯ ⋯	15 10	90 90	35 35	10 10	1271
22	15	45	90	7½ 7½	45 15	45 30	45 45	⋯ ⋯	10 10	896

23	15	45	45	$7\frac{1}{2}$	$7\frac{1}{2}$	...	...	30	45	45	45	15	15	10	10	896
24	15	45	15	$7\frac{1}{2}$	$7\frac{1}{2}$	...	...	10	15	45	45	35	35	10	10	896
25	15	15	90	$7\frac{1}{2}$	$7\frac{1}{2}$	45	15	30	45	15	15	...	...	10	10	646
26	15	15	45	$7\frac{1}{2}$	$7\frac{1}{2}$	...	...	30	45	15	15	15	15	10	10	646
27	15	15	15	$7\frac{1}{2}$	$7\frac{1}{2}$	...	...	10	15	15	15	35	35	10	10	646

This reduction in growth was much greater than with a deficiency of both elements, as in treatment 16 or 20. With the highest amount of calcium (40 m.e.) the successive increases of applied nitrogen gave a general increase in the yield with all crops. At the reduced calcium levels of 10 and 20 m.e.

Table 3

Yields of Spinach, Swiss Chard, and Lettuce According to Variable Levels of Calcium and Nitrogen

| Treatment | Variables | | Fresh Weights* | | |
	Ca	N	Spinach	Swiss Chard	Lettuce
	m.e.	*m.e.*	*gm.*	*gm.*	*gm.*
1	40	40	234.4	634.6	580.0
2	40	20	170.8	487.3	393.0
3	40	10	85.0	391.6	171.0
4	40	5	36.5	32.0	239.0
5	20	40	320.5	486.4	431.0
6	20	20	220.1	693.5	489.0
7	20	10	108.5	333.8	240.0
8	20	5	65.4	212.7	155.5
9	10	40	179.1	233.3	529.0
10	10	20	229.0	243.4	485.0
11	10	10	138.5	215.2	220.0
12	10	5	114.9	171.5	161.0
13	5	40	128.6	179.8	158.0
14	5	20	205.1	133.8	400.0
15	5	10	153.1	116.6	258.0
16	5	5	60.1	104.6	181.0
17	0	40	67.8	....	67.0
18	0	20	197.3	....	260.0
19	0	10	99.9	....	155.0
20	0	5	76.7	....	60.0

* Grams per ten plants.

and especially at the 0 and 5 m.e. levels increases in the nitrogen from 5 to 10 m.e. and from 10 to 20 m.e. also gave a significant rise in yield, but a further increase to 40 m.e. of nitrogen cut production rather sharply in all three crops. Yields were a direct function of the total nutrient supply only when the variables were properly balanced. They point out that a high calcium level must be accompanied by adequate amounts of nitrogen, and a high nitrogen level by sufficient amounts of calcium. Results obtained by growing spinach and Swiss chard at levels of 5, 15, and 45 m.e. each of nitrogen, calcium, and phosphorus in all 27 combinations are summarized (table 4). Potassium was held constant at 20 m.e. and magnesium and sulphate at 5 m.e. for each treatment.

Although responses to nitrogen and phosphorus were outstanding, calcium exerted appreciable influence. Considering calcium, the largest growth occurred at the moderate (15 m.e.) level of calcium combined with the highest of nitrogen (treatments 4–6 inclusive). At a low nitrogen level for both crops (treatments 19–27) and at a medium level of nitrogen for Swiss chard (treatments 10–18) an improvement in growth was obtained when the calcium was reduced to its lowest figure. A rather marked reduction in the yield of both vegetables was noted as the calcium was increased in combination with the lowest nitrogen level.

Increments of phosphorus applied to cultures low in nitrogen (5 and 15 m.e.) failed to give the yield increases possible at high nitrogen (45 m.e.). Conversely, the response to increasing nitrogen was largely governed by the phosphorus supply. When additional calcium was supplied to cultures low in phosphorus, the deficiency of phosphorus was accentuated (compare treatments 12, 15, 18 and 21, 24, 27). The best nutrient-element balance for yield increase was attained in treatment 4, with 45 m.e. as the level of nitrogen and phosphorus and with 15 m.e. as that for calcium. The lack of balance with reference to plant growth was most evident in treatment 21 where 45 m.e. of calcium were combined with 5 m.e. each of nitrogen and phosphorus.

Responses by the tomato plant (variety Marglobe) to combinations of three variable levels of nitrogen, calcium, and phosphorus are portrayed (fig. 1). Yields expressed as fresh weights of vegetation are given (table 5). The plants were grown at 5, 15, and 45 m.e. each of nitrogen, calcium, and phophorus in 27 different combinations. It is evident that a lack of balance among the nutrients was more detrimental than a deficiency in all. The data indicate that phosphorus deficiency in the plants at the 5 m.e. level of this nutrient was greatly accentuated by high calcium and high nitrogen.

Table 4

Yields of Spinach and Swiss Chard According to Variable Levels of Nitrogen, Calcium, and Phosphorus

Treatment	Variables			Fresh Weight*	
	N	Ca	P	Spinach	Swiss Chard
	m.e.	*m.e.*	*m.e.*	*gm.*	*gm.*
1	45	45	45	168.8	227.7
2	45	45	15	197.6	202.6
3	45	45	5	45.5	93.5
4	45	15	45	213.7	232.0
5	45	15	15	176.0	181.0
6	45	15	5	53.8	114.3
7	45	5	45	145.5	206.3
8	45	5	15	171.5	178.7
9	45	5	5	68.3	88.2
10	15	45	45	101.5	67.8
11	15	45	15	82.7	53.4
12	15	45	5	70.1	41.5
13	15	15	45	129.6	68.2
14	15	15	15	102.2	69.1
15	15	15	5	87.8	53.0
16	15	5	45	104.7	112.0
17	15	5	15	103.1	92.3
18	15	5	5	78.5	65.3
19	5	45	45	28.2	20.1
20	5	45	15	18.7	12.8
21	5	45	5	14.7	9.6
22	5	15	45	43.5	24.5
23	5	15	15	24.4	18.0
24	5	15	5	19.5	20.0
25	5	5	45	35.0	35.2
26	5	5	15	28.6	21.6
27	5	5	5	25.4	15.2

* Grams per five plants.

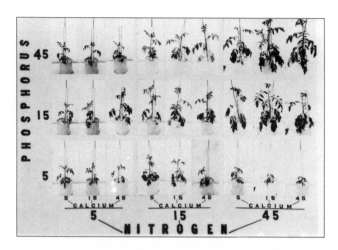

Fig. 1. Tomato plants at variable levels of nitrogen, calcium, and phosphorus. (Numbers indicate m.e. of respective nutrients applied per plant.)

Table 5

Yields of Tomato Plants According to Variable Levels of Nitrogen, Calcium, and Phosphorus*

Phos-phorus	Nitrogen 5 M.E. Calcium, M.E.			Nitrogen 15 M.E. Calcium, M.E.			Nitrogen 45 M.E. Calcium, M.E.		
	5	15	45	5	15	45	5	15	45
m.e.	*gm.*	*gm.*	*gm.*	*gm.*	*gm.*	*gm.*	*gm.*	*gm.*	*gm.*
45	68.6	76.8	57.6	166.0	153.6	169.4	442.0	567.6	516.2
15	60.4	61.0	158.0	202.8	214.8	200.4	345.2	477.6	377.4
5	60.8	48.8	55.4	160.4	119.6	41.2	29.0	25.4	21.2

* Grams per three plants.

With the low level of phosphorus, an increase in the nitrogen from 15 to 45 m.e. depressed the yields. Similarly, at 5 m.e. of phosphorus (and constant osmotic pressure) the increases of calcium gave decreasing yields.

The phosphorus response in tomato nutrition (fig. 1), was dependent almost entirely upon the soil nitrogen supply. By contrast, addition of nitrogen to the soil decreased or increased yields depending on the amount

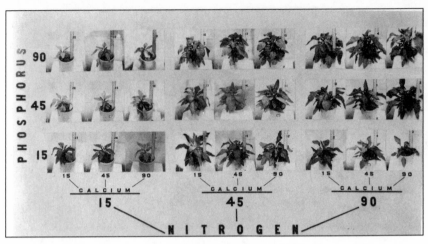

Fig. 2. Tampala plants at variable levels of nitrogen, calcium, and phosphorus. (Numbers indicate m.e. of respective nutrients applied per plant.)

of phosphorus present. With respect to increasing amounts of calcium applied at a high nitrogen and a high or medium phosphorus level, the effects were first an increase and then, with further additions of calcium, a decrease in production. At low phosphorus and high nitrogen levels, the calcium additions progressively diminished yields. In the tomato as with other crops, growth was determined not so much by the total quantities of nutrients added as by the balance relations existing among the elements.

Tampala (*Amaranthus gangeticus*) was grown at nutrient levels of 15, 45, and 90 m.e., each of nitrogen, calcium, and phosphorus in all possible combinations. The nutrient salt additions and clay aliquots were set up in-accordance with the scheme as outlined (table 2). The resulting plant growth and yields of the crop are presented (fig. 2 and table 6). The influence on the yields by a proper balance among the nutrients was again clearly demonstrated. Phosphorus additions either increased, had little effect on, or decreased the growth, depending on the nitrogen and calcium levels. At 15 m.e. of nitrogen, increased phosphorus depressed the yields at all three calcium levels; at 45 m.e. of nitrogen there was little influence, whereas at 90 m.e. of nitrogen, a very significant yield increase was noted. When only 15 m.e. of nitrogen were provided, the addition of calcium accentuated nitrogen deficiencies at all three phosphorus levels. Plants grown with 90 m.e. of nitrogen and 15 m.e. of phosphorus gave noticeably reduced yields, especially when this lack of balance was aggravated by calcium additions.

Table 6

Yields of Tampala Plants According to Variable Levels of Nitrogen,
Calcium, and Phosphorus*

Phos-phorus	Nitrogen 15 M.E.			Nitrogen 45 M.E.			Nitrogen 90 M.E.		
	Calcium, M.E.			Calcium, M.E.			Calcium, M.E.		
	15	45	90	15	45	90	15	45	90
m.e.	gm.	gm.	gm.	gm.	gm.	gm.	gm.	gm.	gm.
90	55.1	52.9	42.1	227.0	230.3	219.9	332.5	372.3	362.9
45	63.8	57.1	52.6	194.7	273.4	265.2	316.7	319.8	333.2
15	87.7	69.5	62.1	184.6	206.9	169.5	186.8	161.7	90.4

* Grams per five plants.

Discussion

In the experiments on nutrient-element balance for growing plants by the sand and/or solution culture method reported to date, it was impossible to control total concentrations of solutions and hence their osmotic pressures as the ions were varied. On the other hand, if the concentrations were held constant, then an increase or decrease in one nutrient ion required that other ions be varied. Exact interpretation of results in terms of a single ion is extremely difficult with sand and solution cultures.

As an approach to the accurate study of nutrient balance, the clay technique of plant growing is admirably adapted. The advantages of this method, and of using other ion adsorptive materials, for refined control of nutritional experiments with vegetables have previously been outlined. Not only do ion adsorptive materials permit the addition of each major cation separately as a carbonate, hydroxide, or acetate without changing other ionic concentrations, but clay holds also the anion of phosphorus in an adsorbed from. Studies conducted by Graham and Albrecht have shown that the nitrate anion may be adsorbed by certain synthetic resins. The adsorbed nitrate was available to plants as readily as were adsorbed cations. Corn plants grew equally well when nitrogen was added in the adsorbed form as in solution. JENNY demonstrated by growing lettuce that adsorbed nitrates were superior to soluble nitrates in amounts above 20 m.e. per plant. The possibility of combining cation and anion adsorptive materials should not be overlooked in plant nutritional studies.

Physical structures of the clay cultures have not gone without consideration. Variations in nutrient levels and colloid content must have a minimum effect on the physical properties of the soil. When combined with large quantities of leached white sand, the clay adheres to the surface of sand particles making up only a small fraction of the total body. Thus the physical properties of the media are not greatly affected. Even a more ideal culture mixture with reference to physical structure can be had by blending clay with "Zonolite." This heat-treated mineral silicate is readily available in several forms as a common insulating material, has a high water-holding capacity, and is practically inert chemically. Its use in combination with clay in nutrient cultures of restricted volume facilitates the addition of large quantities of clay loaded with nutrient ions. At the same time, a physical soil structure is created which is easily penetrable throughout by plant roots, has a high water-holding capacity, and is sufficiently porous for adequate aeration.

Nutrient balance only as it affects yields of some vegetable crops has been emphasized in this report. A few variable levels and combinations of levels of nitrogen, calcium, and phosphorus have thus far been utilized in the approach to fertility balance in nutrition of vegetable crops. These are the nutrient elements most commonly deficient in Missouri soils. An influence of the balance of nitrogen and calcium on the vitamin, mineral, and oxalate contents has been shown. Some of the possibilities of disease and insect control through balanced soil fertility have been demonstrated. The approach offered by the colloidal clay technique of growing plants, provides a means of studying nutrient balance relations in their many ramifications, heretofore not fully appreciated by students of plant nutrition.

Summary

1. The influence of nutrient-element balance on the growth and production of vegetation in spinach, Swiss chard, lettuce, tampala, and tomato was studied by means of growing the plants in cultures prepared by blending colloidal clay with sand or chemically inert "Zonolite." Variable levels of nitrogen, calcium, and phosphorus were supplied.

2. Growth responses by the plants were found to be dependent on relative proportion as well as absolute amounts of variable nutrient elements present in the substrate. Yields were increased, not affected, or depressed by a particular ion, depending on the levels at which the other ions were present in the media. A lack of balance was demonstrated to be more detrimental to plant growth than a deficiency of all the variable nutrients.

3. Advantages of colloidal clay cultures as a means of approach to the study of nutrient-element balance are outlined. Maximum flexibility of variables is possible without concomitant alterations in osmotic pressures or physical properties of the media.

CHAPTER 29

Limestone Mobilizes Other Fertility Too—It's The Soil That Feeds Us

PUTTING LIME ON THE SOILS of the humid region has been practiced under the belief that removal of the acidity of the soil was the benefit from such a treatment. We now know that liming an acid soil is helpful because of the nutritional value of the calcium and magnesium supplied to the crops, by it, and because it helps to mobilize other nutrient elements into the early plant's growth.

Experiments, with a crop like soybeans, demonstrated the need by the young seedlings for calcium early in their life if they were to survive. Any forms of calcium salts showed their benefits. These benefits were the same regardless of whether these salts reduced the soil acidity or whether they increased it. If the soybean seedlings were planted in a lime-bearing sand for no longer time than 10 days and were taken up, washed, and transplanted into a soil, the plants were taller, grew better and gathered more nitrogen from both the soil and the air ever after, than when the first 10 days of their growth were in a lime-free sand. Additional trials with other seeds have demonstrated the earlier emergence and better stands of the crop when the seeds were coated with lime or when this plant nutrient was dusted into the soil along with the planting of the seeds. All of these demonstrations indicate that the calcium of the lime is beneficial by the entrance of the calcium early into the seedling stage of plant growth.

More refined experiments were required to demonstrate the fact that lime as calcium, not as carbonate, serves to mobilize or move other nutrients into the crop. Korean lespedeza, originally imported and claimed to be an "acid-soil crop," showed very clearly its higher concentrations of nutrients other than calcium, when the soil was given this element in the

| Potassium | Magnesium | Calcium | Calcium |
| Chloride | Chloride | Chloride | Acetate |

The importance of calcium, or lime, can be readily demonstrated very early in the plant's life by planting soybean seeds in sand and adding the separate salts of potassium, magnesium and calcium. The effect of the calcium, either as chloride or acetate, is decidedly evident very early in the plant's growth.

soil treatment of liming. By growing test plants in a colloidal clay-sand mixture, it was shown that calcium was required to a relatively high degree of saturation on the clay if the plants were to grow. As this degree of saturation was increased, or as the amount of clay with any degree of calcium saturation put into the sand was larger—to give the plants more calcium—there was more potassium, more nitrogen, and more phosphorus taken into the plants. Lime was the leader, apparently, of the nutrients and was bringing them into the plants.

Quite unexpectedly, it was discovered that when the calcium supply going from the colloidal clay into the plants was very meager, then the nitrogen, the phosphorus, or the potassium might even be going in the reverse direction. This was taking place when plants like the soy beans seemed to be growing fairly well. In no case were any plants grown unless they were increasing their calcium content by its migration from the soil into the plants. Growth was impossible except as calcium was mobilizing itself into the crop early. Soybean plants that would look like a possible hay crop—but could not become a seed crop—had less nitrogen, or less phosphorus, or less potassium, than the seed that was planted because the soil did not offer enough calcium to mobilize these essential elements from the soil into the crop.

Here was ample reason for one to become "lawyer for the defense" of the unsuspecting cow that would be asked to consume a soybean "hay crop" grown on a lime-deficient soil. This would be the case on soils for which the early propagandists for this imported legume said "This is a hay crop if not able to be a seed crop." Fed on hay from this crop grown on such soils, the cow would gain less nitrogen, and less phosphorus, for example, on eating the hay crop than if she had eaten the seed that was originally planted. That a plant may be growing and making vegetative bulk while it is losing nitrogen, or potassium from the planted seed back to the soil may still be doubted. But when some of our animals demonstrate their health disasters on much that is called "feed" because it is "plant growth," we ought to suspect that some thing like nutrients going in the reverse directions might be taking place.

Lime as a helpful soil treatment is quickly indicated by the animal's selection of the vegetation growing on it. All of this may be telling more than just more calcium recognized by the dumb beasts. It may be the indication of the better nutritional values created, or synthesized, within the crop because calcium has mobilized other fertility elements as well as itself into the crop more effectively. Plants create nutritional values by means of the calcium's nutritional service, and not by its removal of soil acidity.

CHAPTER 30

Plants and the Exchangeable Calcium of the Soil

CALCIUM DEFICIENCY in the soil has come to be plant nutrient problem number one in agricultural production. That recognition of this fact should have been so long delayed must unfortunately be ascribed to fallacious reasoning. It has been the common belief that liming the soil is beneficial for plants through the reduction of the hydrogen-ion concentration which this carbonate treatment affects when, in fact, the benefit comes from the introduction of the nutrient, calcium, for plant use. Increasing soil acidity is disastrous to agricultural production, not because of the advent of the hydrogen into the soil, but because of the exit therefrom of the many plant nutrient cations replaced by the hydrogen. Among these, calcium is the most prominent. Soil acidity is therefore in reality a symptom and not the malady.

An understanding of the colloidal behavior of the clay fraction of the soil, with its adsorption of ions and their chemical exchange for others, has done much to provide a clearer concept of the mechanism of those soil and plant root interactions commonly spoken of as plant nutrition. There has always been a wide gap between the behavior of soil in the test tube, by which its stocks of plant nutrients are measured, and its behavior under test against the plant root as computed in terms of crop yield and crop composition. Reasoning from the chemical behavior of the soil in the laboratory to the crop behavior in the field has corresponded to a jump across a tremendous abyss into which most reasoners eventually have found themselves plunged. With the clearer concept of the chemical behavior of the colloidal clay fraction of the soil as it may give, or even take, nutrient cations and anions, it is now possible to bring the clay composition and the plant growth together, and to observe their chemical interactions with laboratory accuracy. We are narrowing the abyss, not only by pushing the chemistry of the soil closer to the plant behavior, but also by using the plant's metabolism as a biological reagent—possibly more delicate than chemical reagents—to give suggestions regarding the chemical nature and behavior of the colloidal clay fraction of the soil.

Colloidal Clay Replaces Aqueous Solutions As Growth Medium
The soil solution has been found an inadequate medium for the relatively large delivery of nutrients from the soil to the plant, and aqueous nutrient cultures may soon be discarded as media simulating plant behavior in the soil. Such solutions demand carefully controlled concentrations, osmotic relations and other physico-chemical conditions that are quickly upset with only partial removal of the ions by the plant. Only the more experienced plant physiologist with continually renewed dilute solutions seems successful with this research tool. On the contrary, the colloidal clay may serve as a nutrient medium which even an embryonic plant physiologist may manipulate successfully. The colloidal clay offers an ease of suspension but yet a low solubility. It gives a large supply, even to excess, of adsorbed nutrient ions but under nearly constant physico-chemical conditions, and it has the capacity to remove from solution those injurious substances bringing about what is commonly known by that cause-concealing term "toxicity." It permits a wide range in kind and amount of nutrient offerings to plants under experiment while other conditions so disconcerting by their fluctuations in aqueous nutrient solutions remain almost constant. At a pH of 5.0 in an aqueous solution, for example, the presence of one hundredth milligram of hydrogen per liter is an approach to the danger point in acidity. In a 2 percent colloidal clay suspension at the same pH of 5.0 there would be 650 times as much hydrogen with no great danger. When the chemistry of the behavior of anions on colloidal clay is understood as well as that of the cations, then the colloidal clay medium will permit laboratory research in plant nutrition to function in the interpretation of field results with a degree of satisfaction which aqueous nutrient cultures do not make possible. The colloidal clay medium was the research tool that brought the exchangeable calcium into its proper importance as a plant nutrient.

Simplified Concept Of Nutrient Absporption By Plants
The ordinary equation of a chemical reaction at equilibrium may be helpful in formulating a concept of plant root and colloidal clay interactions. Suppose we consider the equation as a case of colloidal clay suspension with possibly some ions in solutions as the left side, and the plant cell

protoplasm, also another colloid, plus its aqueous accompaniment as the right side of the equation. Then in place of, or rather along with, the arrows between and pointing in opposite directions, we interpose a membrane like the wall of the root hair. This may be represented as follows:

Imagine the removal of the water to the point of eliminating the solution phase on each side of the equation. Then we can write it as a case of soil colloid and plant colloid on opposite sides of the cell wall of the root hair. This brings us to the concept of two different colloids in contact. We can believe them at equilibrium, or as exchanging ions in either or both directions as regular chemical laws dictate, except for the modifications dependent on the nature of the membrane and its changes in relation to the colloidal interactions or the plant's metabolic effects.

Unfortunately, we know very little about the chemical properties of the plant colloid "in vivo." Chemical behavior of the plant cell contents, like the goose that laid the golden eggs, does not submit to internal observation. Thus, the conditions prevailing on the right side are not well known. In addition, the time factor, as a kind of fourth dimension, must be introduced. Displacement of equilibrium by the plant is a matter of a growing season

Colloidal clay with its exchangeable ions + Solution

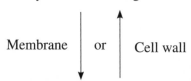

Membrane or Cell wall

Colloidal cell contents of plant + Solution

of approximately 100 days and not an instantaneous performance. Thus, we can measure the accumulated displacement result on the right side of the equation only after that interval of plant growth at which we choose to make analysis of the plants.

More fortunately, the colloidal clay and its properties, its behavior, and possible changes are known definitely enough to serve as the known side of the equation for solving the unknown or the plant side. The beidellite type of clay isolated from the claypan layer in the subsoil of the Putnam silt loam has been subjected to enough physical, chemical, mineralogical and other studies to establish its relative constancy in behavior as an anion. Its capacity for wide variation in kind of, and degrees of, saturation by nutrient cations and anions is also established. It is a large negative molecule of constant size and behavior. By electrodialysis it becomes an acid consisting of a multi-hydrogen alumino-silicate. For its numerous hydrogens, there can be substituted, by simple titration, different amounts and kinds of other cations whether nutrient or non-nutrient for plants. This fact offers in the clay medium, then, wide possibilities of variation in nutrient offering but all under accurate chemical control and yet not in solution.

The relative concentrations of the exchangeable ions are controlled by their respective degrees of saturation on the clay. Their total amounts are controlled by this character coupled with the amount of clay offered the plant. These conditions simulate, then, the degree of ionization and the concentration of the ions, respectively, in the ordinary solutions.

By means of this knowledge of the properties of the clay and its changes on the left side of the equation, we may observe or measure the plant growth behaviors, the incidence of plant disease, and the seed and plant compositions with their indications of the movements of both cations and anions from the colloidal clay into the plant or in the reverse direction. All these and other plant manifestations and clay changes can serve as helps to interpret what has happened chemically on the right side of the colloidal action equation known as plant nutrient feeding. From such we may learn whether plant nutrition may not finally conform to the more commonly accepted laws of chemical behavior.

Calcium is the Most Important of the Adsorbed Nutrients

The experience of farmers with limestone use for legume crops pointed to the irregularities in the growth responses by these crops and cast doubt on the belief that the hydrogen-ion concentration of the soil, or its pH, is the causal factor in legume crop failure. Some acid soils, failing to grow clover, were given limestone and showed no change in pH after a year; yet they produced clover successfully. This beneficial effect of the added calcium, when there was no change in pH, pointed to calcium deficiency in the soil rather than to an injury by excessive hydrogen-ion concentration as the problem of so-called "acid" soils. Aqueous nutrient solutions served to demonstrate calcium as the first requisite for growth of soybeans (Plate I, B), a legume which did not require one nutrient, namely nitrogen, in the medium because of its introduction into the plant from the atmosphere. Growth occurred when potassium and magnesium were not supplied. Incidence of disease with low calcium and, conversely, healthy plants with high calcium, showed calcium to be requisite for healthy plants and plant growth (fig. 1). Clay on which only calcium was adsorbed produced growth (Plate I, C). It was superior to aqueous solutions (Plate I, E)

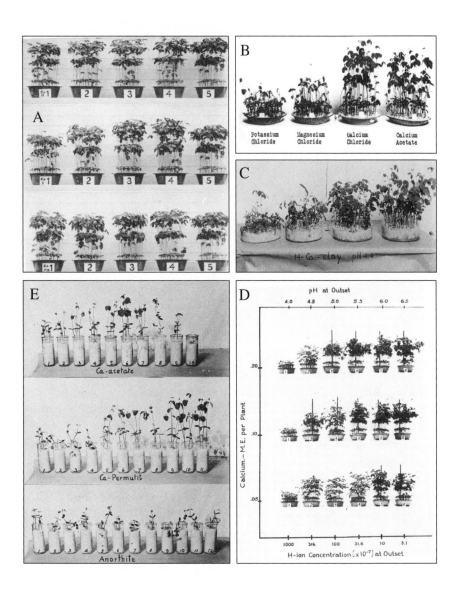

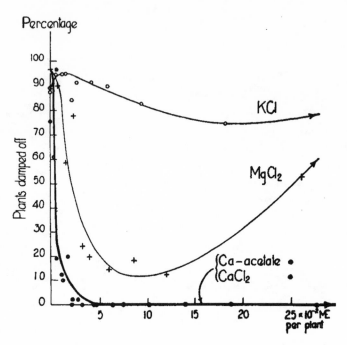

Fig. 1. Damping off as a plant disease was prevalent in the absence of calcium.

in that it produced growth over a wider range of calcium offered the plant. These results suggested that calcium occupying so large a portion of the adsorbed and exchangeable store of cations on the clay is plant nutrient number one in importance, and this is true even for the soybean, a supposedly "acid tolerant" legume.

Separation of Effects of Calcium From Those of Hydrogen-Ion Concentration

Electrodialyzed hydrogen clay on which the exchangeable hydrogen was neutralized by calcium hydroxide to varying degrees to give soils of different pH figures, provided the means of separating the effects of the hydrogen-ion concentration from the direct influence of the calcium

Previous Page Image: Plate I.—A-E.—A. Degree of saturation of calcium is without effect when accompained by methylene blue (lower row) in contrast to its accompaniment by hydrogen or potassium (upper two rows).—B. Calcium, rather than magnesium or potassium, is the first requisite among cations required by young plants.—C. Increasing clay content of sand to supply more calcium (left to right) even at pH 4.4 gives better growth of soybeans.—D. Soybean growth according to different calcium levels through different degrees of acidity of colloidal clay.—E. Calcium adsorbed on permutit was more effective than ionic calcium (acetate) or mineral crystal calcium (anorthite). (Increasing equivalent calcium left to right.)

By use of properly prepared clays, controllable and variable amounts of calcium could be offered to the plant at any pH, merely by varying the amount of the clay that had been titrated to any desired pH. Plant growth on such a series of clays in sand bore some relation to the degree of acidity, or pH, but it was influenced far more by the amount of calcium offered to the plants (Plate I, D). Thus, in trying to relate plant growth to the pH of the soil, the facts indicate that it is related in reality to the approximate reciprocal of the hydrogen saturation and ionization, namely, the calcium saturation.

Some Nutrient Cations May Go In Reverse, Or From The Plant To The Soil

Changes in the pH of the colloidal clay medium as the result of plant growth pointed to a displaced equilibrium, but a displacement toward both the right and the left in the suggested equation. Analyses for calcium of the seed and of the clay at the outset, and again of the plants grown, were the means of determining that the direction of movement of the calcium was to the right or into the plant. Then by calculating the amount of calcium left in the clay and by determining from that the corresponding pH

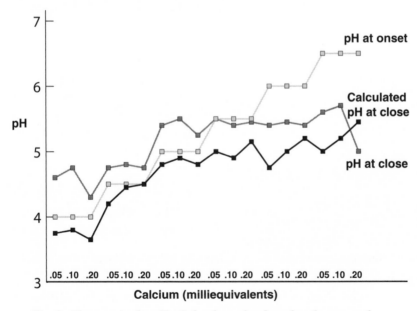

Fig. 2. Changes in the pH of clay brought about by plant growth in contrast to those caused by calcium removal from clay into the plants.

at the close of plant growth, it was discovered that the pH figures for the clays by actual measurement were higher than those by calculation (fig. 2). In other words, the clays were less acid than they should have been because of the calcium removal and its assumed substitution by hydrogen. The increase in calcium in the crop over that in the seed established movement of calcium from the clay soil to the seed and plant in every case. The growth was parallel to the amount of calcium delivered. The fact that the pH was not lowered as calculated for the calcium removal pointed to a return to the clay from the plant of some elements other than calcium, serving as bases or cations, to raise the pH of the clay. Whether anions of plant origin moved to the soil to add to the confusion may well be considered as a possibility.

Here was the first indication that exchange cations—possibly nutrients—may move from the plant to the soil as well as from the soil to the plant. Certainly, as shown by analysis, the element calcium did not go from seed back to the soil. Instead it moved into the plants. Its equilibrium was displaced by movement to the right. At the same time, some displacement toward the left occurred because of movement of other cations in that direction.

Changes In pH Of Clay Caused By Plant Growth Are Related To Calcium Supply

When the pH figures of the clays were below 5.5, the calculated reduction in pH by calcium removal and hydrogen substitution as shown by calcium increase in the plant over that in the seed corresponded to an average of approximately 0.12 pH. In clays with pH figures above 5.5, the lowering of pH through calcium removal was greater according as the pH figure was higher for the initial clay. These reductions were 0.45, 0.90, and 1.25 pH for clays at pH 5.5, 6.0, and 6.5, respectively. Equilibrium displacement through calcium removal from the clay by the plants was greater as the clay was more nearly saturated by calcium, or as its pH figure was higher. The plants removed a larger share of the exchangeable calcium as calcium occupied more of the exchange capacity of the clay.

In spite of the calcium removal from the clay, which lowered the pH figure, the measurements of pH of the clays showed these to be higher by some rather consistent amounts than those obtained by calculations. These amounts of pH shift were not related to the pH level of the clay growing the crop. They were seemingly related inversely to the total calcium offered to the crop. With offerings of 0.05 M. E. of calcium per plant the clay became more alkaline by an average of 0.55 pH. For 0.10 M. E. of calcium offered, the induction of alkalinity was but little less, but where 0.20 M. E. of calcium were allotted, there was a shift toward alkalinity of only 0.25 pH. Even at the higher degrees of soil acidity, or with pH figures below 5.5 to 4.5, the plants gave less of their cations back to the soil as more total calcium was offered to them.

Not Only Ammonium Cations Go In Reverse Direction

Nitrogen determinations of the seed and crop showed losses of this element at the pH figures below 5.5 (fig. 3). Here may have been a cation that was going back to the clay in the form of ammonia to make it more alkaline. But since an increase in nitrogen in the system occurred at and above pH 5.5 for the offerings of 0.10 and 0.20 M. E. of calcium per plant, nitrogen fixation or use of atmospheric nitrogen was involved, with an increase of nitrogen in the system. This raises the question as to whether nitrogen fixation may be going on at the same time that losses of it to the soil are occurring. Since the shifts in pH were so consistent for the calcium offer-

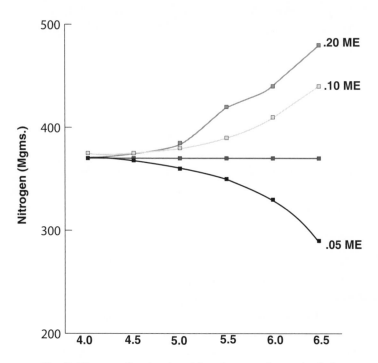

Fig. 3. Nitrogen fixation (positive above and negative below horizontal line for seed content) as correlated with calcium levels rather than with degree of acidity.

ings at all six pH levels used, it seems doubtful whether the plant losses of the ammonium ion could be so consistent in affecting this change when coming from such widely varying sources as seed alone in some cases, and from seed plus atmospheric fixation in other cases. Doubtless the shift toward higher pH by cation movement from seed to soil must be ascribed to cations other than the ammonium of seed origin in this case, where a calcium-hydrogen clay delivering only calcium to the plant is used.

Calcium Delivery To Plants Related To The Degree Of Calcium Saturation Of The Clay

In order to test more accurately the significance of the degree of calcium saturation in the delivery of this element to the plant, clays were prepared with different degrees of calcium saturation, ranging from 40 per cent to complete saturation. The balance of the exchange capacity of the clay was taken individually by hydrogen giving variable acidity, by barium, magnesium, and potassium all giving complete neutrality in the form of readily exchangeable ions, and finally by methylene blue, a large, non-exchangeable ion of organic matter. Such quantities of clay were added to sand for the growth of soybeans as would supply equal amounts of calcium per plant.

Plant growth followed the degree of clay saturation by the calcium, whether it was accompanied by hydrogen or by the other inorganic cations. In all of the trials in this test, as was true in the others, growth was insignificant unless the seed content of calcium was doubled within the growth period, which was five weeks. Increased degrees of saturation resulted in the delivery into the crop of an increased percentage of the exchangeable calcium on the clay, figures varying from six to twenty-five percent of the constant but exchangeable supply (fig. 4). When a large complex organic ion like methylene blue accompanied the calcium, then the degree of saturation was without effect on growth (Plate I, A).

These situations are not easily explained on chemical bases, though they certainly exclude any effect of the hydrogen-ion or the soil acidity. Seemingly, as more calcium is placed on the individual clay molecule, those calcium ions added at the more nearly complete saturation stage are more active in entrance into the plant, or they may be less forcibly held to the clay molecule. Much less of the same total exchangeable calcium moves into the plant when it it is present at a low degree of saturation on many clay molecules, than when it is present at the higher degree of saturation on fewer clay molecules. Seemingly, chemical equilibrium pressure

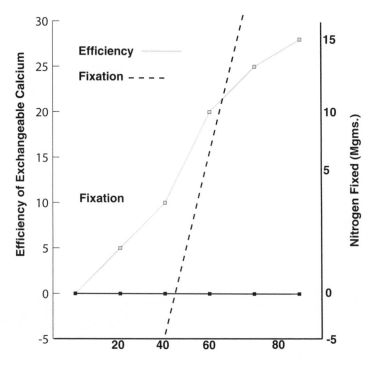

Fig. 4. Nitrogen fixation and efficiency of exchangeable
calcium as related to the degree of calcium saturation.

is changed; that is, it is increased when the clay surface for root contact
offers the nutrient in the higher degree of saturation.

Such results suggest that if the calcium is to have the most pronounced
effects, and if the application is to be used most efficiently, then we should
place the calcium into limited soil areas for more complete clay saturation
rather than place it throughout the root zone for only partial saturation.
In agricultural practice this would suggest drilling the limestone in the
manner used for fertilizers. It also gives credence to the theory of increased
efficiency of fertilizers through their granulation.

**Losses of Other Nutrients From Plant To Soil Under Calcium
Deficiency**

A more complete chemical inventory of seed and clay at the outset was
undertaken in order to determine the behavior of other nutrient ions beside
calcium and nitrogen. The latter had been found to move seemingly from
plant to soil. The former had been shown to pass from soil to plant whenever growth occurred. Trials were undertaken to determine the behavior

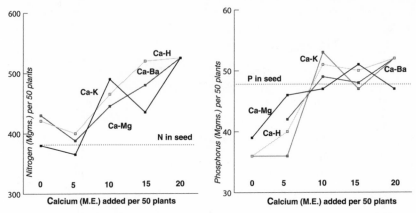

Fig. 5. Nitrogen and phosphorus contents of the soybean crop in relation to calcium levels. (Seed nitrogen = 385 mgms., seed phosphorus = 47 mgms.)

of phosphorus in connection with different amounts of calcium offered the plants. The element phosphorus, though a cation, should be classified with nitrogen in that it moves from plant to soil. Unless larger offerings of calcium were given the plant, it failed to contain all the phosphorus originally in the seed. The phosphorus seems, therefore, to have gone back to the soil (fig. 5).

Phosphorus and nitrogen, both constituents of protein, are apparently moved into the plant from its seed only at high levels of calcium delivery by the soil to the plant. Whatever the nutritional role of the calcium in the plants may be, the question may certainly be raised as to whether it is not instrumental in metabolizing the nitrogen and phosphorus within the plant into insoluble protein to keep equilibrium displaced to the right. There is the further question as to whether it may not play some role in determining the nature and activity of the plant membrane interposed. The latter may be one of its functions, according to the work of the late Professor True; the former can scarcely be denied when calcium, nitrogen and phosphorus run so closely parallel in the plants growing near the lowest possible levels in these different trials. If calcium plays this role in membrane activity, its significance in the early life of a plant is greater than that of merely adding calcium to the original content of the seeds.

In some other trials it was revealed that potassium moves from the plant back to the soil (fig. 6). Although this element appears in the seed in quantities larger than those of calcium or of phosphorus by fifteen and three times, by weight, respectively, it is interesting to note that, despite this fact, the potassium movement to the left in our type equation has been as high as 50 per cent of the seed content. It might be easy to imagine a "sour" soil serving as an acid extracting agent for taking potassium out of the plant. The potassium, however, moved back to the soils, even when they were neutral, moderately saturated with calcium and free of potassium. When one crop exhausted only part of the applied potassium the second or the following crop brought potassium returns to the soil. This brings our view-point nearer to the equilibrium concept again and to the belief that potassium must occur liberally on the clay, with calcium accompanying it, if the potassium content of the crop is to increase over that in the seed.

The Small Supply Of Calcium In The Seed May Be Significant

The full significance of calcium in these cases where nitrogen, phosphorus and potassium have gone from the plant back to the soil, unless calcium was liberally supplied, is not yet determined. It may not be as important as at first indicated, but it is significant that in no case has growth been possible unless calcium moved into the plant in its early life. Growth has taken place, however, during the time when nitrogen, phosphorus, and potassium are being lost from the plant to the soil. The quantities of these different nutrients in the seeds may have some meaning when we note that calcium is present in soybeans in a lesser amount than any of the other nutrients. The calcium, magnesium, phosphorus, potassium and nitrogen occur there in the approximate ratio of 1:1:2:7:42 as molecular equivalents, respectively. Those present in the seed in larger quantities may be more readily lost from the plant to the soil, yet permit plant growth. The short-

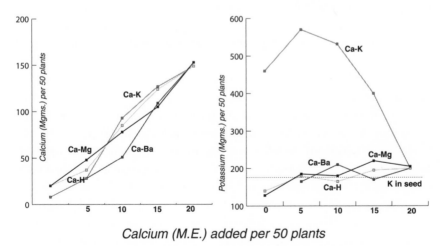

Calcium (M.E.) added per 50 plants

Fig. 6. *Potassium contents of soybean crop with increasing calcium.*
(Seed potassium = 171 mgms.)

age of calcium in the seed may be related to the need for delivery of it by the soil in the early plant growth, or even in seed germination.

Magnesium and Manganese May Bear A Relation To Calcium

When magnesium is considered in relation to its influence on soybean growth and nitrogen fixation, its importance is seen to be indirect. Improvements in general plant performance, including nitrogen fixation, were not related to the amounts of magnesium taken in by the plant, but rather to the increased amounts of calcium from a constant source which went into the crop as the exchangeable magnesium on the colloidal clay was increased. Magnesium is apparently instrumental in bringing about greater effectiveness in calcium use by plants in much the same manner that calcium is important in making nitrogen and phosphate more effective in the plant.

Another interesting relation is that of the calcium to manganese. Recent studies of this so-called "minor" or "micro-nutrient" element in plant nutrition, which is present in such minute quantities that spectrographic technique is required to measure it, show that as more calcium carbonate is mixed throughout the soil, there is a reduction in the amount of manganese taken by such crops as bluegrass, redtop, lespedeza, and sweet clover. When, however, these same amounts of limestone are put into the surface part of the soil only, to "feed" larger amounts of calcium into the plants, then the plants take more manganese from the soil. Here calcium carbonate seems to inhibit manganese delivery to the crop by its neutralizing effect when it is evenly distributed throughout the soil, but to stimulate the same when it is provided to the plant as a nutrient in only a limited zone of the soil. Two distinct effects of calcium are here shown, if this visualization of its role is correct.

Calcium Significant In Ecological Array In Nature

If calcium is so significant in the plants, this may have come about by adjustment, during the course of evolution, to this one chief and widely fluctuating variable, which makes soils different according to climatic differences. The degree to which soil development has progressed is measured in terms of calcium depletion. Vegetation in its ecological array fits into the picture of the variable calcium as it gives plants of different chemical compositions. Soils liberally stocked with calcium support nitrogenous vegetation. Calcium depletion, and therefore potassium dominance, in the soils means a highly carbonaceous vegetation. Calcium fluctuation, then, may determine the different crop possibilities on our different soils. Alfalfa with its protein-rich herbage is commonly established without soil treatment in Kansas or Colorado because the low rainfall has not leached the calcium from the soil. Cellulosic cotton fiber, sugar cane, and other crops, rich in carbohydrates and deficient in proteins and minerals as animal feeds, dominate in regions of high rainfall and soils so highly developed that human and animal populations are disturbed by mineral deficiency diseases. Such relations of plant composition and of animal nutrition to the calcium levels in the soil will be no anomaly in the climatic scheme of plant arrangement when the full significance of calcium in the plants and the soils is understood.

Possible Chemical Linkage Of Calcium To Phosphorus Sugested

The close linkage of phosphorus to calcium in behavior deserves particular attention in future studies in physiology in respect to their possible molecular as well as ionic activities. Plant behavior suggests that the two are used in combination, and the same thing is seen in the animal world among the vertebrates. This is suggested bio-chemically by bacterial behavior when colloidal clay with adsorbed calcium and phosphorus is used as a medium. It is suggested in a purely chemical way when phosphorus shows a different chemical behavior when adsorbed on a calcium-saturated beidellite clay from its behavior on the same medium carrying no exchangeable calcium. Plant services credited commonly to phosphorus may in some measure be found to be services by calcium.

Summary

Calcium is important because of the roles it plays directly. In addition it is significant in relation to the behavior of other ions and to the entire physico-chemical relationship of plants and soils.

To date, the behavior of all the plant nutrient ions adsorbed on the colloidal clay complex, or in the exchangeable form, can by no means be cataloged completely. However, a beginning has been made which has called attention first to calcium. Other cations also have come into the picture. Anions and their reactions to the colloidal clay and to the humus as an organic colloid are still unknown. One nutrient after another can doubtless be brought into the picture with respect to its relation to calcium, and then to the other nutrients, both cations and anions. If these relationships can be worked out, we may learn to understand the influence of these nutrients on the behavior of the root hair wall or membrane which intervenes between the plant and soil colloids.

The colloidal clay concept, and the clay behavior as it establishes an equilibrium with the plant colloids on the other side of a cell wall has suggested that the humus as a colloidal, organic matter fraction may be serving similarly as a nutrient ion carrier. This concept has opened fields of study in plant physiology and soil fertility that are bringing the soil and the plant closer together. These studies may have a much greater significance as their results are applied to animal and human physiology. Perhaps in time, even the mysteries of plant growth can be analyzed in terms of simple chemical behaviors.

CHAPTER 31

Calcium Saturation
and Anaerobic Bacteria
as Possible Factors in Gleization

THE AGENCIES AND chemical changes concerned in the production of the blue-gray horizon in the deeper part of the soil profile, commonly spoken of as "glei development," have provoked much discussion. This process of gleization has regularly been associated with standing water and the consequent iron reduction to give the gray color. Calcium as a nutrient for the responsible bacteria has not been suggested, and as a contributing factor, calcium has not been segregated.

Since this horizon usually consists of a sticky, compact, and structureless clayey mass, its water retention is generally high and movement through it very slow. Its location deep in the solum would exclude influences by atmospheric oxygen but would not necessarily prohibit the infiltration from the soil surface of energy-supplying materials of organic origin. These might serve for use by anaerobic bacteria. Since recent studies emphasize the encouraging role of mineral nutrients, particularly of calcium, in organic matter decomposition and the diminished decomposition, or organic matter accumulation, under limited calcium supply, it seems possible that gleization occurs in the zone where the three factors, ample calcium, organic matter infiltration, and standing water, all operate jointly for anaerobiosis.

That this may be true is suggested by an observation of clay standing under water. Putnam subsoil had been treated with acid and washed thoroughly to produce the resulting acid clay. Three lots in suspension were then treated separately with calcium hydroxide, magnesium hydroxide, and aluminum hydroxide. All were preserved under waterlogged conditions. After 3 months, the samples of the calcium-treated clay and of the magnesium-treated clay had developed the bluish-gray color resembling that of glei. The sample treated with aluminum showed no color change throughout its depth.

Since these clays contain some relatively stable organic matter representing the residue of microbial action which has been moved downward by podzolization, such organic residue would of necessity be relatively deficient in calcium and in magnesium as bacterial nutrients. It would still be of service as a source of microbial energy, however, and the promotion of microbial growth might occur when these mineral shortages were restored.

That an attack on this organic material by anaerobic microorganisms occurred where the calcium and magnesium were applied to the clay was indicated by the color change, and pointed to the reduction of the iron for the organic matter oxidation. Where neither calcium nor magnesium was applied to serve as nutrient bases, but where aluminum, a nonnutrient, or potassium was substituted, these anaerobic performances were not initiated.

That the exchangeable calcium plays a role is suggested by some studies by Wilde, of the Wisconsin Experiment Station. Calculations from his determinations of exchangeable calcium in different horizons of alpha, beta, and gamma glei soils show that the glei horizon occurs where the calcium saturation of the clay was increasing in the successively deeper layers approaching the glei layer. In one of his soils, which he assigns to the Colby series, the percentage of calcium saturation in the zone of glei formation was slightly less than 50 per cent. In another, assigned by him to the Miami series, it was above this figure.

That at least 50 per cent calcium saturation of the clay should be required to foster anaerobic bacterial activity is in interesting agreement with the approximate 50 per cent calcium saturation of colloidal clay required for significant growth and nitrogen fixation by soybeans. It raises the question whether the profile horizons above that of glei formation are not simply of too low a degree of calcium saturation for microbial activity, so that the percolating organic matter is not of service until it has moved downward to the horizon of sufficient calcium saturation and the corresponding relative saturation of other bases.

These observations prompted a simple laboratory test. Untreated Putnam clay and Putnam clay saturated with different cations were taken in equal amounts and mixed with equal amounts of the humus compound extracted from a calcium-deficient soil. They were all stored under water. The soil given calcium became gray. No significant color change occurred in the clay saturated with aluminum, potassium, or hydrogen, or in the untreated clay.

These changes were noticeable in less than 4 weeks and became very distinct in 8 weeks or at the intervals of closer observation. After this latter period the stoppers were removed, cleaned, and the upper part of the cylinder cleaned in connection with the examination for odors. A distinct odor of hydrogen sulfide was detected over the calcium clay. It was less noticeable but yet present over the natural and potassium clay. There was none over the hydrogen clay or the aluminum clay. The stoppers bore dark stains corresponding to the hydrogen sulfide production. The supernatant liquids gave corresponding suggestions of iron in solution after enough time following the odor test had allowed them to clarify. Opalescence, suggesting colloidal iron, appeared over the natural and potassium clays, and a rusty-colored flocculate was over the gray-colored calcium clay. Thin horizons of gray color, of intensity corresponding to that of the calcium clay, appeared at the top of the natural and potassium clay columns. Here the production of soluble iron is suggested, not in an acid soil, but rather at the maximum in the neutral clay saturated with calcium and providing nutritive conditions encouraging microbial performances.

These observations and tests suggest that the process of gleization may center about the presence of calcium in sufficient degrees of saturation of the clay to serve in the bacterial nutrition if the horizon of standing water is to leave its historic record as a bluish gray layer. When such calcium is absent, and apparently because of this calcium deficiency in the bacterial ration, the event of standing water remains unrecorded, regardless of the period of its presence or the possible percolation of the organic matter downward to it.

This hypothesis regarding the importance of the degree of calcium saturation in the process of gleization is submitted not as a proved fact but in the hope that students of soils in the field will test it either for verification and acceptance or for disproval and discard.

CHAPTER 32

Calcium and Hydrogen-Ion Concentration in the Growth and Inoculation of Soybeans

THE COMMON FAILURE OF legumes on sour soils has led us to believe that the soil acidity, or degree of reaction, is responsible. Little attention has been given to the deficiency of calcium as the possible cause, and further consideration needs to be given the question whether legume failure is caused by the harmful effects of the excessive degree of acidity, or by the failure of the plants to obtain sufficient calcium. In mineral, humid soils, the increased deficiency of calcium usually parallels the excessive degree of acidity. Also the use of calcium carbonate on sour soils functions both to supply calcium and to reduce the degree of acidity. Thus, the two possible causes have not been differentiated, and it is readily possible that casual significance has been ascribed to the wrong one of two contemporaneously variable factors. It seems highly essential that we separate these to learn whether legume failure can be ascribed wholly to the excessive hydrogen-ion concentration of the soil or to the deficiency of calcium and its proper functioning in the legume growth.

The particular function of calcium in the plant can not be so readily determined because of the difficulty of controlling accurately the calcium in the soil, and the fact that its ionic form in a water culture may function differently than the adsorbed soil form. Recent developments in the technic of manipulating soil colloids suggested a means of controlling calcium conditions to greater refinement than possible in simple quantitative chemical methods, and a study of the importance of calcium in growth and nodule production of legumes was undertaken with the hope of understanding better the significance of the element calcium in these crops.

Previous work has pointed to calcium as important in soybean inoculation and suggested that it does not exercise this importance so much through its direct influences on the bacteria. These remained viable in an acid soil even though they failed to produce nodules. Inoculated sour soils which failed to produce nodules gave a nodulation increase of 300% when given calcium but no additional bacteria. That the lime functions through the plant more than through its effects on the bacteria is indicated by a significant increase of nodules on the plant grown for 10 days on a calcium-bearing sand and then transplanted to an acid, but well inoculated soil. This same preliminary treatment of the plants for 10 days in calcium-bearing medium also gives greater growth and greater nitrogen fixation in the plants' early history. These facts led to a more careful study of legume growth and inoculation by the use of electrodialyzed colloidal clay as a means of supplying calcium under conditions controlled for (a) the reaction and (b) the amount of calcium supplied.

Methods

The electrodialyzed clay titrated with different amounts of calcium hydroxide served to give varied hydrogen-ion concentration (pH), and an inversely varied amount of calcium. The colloid of this type contains mainly adsorbed calcium and hydrogen ions and introduces no other significant disturbing factors. The selection of different degrees of calcium saturation made possible constant but different pH values, while the use of different quantities of clay per seed gave different but constant amounts of calcium. Clays so selected were mixed with a leached silica sand and served as a medium for the growth of soybeans previously germinated in plant-food-free sand. The treated clay permitted an approximate range in pH from 3.5 to 7.0. The concentrations of clay in the sand ranged from almost insignificant amounts to quantities never large enough to disturb the good physical condition of the sand. In the early work this never exceeded 2%.

No other plant foods were added, since inoculation may take place under normal conditions of the soybean as early as 14 days, and the cotyledon probably carries a reserve of the elements necessary for this short period of growth. Ionic calcium in the form of solutions of acetate and chloride titrated with their acids was used for comparison with that adsorbed on the clay colloid. The plants were grown in different trials, first, by varying the amount of calcium and inversely the degree of acidity, second, by varying only the acidity at constant amounts of calcium, and third, by varying only the calcium at constant acidity.

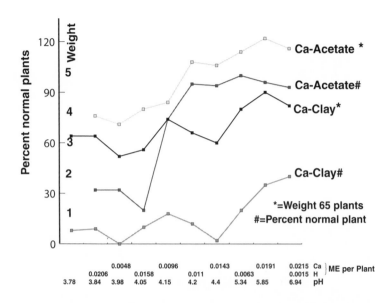

Fig. 1.—Growth of soybean plants on varying amounts of calcium and inversely varying acidity, maximum calcium 0.0215 M.E. per plant.

Experimental Results

In the first trials, which used the clay titrated to different degrees of saturation, the amounts of calcium were so low that difficulty occurred in obtaining growth of the plants. Their very earliest growth seemed normal but was followed by a diseased condition resembling damping-off. The number of plants with apparently normal growth varied with the treatment, becoming more numerous with increased calcium and lessened acidity. This effect was far more pronounced for the calcium as acetate than for the calcium in the colloidal clay, suggesting the more ready availability of calcium in the acetate or free form than in the adsorbed form. The growth, or weights, ran parallel with the percentage of healthy plants, as shown in Fig. 1. A trial along this same plan, supplying large amounts of calcium, produced good growth with most of the plants normal as shown in Fig. 2. The introduction of the proper bacteria failed to produce nodules. Very few of the plants grew to significant size and the study was directed to work out more fully the relation of growth and nodulation to calcium and the acidity.

Clays were prepared at different degrees of saturation, and therefore different degrees of acidity within a pH range from 3.84 to 6.94. The calcium was maintained constant as amounts per seed by using more clay

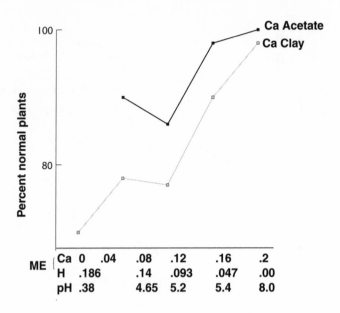

Fig. 2.—Growth of soybean plants on varying amounts of calcium and inversely varying acidity, maximum calcium 0.20 M.E. per plant.

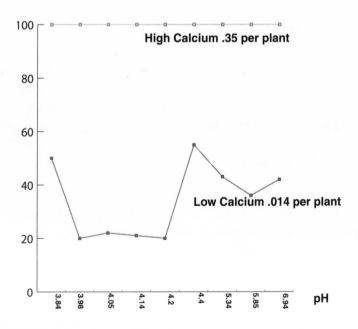

Fig. 3.—Percentage of normal of soybean plants as grown on low and high amounts of calcium per seed through a pH range from 3.84 to 6.94.

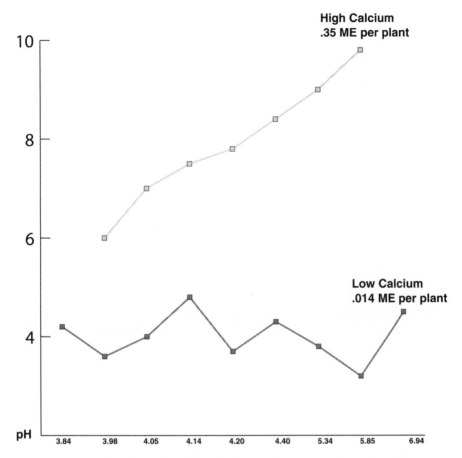

Fig. 4.—Weights of soybean plants grown on low and high amounts of calcium per seed through a pH range from 3.84 to 6.94.

of the higher acidity and less of the lower acidity. Two levels of calcium were taken, *viz.*, low calcium at 0.014 M.E. per plant and high calcium, at 0.35 M.E. per plant. The results of this trial are given in Figs. 3 and 4, and point clearly to the fact that with the low supply of calcium the growth, measured in terms of both normal plants and weights, was erratic, irrespective of pH, while with the higher supply of calcium, the growth was good regardless of the degree of acidity.

Since the previous trial points to the importance of the calcium more than to the hydrogen-ion concentration, it was necessary to determine the significance of the amount of calcium in the plant growth. Another trial was undertaken in which this was varied in one series through a range from 0 to 0.042 M.E. per seed at a pH of 6.94 (neutral) followed with a duplication at

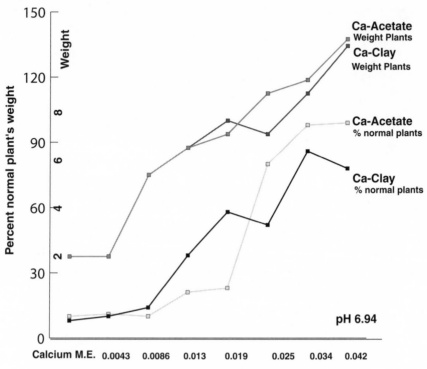

*Fig. 5.—Growth of soybean plants on varying amounts
of calcium per seed at pH 6.94.*

pH 6.92 through calcium from 0–0.35 M.E. per plant grown as individual plants, and another series through a variation from 0.0086 to 0.0308 M.E. at a pH of 4.4 (acid). The results in this trial as given in Fig. 5 and in Tables 1 and 2 show that the growth is associated with the amount of calcium (within the ranges used) and that growth is quite independent of the pH. The acetate serves better to supply the calcium than does the clay colloid at these low amounts of calcium. This points rather definitely to the significance of the calcium in producing the growth and emphasizes the fact that if this element is present in either the free or adsorbed form in sufficient amount, growth seems normal irrespective of the degree of acidity.

Inoculation was applied in all these trials, but no significant nodule production occurred except that there was a suggestion that the nodulation will occur as larger amounts of calcium (approaching 0.30 M.E.) are available to the plant. Growth was terminated after relatively short intervals, though long enough to permit nodulation under normal conditions. Since growth was obtained with difficulty, it is readily possible that even this growth was an abnormal condition for nodule production.

Table 1

Growth as Related to the Amount of Calcium at Constant pH (Neutral, 6.92), Summary of 200 Plants Grown Individually

M.E. of calcium per plant	Normal plants %	Weight of one plant, grams	Nodules per plant
Calcium clay			
0	0	0.0829	0
0.005 to 0.05	71	0.1244	0.04
0.06 to 0.20	93	0.1828	0.23
0.25 to 0.35	97	0.2003	0.13
Calcium acetate			
0	0	0.0829	0
0.05 to 0.10	75	0.1554	0.5*
0.30	100	0.2571	5.6

Only near 0.10 M.E. per plant.

Since growth in these trials was closely correlated with the presence of calcium and its concentration and not with the hydrogen-ion concentration, it points out clearly that calcium is far more effective in producing growth than excessive hydrogen-ion concentration is in prohibiting it.

In the preceding trials attention was directed only to calcium and hydrogen. There arises also the question whether other nutrient cations might not function likewise and play a role correspondingly as important

Table 2

Growth as Related to the Amount of Calcium at Constant pH (Acid, 4.4).

M.E. of calcium per plant*	Normal plants %	Total weight of 65 plants, grams	Average weight of single living plant, grams
0	0	4.26	0
0.0086	60	4.39	0.0687
0.0192	92	5.67	0.0890
0.0308	100	6.37	0.0980

Calcium clay.

Table 3

Nodulation of Second Crop of Soybeans on Sands given Calcium Carbonate as
Supplement to Treatments of Preceding Crop.

Previous treatment	Total plants	Total nodules	Infected plants, %
Potassium chloride + inoculation	69*	89†	76
Magnesium chloride + inoculation	66	81	71
Calcium chloride + inoculation	69	111	87
Calcium acetate + inoculation	66	51	40

* Eleven pots with five to eight plants each were used in each treatment.
† The check contained three jars with 21 plants. Only two nodules were found on one plant.

as that of calcium. Methods of test, similar to those used previously, were employed to try the importance of potassium and magnesium as chlorides in comparison with calcium in this and the acetate forms, all at initial pH 7.00. The results are given in Figs. 6 and 7. Increasing amounts of each salt improved the growth. With potassium chloride this ranged from 6 to 26% normal, with magnesium chloride from 4 to 88% and for calcium chloride and calcium acetate marked improvement occurred with every increment, while normal growth was obtained as soon as a certain minimum of calcium (approximately 0.023 M.E. calcium per seed) was reached.

Nodulation was observed in these trials testing calcium, magnesium, and potassium only in the higher concentrations of calcium as acetate (at 0.017 and 0.043 M.E. calcium and above). Consequently, the sands as used were given calcium carbonate, reseeded, but not reinoculated. Growth was normal and nodulation developed, according to the data in Table 3. This points clearly to the greater significance of calcium in larger amounts to bring about nodulation that had previously failed.

Gedroiz used oats, mustard, and buckwheat plants in soils dialyzed free of their calcium but saturated with other bases and reports that, "Plants are thus able to utilize the elements magnesium and potassium in a soil from which the exchangeable bases of these elements were removed practically completely. When the other nutritive elements were provided, high yields were obtained. Totally different results are obtained concerning the role of calcium in the plant nutrition; if practically all the exchangeable calcium is removed from the soil and is then replaced by a base, the presence of which does not prevent the development of the plant in one way or another,

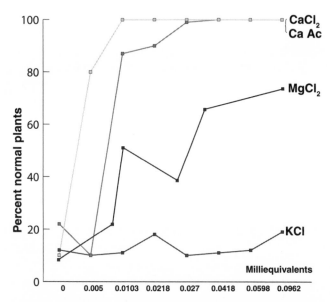

Fig. 6.—*Percentage of normal of soybean plants as grown on salts of potassium magnesium, and calcium supplying varying amounts of each, initial pH 7.00.*

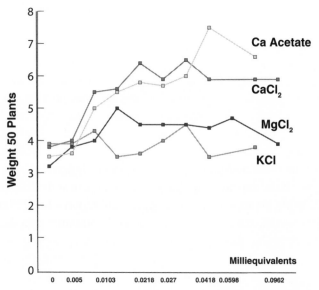

Fig. 7.—*Weight of soybean plants grown on salts of potassium, magnesium, and calcium supplying varying amounts of each, initial pH 7.00.*

then…the plant dies entirely when no calcium salts are added to the soil." This points to a similar significance of calcium for non-legumes, such as oats, mustard, and buckwheat, as suggested for soybeans in the tests reported here. Gedroiz places the importance of calcium not only over magnesium and potassium, but also over the other bases sodium, aluminum, iron, hydrogen, manganese, lithium, and ammonium. This can not be with the same force in connection with strontium, which he believes "may to a certain extent take the place of calcium for plant growth." Nevertheless, of a total list of 16 bases used to saturate the soil fully, he believes that "the plant…points to a very special position of exchangeable calcium among all the bases tested."

As for the base hydrogen, Gedroiz believes this ion injurious, contrary to the results suggested in the studies here presented. In failing to obtain crop growth on a soil fully saturated with hydrogen-ions and given no calcium carbonate, he says, "Two causes prevented their growth: the absence in such a soil of available calcium, and the acid reaction." He points to the injurious effects by the acid reaction, since his introduction of calcium sulfate in place of calcium carbonate into a hydrogen-saturated soil fails to produce a crop. Yet, in his explanation, it is suggested that the sulfuric acid formed from the introduction of calcium sulfate into a hydrogen-saturated soil may be the cause of plant growth failure, which is a detrimental factor quite different from the adsorbed hydrogen-ion of the soil, and does not necessarily prove the hydrogen-ion in acid soil as the injurious factor.

These results thus far emphasize the significance, first, of the element calcium itself; second, of the quantity of calcium present; and third, of its association with different cations (acetate, chlorine, clay). The latter point suggested a trial of calcium in different forms to include (a) the acetate, providing calcium in the free, diffusible, ionic form; (b) calcium permutit, with calcium in the adsorbed form, becoming free through exchange with other cations; and (c) anorthite, carrying calcium in the insoluble crystal form of this alumino-silicate mineral. The individual plants were grown at pH 7 with a supply of calcium varying through a range from 0.0125 to 2.50 M.E. per plant. The calcium acetate produced normal plants, the permutit produced such only at higher concentrations, while the anorthite failed at all concentrations. This points out clearly that the "availability" of the calcium or degree of being free is a significant factor as well as the amount of this element per plant.

Though inoculation was applied regularly in all the preceding work, irregularity of growth was the outstanding result and nodules failed to

Table 4

Nodulation of Soybeans with Varying Amounts of Calcium (pH 7.00), Nodules Per Plant as average of Eight Plants.

M. E. of calcium per plant	0.01	0.02	0.03	0.04	0.05	0.06	0.07	0.08	0.09	0.10	Total
First Trial											
Calcium acetate	—	0.37	0.10	2.50	2.62	2.62	0.25	3.50	4.37	4.25	20
Calcium carbonate	0.75	0.62	2.75	3.25	3.50	4.62	6.25	5.50	3.37	4.50	35
Second Trial											
Calcium chloride	—	2.13	3.00	3.00	4.37	2.50	2.75	5.62	6.00	5.50	33
Calcium permutit	—	—	—	1.13	—	2.13	—	1.87	—	3.50	9
Calcium acetate	—	—	1.50	2.25	1.87	2.50	2.37	2.00	2.13	2.00	16
Calcium clay	—	—	0.37	2.00	4.13	3.62	4.50	3.00	4.13	4.13	26
Calcium bentonite	—	—	—	1.00	2.13	2.37	3.13	4.75	2.87	3.62	20

develop in most cases, except when increasing amounts of calcium were applied. This led to other attempts to produce nodulation by still larger amounts of calcium per seed applied by means of clay. The plants were grown in the individual containers and given variable amounts of calcium at the constant pH 7.0 (neutral) and associated with different cations. Two different trials are represented. The results are given in Table 4. In these trials nodulation was obtained in few cases of the lower calcium concentration, but increased with increasing amounts of calcium. These confirm, in part, the previous trials in which nodulation failed in the lower calcium concentration but developed in the calcium acetate above 0.043 M.E., and in the calcium clay above 0.05 M.E. per plant (Table 1). At this concentration and all those above it, nodulation occurred, suggesting this as a possible lower limit for nodulation under the conditions of the experiment.

Again the amount of the calcium, its form, and the associated cation emphasize themselves. The ionic, free forms produce nodulation at a concentration lower than that of the adsorbed form. It is particularly interesting to note that the calcium carbonate was as effective, if not superior, to all other forms. At the much larger amounts of calcium used in these trials growth was always normal and nodulation very satisfactory. Further trials of these larger calcium amounts at other hydrogen-ion concentrations are needed.

Summary

The data as a whole suggest that, with the minimum amounts of calcium used, the plants are readily attacked by disease and that only poor growth without nodulation occurs. With increased amounts of calcium, growth improves and seems to be normal, but only as still greater amounts of calcium are available to the plant will nodulation occur. Though only two trials of larger amounts of calcium at one hydrogen-ion concentration were used to bring about nodulation, they suggest a minimum necessary calcium for nodulation with improved nodule production as this is increased. This suggests that the calcium supply must first meet the requirements for growth and then an additional amount of this element is needed to permit the nodulation. Further, the data point out clearly that the significance of calcium for the soybean plants rests on its function as an element in the plant's activities rather than on that of reducing the hydrogen-ion concentration of the soil or growth medium.

CHAPTER 33

Growing Legumes on Acid Soils

A SIGNIFICANT DEGREE of soil acidity has long been considered a troublesome condition for legumes, particularly those more desirable as forage for livestock. Yet it is highly probable that native legumes once grew well on those same troublesome soils when they were first cleared of virgin timber or plowed out of the prairie sod. Failures of many legume crops to return the cost of their seedings have generated the desire to find some acid-tolerant legume of high feeding value. The hope of finding such a legume has long been a tantalizing problem for many agronomists.

Now that we are moving forward to a better understanding of how the clay, or the dynamic fraction of the soil, becomes acid and sour, and how it is a kind of a jobber that may carry in stock the supply of plant nutrients from which it takes acidity, we have come to realize that legumes may actually tolerate acidity. We now know that this is true, provided they have access to a well-balanced supply of nourishment from the soil, or have ample fertility in the presence of acidity.

Soil Acidity is Natural

An acid condition is perfectly natural in regions where intensive and productive agriculture is located. Such an industry establishes itself by the help of, and on soils formed by, annual rainfalls high enough to have water going down through the soil. It demands moderate temperatures. Such climatic conditions leach the soil with carbonic acid and carry plant nutrients away in solution as we know from the hard waters that make up the ground water. These are the conditions that prevail in the Eastern half of the United States. They also prevail in the temperate zone where annual rainfalls are more than approximately 30 inches. In other words, they prevail where the precipitation exceeds the evaporation. Such combinations of climatic forces of soil development produce a clay, the particular chemical composition and structure of which give it a high capacity to adsorb and exchange, that is, to take up and to give up, many elements of both nutrient and non-nutrient values to crops. It is, in reality, a fortunate natural circumstance, namely, that where the rainfalls are high enough to grow crops abundantly there should also be this large capacity of the clay to hold acidity to a correspondingly high degree. This is good fortune because such high capacity for holding soil acidity is also the same high capacity for holding fertility or crop nourishment.

Since the highest agricultural productivity now exists in those soils recognized as acid, and also in those which were acid to possibly a lesser degree in their virgin state, can the soil acidity itself be the cause of the difficulties in growing legumes? If these virgin soils built themselves originally to high levels of organic matter by taking nitrogen from the only ultimate source, which is the air, surely there must have been some legumes and some nitrogen-fixing bacteria growing in them.

Acidity and Fertility on Clay

In breaking rock down to make soil, it is the carbonic acid in the rain water that is the main responsible chemical reagent. Clay is a residue of that process. Different kinds of clay result according to different combinations of temperature and rainfall. At the same time that these different clays are being produced, they are also being stocked with varying amounts of the different chemical elements, both plant nutrients and non-nutrients. This happens while these separate elements are being broken out of the rock and while moving down through the soil in dilute solution. They are being concentrated on the clay through its action both as a filter and as an adsorber. Some elements are held more firmly by the clay than others. Then too, since the clay of our most productive soils is highly negative in its electrical charge, it necessarily holds chemical elements of the opposite or positive charge. But when hydrogen in the soil is also positive in charge, such as calcium in lime, potassium, or magnesium, we may well expect that the clay should be holding hydrogen or acidity as a non-nutrient along with these other elements which represent the fertility.

When carbonic acid is spending its soluble hydrogen or its acid in breaking down rocks to make their calcium, potassium and other elements soluble and available for plants, it should be no surprise to us that this mixture of positively charged elements, whether nutrient or not, should be caught up by and concentrated on the negatively charged clay. Can it not be readily appreciated then that acidity and fertility are therefore inter-changeable and that any root growing into a soil center or spot of fertility is also going into possible acidity?

Here then in these facts is a good foundation for our thinking about and understanding of the acidity-fertility situation in the soil. Acidity helps to develop a fertile soil under moderate rainfalls and stocks it with fertility, but under higher rainfalls this same acidity that puts nutrients on the clay can be excessive enough to take them off. Thus, when the soil has naturally become acid to a high degree, this condition merely means that the fertility has been removed to a dangerously large extent. In reality, it is then the starvation of the plant for nourishment in an acid soil rather than the excessive degree of acidity that makes what we call soil acidity, so troublesome in the growing of crops. It is not the arrival in the soil of the hydrogen or acidity, but rather the departure of the fertility that is the real trouble.

It is this interchangeability of acidity for fertility on the clay that makes possible the very feeding or nourishment of the plant by the soil. Experimental studies using the clay as a medium for growing plant roots have shown that the root gives off carbon dioxide and thereby surrounds itself with acidity from carbonic acid. This acidity then exchanges place on the clay with some of the nutrient elements like calcium, ammonium, magnesium and others, which are then free to move into the plant roots. It is by this trade of acidity to the soil that the plants are fed.

Liming Restocks the Soil

When limestone is put on the soil, it accepts acidity from the clay, just as other minerals do in the rock weathering processes. As a carbonate, it changes the active acid, or hydrogen, into water, of which compound the hydrogen is not such a highly active acid element. Therefore, the limestone corrects or neutralizes the soil acidity.

It has, however, been shown that this neutralizing effect from the liming operation is not so much the particular benefit derived by the crop, because compounds of calcium that do not neutralize the acidity, like calcium chloride, calcium sulfate or gypsum, and even ordinary cement for example, can improve the legume crop as well as calcium carbonate. Liming the soil puts calcium (or both calcium and magnesium if dolomitic limestone is used) on the clay, and thereby makes up this shortage on the list of nourishment of the crop. It feeds the plant this one nutrient which the better forage legumes need so badly for their good growth and which is so readily removed from soils under higher rainfalls. It is the calcium put in, more than the acidity put out, that comes as the beneficial effect from liming the soil.

Shortage of Fertility

Experimental studies that provide accurate control of soil fertility, have demonstrated that the better legumes require large amounts of fertility in addition to nitrogen. Though they can take nitrogen from the free gaseous supply in the air, they do not carry on this special activity of cooperating with their nodule-producing bacteria unless the soil generously provides calcium, potassium, phosphorus, magnesium, and all the other strictly soil-borne or mineral nutrients. In spite of the fact that a legume may take much nitrogen from the air, it is equally true that usually more than half of the nitrogen content in such a legume is taken from the soil. Legumes are apt to be overrated in our belief that they can provide their necessary nitrogen wholly from the supply in the air. They are also perhaps generally overrated in our speaking of them so commonly as soil-builders. They are, however, better feeds because all the other elements of fertility besides nitrogen contribute much to make them so. These extras must be supplied through the soil.

It may seem unusual, yet very good yields and fine appearing crops of soybeans have been grown experimentally only to have less nitrogen, and thereby less protein, in the final crop (including both roots and tops) than was in the seeds originally planted. The reason for this was that the calcium supply in the soil was low. Nitrogen had gone from the crop to the soil rather than in the opposite direction, as is commonly expected. Deficient calcium in the soil was also the occasion for deficient phosphorus in the crop. Then, too, unless potassium was amply provided in the soil, this element, too, like the nitrogen and the phosphorus, was wandering in the wrong direction while the crop was growing. That the bulk of the crop should be increasing and the plants seemingly growing well while the final crop was containing less nitrogen, or less phosphorus, or less potassium than was originally in the seed, may seem impossible, but such is what feeding results with animals seem to suggest.

Experiments at the Missouri Station, using different degrees of acidity, controlled in the soil, for soybeans, have shown more nitrogen taken from the air by this legume crop when the soil was acid and fertile, than when nearly neutral and of exactly the same fertility. Soybeans started in a soil at a high degree of acidity measured as pH 5.7, made that soil much more acid when they brought it to the pH 4.2 during their growth. And yet in spite of that increase in acidity, they were taking nitrogen from the air amounting to as much as 25 per cent of the total in the crop. The comparison crop that started on nearly neutral soil of the same fertility also made its soil more acid, but it did not fix so much nitrogen from the air. Here, then, in these trials the legumes fixed more nitrogen, or would have been considered better soil builders, where the soil was left more acid but was given the fertility by calcium, phosphate, potassium, and other nutrient elements. These legumes were tolerating acidity and functioned as nitrogen-fixers when given the necessary fertility.

Non-legume crops fit into the same category as legumes. They, too, have their troubles in growing on soils where there is increased acidity that means less fertility. They are not taking the mineral nutrients from the soil, nor are they synthesizing their complex compounds of such high food values, even though they may be producing bulk or tonnages per acre. For example, spinach, a non-legume, so often considered for the minerals it might put into the diet, contained less calcium and magnesium when grown on a neutral soil with ample fertility, than when the equivalent fertility was provided for the crop and the same soil left acid. In addition, the crop on the neutral soil contained more than enough oxalic acid to make all the calcium and magnesium it contained insoluble, and therefore indigestible. On the acid soil the crop contained more of these mineral nutrients than its oxalic acid contents would take out of digestive use.

Acidity not Detrimental

Our troubles in growing legume crops have not been so much with the soil acidity itself. They have been rather with our measurements of the acidity, and our emphasis on it when we had no convenient and accurate enough means in the laboratory for observing and measuring the fertility. Now we have been shown that soil acidity is simply the indicator of the degree to which the clay must keep holding hydrogen, when there are not significant amounts of the elements of fertility to take its place. It is the acidity, or hydrogen, that has the highest activity in the soil of all the chemical elements. Without acidity there is less trading, or less business going on, in the soil. When all plants, both legumes and non-legumes, produce acid by which to feed themselves, shall we condemn this character by which they barter? It therefore behooves us to think about liming more as a provider of calcium for plant nourishment, than as a carbonate to remove acidity. We should also provide other elements of fertility as well as calcium. With legume and non-legume crops, our acid soil trouble is not a question of their tolerating the acidity, but of our failure to appreciate that no plant can tolerate starvation. Yes, legumes can tolerate acidity if given fertility.

CHAPTER 34

Relation of Calcium to the Nodulation of Soybeans on Acid and Neutral Soils

AS A RESULT OF RECENT TESTS on the effects of calcium-bearing soil treatments, such as lime, acid phosphate, and calcium salts, upon nodulation of soybeans, there is an indication that the beneficial effect of these materials is essentially one of calcium stimulation. Frequent and repeated reports of failures to obtain nodulation of legumes by the pure culture method on certain acid soil types of northeastern Missouri and southeastern Illinois led to a search for the responsible factors. Soybeans, as an acid tolerant legume, have taken a prominent place in this territory within recent years, but thorough inoculation of even this crop has been difficult unless the soil was well limed. A study of the beneficial effects of lime on soybean inoculation, reported herein, leads to the belief that much of this is due to the element calcium.

Historical

Harper and Murphy, have recently given a review of the literature dealing with the factors affecting nodule formation by soybean plants. Other recent papers summarize the literature similarly, including specific phases of inoculation. Wilson, Scanlan, and Karraker, have each reported an increase in nodulation in consequence of the application of calcium as the carbonate or as a soluble salt. Alway, who was comparing the effectiveness of inoculation of alfalfa by soil transfer with that by pure cultures on lime-deficient sandy soils, found these two methods of equal efficacy when the land had been limed well in advance of seeding. But when the land had not been limed, the soil transfer method was far more effective. An increase in the amount of culture, many times beyond the usual rate, did not make it as effective as soil transfer. This seems to indicate an adaptation of the organism to a lime-deficient soil habitat in consequence of several previously grown, host crops. Bryan, in a study of the effect of acid soil reactions on nodulation of soybeans, found that, in general, the hydrogen-ion relations for the organisms tend to be the same as those for the host plant. He secured a maximum nodulation at pH 6.5 and none below 4.9, although the critical hydrogen-ion concentration for the organisms was found to be pH 3.5 to 3.9. Scanlan concluded that hydrogen-ion concentration must have no direct effect upon inoculation of soybeans by *Bacillus radicicola*. Although both calcium carbonate and calcium acetate stimulated inoculation tremendously, the carbonate neutralized the hydrogen-ion concentration and the acetate had no effect upon it. Fellers noted that the bacterial infection of roots did not take place readily on acid soils even when a good supply of bacteria was present.

Karraker, working with alfalfa, single plants of which he grew with part of the roots in a limed and part in a lime-deficient, acid soil, found that there was a difference in the nodule formation of the two parts of the root system, and that this difference was as great as the difference between the nodulation of plants grown wholly on the limed and those on the lime-deficient soils. He concluded that the effect of soil reaction upon nodule formation must be one of localized character in the plant, a direct effect of soil hydrogen-ion concentration on the bacteria in the nodules, or an antecedent effect of the soil on the bacteria while they are existing non-symbiotically in the soil.

It has been pointed out by Lohnis and Smith that bacteria undergo a fairly definite cyclic change. Bewley and Hutchinson found similar cyclic changes and that these are even specific with reference to cultural conditions. They stated that as long as there was sufficient available carbohydrate to support growth, the organism remained in the motile rod form with no changes. Their "pre-swarmers" (one of their cyclic forms); could be induced by the addition of calcium or magnesium carbonate to the medium. Of a considerable number of compounds other than carbohydrates, calcium phosphate alone was capable of bringing about the change from "pre-swarmers" to rods. The response to the reaction of the soil, in the main, was a rapid change from the normal rod form to "pre-swarmers" in calcareous soils; a production of a highly vacuolated form and the eventual death of the organisms in acid soil; and a continuous growth without significant change of form in a slightly alkaline soil. Thornton and Gangulee, in an even more recent investigation along this line, also noted a similar, regular cycle of change, in which unbanded rods, cocci, and banded rods successively followed each other. They stated that an increase in the percentage of cocci was associated with increased bacterial numbers and with the appearance of motile forms. They found that by modifying the liquid used to suspend the inoculum added to the soil, the time of appearance of cocci in predominance could be altered, and on this basis they recommend the inoculation of the soil with a bacterial suspension in milk to which is added 0.1 per cent of calcium acid phosphate.

That calcium may play some significant part in establishing legume bacteria in certain lime-deficient soils was suggested by previous workers and served as the main hypothesis in the work reported herein.

Experimental

Part I

Increased nodulation of soybeans, upon an already well-inoculated soil, resulted from the use of calcium treatment on such soil in the greenhouse. This was an acid soil (pH 5.5), taken from the experimental field, and already well inhabited with the symbiotic organism in consequence of inoculated crops of soybeans of the three preceding seasons. Limestone, equivalent to 4 tons per 2 million pounds, was added to part of the soil. The seed from a single mother plant was used for a stand of 5 plants per pot on 30 pots from both the limed and the unlimed soil. They were grown for 5 weeks, after which the uniform and healthy plants were taken up and the nodules counted. Although Erdman, has presented an argument for the importance of the size as well as the number of nodules in determining the effectiveness of inoculation, the numbers only were taken. The data are summarized in the first half of table 1.

The results show an increase of 336 per cent in numbers of nodules formed as a result of liming, even though the soil was already well inoculated with the organism. In spite of the fact that these data show a correlation between inoculation and neutralization of the soil acidity, this does not necessarily establish a causal relationship.

Part II

In consequence of the fact that an application of calcium as the carbonate, produced an important increase of nodulation on an already well-inoculated soil, and of the belief that this stimulation was not necessarily the result of a change in hydrogen-ion concentration, or at least not entirely so, a test was made of the effect of calcium, as the chloride, upon the inoculation of soybeans by the pure culture method on an acid soil which was sterile with regard to *B. radicicola* of soybeans. To each of 30 pots of a rather heavy Union silt loam (pH 5.4), there were added at planting time 25 cc. of a solution of calcium chloride supplying calcium equivalent to that of 200 pounds of calcium carbonate per 2 million of soil. Thirty pots of the untreated soil were planted also. Liberal quantities of an inoculating suspension were supplied directly to the beans at the time of planting. Eight pots of untreated and uninoculated soil were planted as checks. When, at the end of 5 weeks, the examination for nodules revealed none formed, 16 pots each of the inoculated, calcium treated and of the inoculated, untreated soil were immediately replanted with sprouted beans in the same pots. After 5 weeks of growth, these were likewise carefully taken up, washed, and examined for nodules. The complete data are summarized in the latter half of table 1.

The nodulation of the beans of the second planting indicates that the calcium as a chloride has a stimulating effect upon the longevity and viability of the organism in the acid soil. This agrees with Scanlan's results of increased viability of the organism in water cultures.

Part III

Since the addition of a small amount of a neutral calcium salt to an acid soil (pH 5.4) had kept *B. radicicola* viable within the soil from the time it was applied by pure cultures on the first crop until the second planting, and since an addition of large amounts of calcium carbonate produced important increases in nodulation of soybeans on an already well-inoculated soil, it was thought possible to determine whether this stimulating effect was due, (*a*) to calcium within the plant, (*b*) to an effect of calcium upon the organism in the soil, or (*c*) to an effect of calcium upon the soil as the habitat of the organisms, by growing plants so arranged that one part of the root system of each was growing in an acid soil and the other part in the calcium-treated soil.

Soybean seedlings were grown in sterile sand from 10 to 14 days, or until the lateral roots about an inch long were sufficient to support the plant. These seedlings were taken up, washed, and the tap roots cut off just below the longest lateral roots. They were then planted with half of their roots on one side and half on the other side of the water-tight partition of

Table 1

Nodulation of Soybeans on Acid Soils as Influenced by Calcium Compounds

Soil treatment		Number of pots	Total number of plants	Range in nodules per plot	Average nodules per plant	Per Cent increase
Soil already inoculated given calcium carbonate						
None..........		30	130	10–81*	12.0	
Calcium carbonate—4 tons..............		30	133	64–247†	40.2	336
Sterile soil given calcium chloride with inoculation						
First crop	None........	30	130	—	—‡	
	Calcium chloride......	30	133	—	—‡	
Second crop	None........	16	72	—	—‡	
	Calcium chloride......	16	80	1–26	1.8	

* Three pots exceeded this range greatly, having 110, 140, and 142 nodules.
† Two pots exceeds this range greatly, having 297 and 380 nodules.
‡ Three plants had one nodule each in these trials.

Table 2

Nodulation of Soybeans Grown with Part of Root System in Calcium-Treated Soil and Part in Untreated Soil

| | Plants with divided roots | | | Check plants | | | |
| | | Nodule production | | Calcium-treated soil | | Untreated soil | |
Treatment	Number of plants	Roots in Calcium-treated soil	Roots in untreated soil	Number of plants	Number of nodules	Number of plants	Number of nodules
Uninoculated............	4	0	0	6	0	5	0
Inoculated............	23	160	77	28	494	31	302
Avearge per plant............		6.95	3.34		17.64		9.74
Per cent increase through calcium............		208			181		

a two-compartment pan. The moist acid soil was filled in around the roots on one side, and moist calcium-treated soil on the other. Liberal quantities of the inoculating suspension were supplied directly to the roots. The soil used was a Putnam silt loam (pH 5.14). Five plants were planted with their roots divided by the partition and five more plants with their tap roots similarly pruned were planted wholly on each side of the partition as checks. Although there was a high mortality of plants, those that lived grew satisfactorily for the five weeks, after which a count of the nodules was made. The results are given in table 2.

The increase in nodulation on the parts of the root systems growing in the calcium-treated soil over those parts growing in the untreated soil was comparable to the increase obtained in the checks or those whose entire root system was within a single soil treatment. This agrees with the results obtained by Karraker on alfalfa. Although this type of experiment is unsatisfactory because of unequal development of the divided parts of the root, the results indicate that the stimulating effect of the calcium upon nodulation was due to an effect upon the bacteria in the soil, or to a physiological effect within the plant. In addition, the effect was local in character, and limited to the roots. The calcium was not translocated to all parts of the plant root system sufficiently to make its influence uniform on the degree of inoculation, at least not within the time limits of this experiment.

Part IV

The preceding results raised the question whether there is an effect upon nodulation by the calcium already within the plant tissues. An attempted answer was undertaken by growing some soybean seedlings in calcium-free and some in calcium-bearing substrates and then transplanting from both into an inoculated soil. The calcium-free substrate was prepared by treating sand with $5N$ hydrochloric acid for 3 hours, washing with water until acid-free according to the silver nitrate test, drying, and sterilizing in an oven at 110°C. for 48 hours. For the calcium-bearing substrate, calcium carbonate was mixed with the same quartz sand at the rate of 10,000 pounds per 2 million. This was also sterilized in the oven 110° C.

The total yield of beans from a single plant was sterilized, germinated for 24 hours, and planted into pots of these sterile substrates, half into the calcium-free and half into the calcium-bearing sand. The pots were set to their shoulders into moist soil, which was sterile with regard to *B. radicicola,* and after 10 or 11 days the plants were taken up, washed, and replanted to the inoculated soil which had been prepared and silted at a suitable moisture content into ordinary greenhouse flats. Both the calcium-bearing and calcium-starved seedlings were grown simultaneously on their respective halves of the same flat and within the same soil. Seedlings so treated were transplanted and grown on two different soils, one an acid, lime-deficient soil, and the other, a neutral, fertile, garden soil. No inoculation was added, since both soils had grown well-inoculated crops of soybeans during two consecutive seasons just previous to this test. After a growth of 5 weeks, the plants were taken up readily without injury to the roots and the nodules counted. The data from the count are summarized in table 3. Included in the table are also the analytical data giving, (*a*) the calcium content of the soybean seeds from a single, similar plant, (*b*) the calcium content of 10-day-old calcium-bearing and calcium-starved seedlings, and (*c*) the total electrodialyzable calcium of the soils as determined by Bradfield's method of measuring the total electrodialyzable base. These analyses were made in order to correlate the nodulation with the calcium content of the plants as influenced by the treatments.

The increased nodulation of the calcium-bearing seedlings on the calcium-deficient, acid soil demonstrates that the presence of calcium within the plant increases nodulation of soybeans on such soil. On the other hand, the lack of difference in nodulation of the seedlings on the neutral, calcium-laden soil indicates that the presence of this element within the plant on a calcium-sufficient soil does not affect nodulation, or that if it does, the calcium-starved plants are able to take calcium from the soil rapidly enough to offset the measurable differences in nodulation.

The increase in calcium content of the calcium-starved seedlings over that in the seed, as shown by the analytical data, was due to the calcium that was carried back into the acid-extracted sand by the tap water with which it was washed. An elimination of this factor might have served to intensify further the differences obtained.

Part V

Since calcium exerted an intimate effect upon inoculation by the organism *B. radicicola*, this effect was deemed possible through an inter-relation with the soil colloids, the main chemically reactive part of the soil. It is known that the colloids are highly absorptive, and that minute quantities of calcium are effective in flocculating them, hence this phase of the experiment was undertaken to detect such possible relation.

Table 3

Nodulation of Soybeans in Neutral and Acid Soils as Influenced by Calcium in the Seedlings

Soil character	pH	Seedling treatment	Number of plants	Nodule numbers pee plant		Calcium content		
				Range	Average	Per 100 seedlings	Electrodialyzable per 10 gm. soil	Per 100 seeds
						mgm.	mgm.	mgm.
Neutral..........	7.8	None	60	12–77	36.6	17.07		
		Calcium	67	9–67	38.9	30.14	24.07	6.85
Acid............	5.5	None	69	1–7	3.4	17.07		
		Calcium	79	2–25	15.1	30.14	11.78	6.85

A suspension in distilled water of the organisms from several agar cultures was added to a 0.4 per cent solution of colloidal clay in a ratio of four parts of the bacterial suspension to five parts colloidal solution. To this mixture was added one part of water containing the desired amount of flocculating agent.

Those mixtures left unflocculated received the equivalent of distilled water. Thus the resulting solutions contained 0.2 per cent colloidal clay and equal numbers of organisms throughout. These were made up in units of 100 cc. in test tubes. The chlorides of potassium and calcium were used

Table 4

Nodule Numbers on Soybeans Inoculated by Colloidal Clay Suspensions of Bacteria

Kind of inoculating suspensions	Range in number of nodules per pot*	Description of nodulation
Distilled water............	72–90	Variable size. Scattered over entire root system
Colloidal clay............	84–112	Uniform size. Clumped at plant crown
Tap water..................	56–71	Variable size. Well scattered
No inoculation............	0–0	Plants yellow. Grew for time of test
Full inoculation...........	98–161	Variable size. Well distributed
Calcium chloride supernatant................	0–6	Not over one plant per pot infected
Calcium chloride flocculant....................	64–133	Variable size. Clumped at plant crown
Potassium chloride supernatant................	85–169	Variable size. Well distributed
Potassium chloride flocculant.................	148–162	Indiscriminate size. Clumped at base, some scattered

* Duplicate pots were grown with 5 plants each.

as comparative flocculating agents at the rate of 0.5 milliequivalents, or the minimum requirement of potassium chloride as electrolyte at this concentration of colloidal clay. Mixtures of the organism at the same concentrations in the natural colloid, in distilled water, and in tap water were set up as checks.

The tubes were incubated for 7 days, after which the liquid supernatant to the flocculated clay, the flocculated clay itself, the natural colloidal clay, and the suspensions in water, were tested for the presence of the viable organism by applying specific quantities to sterile, germinated soybeans as they were planted into sterile sand. At the end of 5 weeks the plants were taken up and the nodules per plant counted. The data are presented in table 4.

The results obtained in this experiment were duplicated almost identically in a repetition of the experiment 6 weeks later. The nodulation obtained indicated that the colloidal clay absorbed the bacteria but did not destroy their viability. Flocculation of the clay with calcium chloride carried the organisms down and retained them within the flocculant. This was not the case for the potassium chloride. In the potassium chloride the supernatant was as effective for inoculation as the flocculant.

Table 5

Plate Counts of Bacillus radicicola as Influenced by Colloidal Clay Treatments

Portion of treatment sampled	Average count per cubic centimeter
Supernatant to calcium flocculant...................….....	8
Supernatant to potassium flocculant...................…...	13,100
Upper half calcium-bacteria suspension..............…	200
Upper half potassium-bacteria suspension...........…	7,000
Lower half calcium-bacteria suspension..............….	4,300
Lower half potassium-bacteria suspension...........…	1,000
Supernatant to centrifuged inoculated colloid.......	22,100
Inoculated colloid—not centrifuged....................…	9,550,000
Tap water suspension...…...	3,600

In order to verify the accuracy of this test and to determine whether the calcium chloride or the colloid is the active factor in carrying the organisms out of suspension, this experiment was repeated. Platings were made from the solutions into sterile petri dishes at the time of planting. Also, the pure bacterial suspensions were flocculated by potassium chloride and calcium chloride and then plated. A sterile colloidal clay inoculated 7 days previously was also plated. The effectiveness of the absorption of the bacteria by the colloid was tested by centrifuging the colloidal material out of an inoculated colloidal clay and then plating the centrifuged solution. The counts are given in table 5.

The relation of the calcium to the retention of the bacteria by the flocculated clay, as previously found, was substantiated in this trial. The liquid, supernatant to the potassium chloride flocculant contained over 13,000, whereas that over the calcium chloride flocculant contained but 8 bacteria per cubic centimeter, showing that the calcium flocculated clay carried the bacteria out almost completely whereas the potassium flocculated clay did not. Calcium used independently of the clay, carried out the bacteria, since the water suspension given potassium chloride contained a count of 7,000, whereas the treatment with calcium chloride reduced this to 200 per cubic centimeter. In comparing the inoculated colloid suspension with the same after centrifuging, the number of about ten million in the former was reduced to about 22,000 in the supernatant in consequence of centrifuging.

These data suggest that though the clay carries the bacteria out of suspension, certainly the calcium does likewise, whether used alone or whether combined with the clay colloid. When the calcium is used in conjunction with the clay, however, a more nearly complete removal of the organisms is obtained. This is no doubt due to the simultaneous coagulation of the bacteria and to the flocculation of the colloid. This does not hold true for the potassium chloride.

Part VI.—Field Trials

After finding that applications of lime may stimulate nodulation on an acid soil already inhabited by the organisms, and that small amounts of calcium in the soil, as well as small amounts within the plant tissues, are important in stimulating nodulation, it seemed quite plausible that liming a soil may exert its influence not wholly as a secondary effect through the correlation of hydrogen-ion concentration, but also in consequence of its content in calcium. Work was done in the field to test whether small

Table 6

Nodulation of soybeans on acid soils in field treatments of calcium

Inoculation treatment	Marion silt loam*					Putnam silt loam (better phase)†			
	Nodules per plant	Per cent infected plants	Nodule Volume, $\frac{cc.}{1000}$ per nodule	Nodule Weight, mgm. Per nodule	pH	Nodules per plant	Per cent infected plants	Nodule Volume, $\frac{cc.}{1000}$ per nodule	Nodule Weight, mgm. Per nodule
None‡...........	0.2	20.0			6.4	0	0		
Culture...........	0.6	6.6	900.0	133.0	6.1	3.5	43	9.5	9.2
Culture and calcium chloride...........	26.6	100.0	24.1	24.4	6.0	3.3	67	25.0	21.2
Culture and calcium nitrate...........	22.9	100.0	28.6	28.9	6.0	3.6	50	23.3	23.0
Culture and calcium hydroxide...........	22.9	100.0	21.1	23.0	6.0	8.9	83	33.4	36.8
Inoculated soil...........	16.0	100.0	31.2	30.0	6.4	2.6	57	40.2	38.8
Soil and calcium chloride§...........	13.4	100.0	45.5	44.4	6.4	6.6	87	19.7	17.1
Soil and calcium nitrate¶...........	11.6	100.0	53.5	58.3	6.4	3.7	60	25.4	20.0

* The initial soil contained 0.9785 as total base (cc. normal acid) and 23.3 mgm. as electrodialyzable calcium per 10 gm. soil.

† The initial soil contained 0.7563 as total base (cc. normal acid) and 18.2 mgm. as electodialyzable calcium per 10 gm. soil and had a pH of 5.6.

‡ About 30 plants were examined in each case. They contained 1.23 per cent nitrogen in the tops and 0.76 per cent in the roots.

§ The plants in this treatment contained 2.39 per cent N in the tops, 2.04 per cent in the roots.

¶ The plants in this treatment contained 2.16 per cent N in the tops, 2.13 per cent in the roots.

Table 7

Nodulation of Soybeans on Acid Soils in Field Treatments of Calcium

Inoculation treatment	Putnam silt loam (rolling phase)*				Putnam silt loam (flat phase)†			
	Nodules per plant	Per cent plants infected	Average nodule Volume, $\frac{cc.}{1000}$	Weight, mgm.	Nodules per plant	Per cent plants infected	Average nodule Volume, $\frac{cc.}{1000}$	Weight, mgm.
None(a)...............	0.6	20	105.5	106.7	0	0		
Culture...............	10.2	100	48.9	51.1	5.6	66	30.1	30.1
Culture and calcium chloride(b).........	5.2	90	31.2	31.8		Base	Dialyzable	Calcium
Culture and calcium nitrate..............	9.2	93	29.3	29.9	(a)	0.7665		14.5
Culture and acid phosphate...........	8.0	100	37.5	38.3	(b)	0.9647		20.6
Inoculated soil.........			Dialyzable		3.8	83	47.8	50.4
Soil and calcium chloride............		Base		Calcium	2.1	57.1	50.9	52.1
Soil and calcium nitrate............	(a)	0.6597		18.2	1.1	33	26.4	28.2
	(b)	0.6597		14.5				
Soil and limestone‡.........	25	100	26.8	27.7				

* This untreated soil had a pH of 5.75, given limestone it had a pH of 6.3. The electrodialyzable base and calcium were determined on 10 gm. of these soils after the crop was grown. Limestone was applied at the rate of 3 tons per acre.

† The untreated soil had a pH of 5.14.

‡ Limestone applied was equivalent to 5 tons per 2,000,000 pounds soil.

amounts of soluble calcium with no neutralizing capacity would improve nodulation by the pure culture method on acid soils that were difficult to inoculate without liming.

The work was done in cooperation with farmers experiencing difficulty in getting inoculation on unlimed land. The soybeans were inoculated at planting time with a tested strain of the organism, and applications of calcium chloride, calcium nitrate, calcium acid phosphate, and calcium hydroxide were made through fertilizer attachments on the seeding machinery. In addition to these, tests were made using inoculated soil, both with and without calcium salt treatments. The salts, including calcium chloride and calcium nitrate, were mixed, as a $2N$ solution, into the dry pulverized soil and the soil was then dried until it would operate through the fertilizer attachment. A determination of the nodulation was made when the beans were at full growth, just shortly before maturity. Samples of the soil were also taken then for hydrogen-ion measurements and for determinations of dialyzable base and calcium. Tables 6 and 7 give summaries of the data on nodulation in these field trials.

The data show that the culture inoculation was successful on the Marion Silt Loam in every case where it was supplemented by applications of small amounts of calcium salts, but failed wherever the calcium was omitted. These differences were very noticeable in the color of the plants. Soil inoculation was successful on this soil type without added calcium. The inclusion of calcium, however, increased the size of the nodules significantly. The lessened number of nodules per plant, when calcium was added to the inoculating soils, suggests possible death to the organisms by this salt treatment, though this is not significant enough to reduce the percentage of plants inoculated.

On fields other than the Marion Silt Loam, the culture used alone was successful without special treatment. However, in many cases the addition of the calcium, especially the hydroxide, which distributed itself more thoroughly on account of its fineness, gave increased nodules per plant, and increased the percentages of infection. On these fields the color differences were less pronounced than on the Marion Silt Loam, but yet significant differences in growth were evident.

Determinations of the hydrogen-ion concentration revealed a pH of 6.0 on the Marion Silt Loam where the calcium was beneficial to inoculation, and a much lower figure for the pH where calcium was less effective. Just what relations exist between the hydrogen-ion concentration and the effectiveness of the applied calcium, or between the effectiveness and the electrodialyzable base or calcium, is still a question. The total electrodialyzable base and electrodialyzable calcium content seem to decrease as the calcium additions were less effective.

Part VII

In an attempt to determine the relation of dialyzable base or calcium of the soil to inoculation, the flat phase of the Putnam Silt Loam of the field trials was used in the greenhouse. Seedlings were started for 10 days in calcium-deficient and calcium-laden substrates and then transplanted to this soil given no treatment, given calcium carbonate equivalent to 5 tons per acre, and given calcium chloride at the rate of 1 part per 1500 parts of soil solution, considering the soil at 25 per cent moisture. Thorough inoculation was applied at planting and the plants were grown for 5 weeks, when they were examined for their nodulation. Analyses were made of the seedlings for their calcium content, and of the soil for the total electrolyzable base and calcium. The hydrogen-ion concentration was also determined. The complete data are given in table 8.

Though no statistical manipulation was undertaken to express the reliability of the data in the usual way, it is interesting to note that even though this soil gave no great improvements in its inoculation through calcium applied in the field trials, a significant increase occurred in the nodule numbers when the seedlings carried a liberal calcium supply. This difference was obliterated when the soil was given calcium, either as carbonate or as chloride. No correlation seemed to exist between the electrodialyzable calcium and the nodule numbers per plant. However, it is interesting to note that the insoluble calcium carbonate was less effective in increasing nodule numbers per plant, than was the soluble calcium chloride or calcium within the seedlings, for the short time of this trial.

Measurements of the electrodialyzable calcium within the soils in this study were not numerous enough to establish whether or not this quantity of the element might serve as a possible indication of the soil's deficiency in calcium with reference to inoculation. Further data of this kind will be necessary to decide the question fully. However, the data thus far suggest that electrodialysis is scarcely a criterion as to whether or not the soil will yield sufficient calcium to guarantee thorough inoculation or whether added calcium mightimprove the establishment of the relation between nodule bacteria and their host plant. Under certain conditions, certainly, very small amounts of calcium are beneficial in establishing thorough

Table 8

Nodule Production by Soybeans on Acid Putnam Silt Loam

Soil and Treatment	Untreated*		One part CaCo$_3$ per 200 soil		One part CaCl$_2$ per 1,5000 solution†	
Seedling treatment	None	Calcium	None	Calcium	None	Calcium
Number of plants	73	61	62	79	70	72
Average number of nodules per plant	7.9	12.8	8.0	7.3	11.9	11.0
Range in number of nodules per plant	0–23	1–26	0–19	0–20	0-34	1-41
Number of plants not inoculated	1	0	2	2	1	0
Calcium content of plants at replanting: mgm. Ca per plant	17.07	30.14	17.07	30.14	17.07	30.14
Total electrodialyzable base in soil at end of plant growth: titrable milliequivalents of base	0.78582		2.15754		0.83412	
Total electrodialyzable calcium in soil at end of plant growth: mgm. Ca per 10 gm. H$_2$O-free soil	12.9		41.6		13.4	
pH of soil at end of plant growth	5.82		7.40		5.25	

* Orginal pH of soil—5.14.

†Porosity of treated soil—48.7 per cent. Calculations of soil solution were made for 25 per cent moisture.

inoculation and consequently the legume crop itself. This possibility might be inferred from the work of McCool and by the report of Jaeger. How small this amount may be in any case is still a question. Attention may need to be given to ionizable calcium or some other forms before soil analysis can contribute a simple chemical answer to this complex question of biological behavior.

Summary and Conclusions

1. The study reported herewith suggests that the beneficial effects of liming for establishing thorough inoculation of legumes on acid soils may be due in part to the element calcium as well as to a change in the degree of acidity.

2. The use of calcium carbonate on an acid soil already well inoculated with *B. radicicola* of soybeans, gave decided improvement in the inoculation of this crop.

3. The addition of calcium chloride to an acid soil, sterile to the soybean organism, favored its longevity from the time of introduction, and improved inoculation on the later planting.

4. A part of the root system of soybean growing in calcium-bearing soil had better inoculation than the part of the same root system growing in calcium-deficient soil. This effect was, then, not readily transmitted to roots in environment deficient in calcium but supplied with the necessary organisms.

5. A liberal supply of calcium within 10-day-old soybean seedlings improved their inoculation when they were transplanted into acid soils.

6. The soybean organisms in colloidal clay suspensions were carried down when flocculated with calcium chloride but not significantly when flocculated with potassium chloride.

7. Field trials found very small quantities of calcium, applied as different salts, a very effective help in increasing inoculation on certain soils and scarcely significant on others.

8. The effect of calcium in stimulating inoculation failed to show a significant correlation to the hydrogen-ion concentration, or the electrodialyzable calcium in the soil in the few cases studied.

9. Though thorough inoculation may be stimulated in some cases by the addition of calcium, many factors, as fertility of soil and cultural practices are also of significance.

CHAPTER 35

Liming Alone
will not Cure a Sick Soil

LEGUMES, AN INDISPENSABLE forage crop, are unfortunately not grown universally. We have ascribed their frequent failure to the acidity of the soil, a diagnosis which is open to question.

Acidity, a common soil condition in the temperate zone, occurs when rainfall washes away fertility or when much vegetation has leached the soil of its supply of nutrients. Thereafter, the soil grows mainly carbonaceous or woody vegetation. Soil acidity is in reality, then, a shortage of plant nutrients. How can we restore the soil to its original fertility?

Liming as an agricultural art was known even to the Romans, and to Benjamin Franklin, who used gypsum or land plaster on clover. The growing agricultural science of the early years of this century brought back liming as a general practice, particularly under the encouragement of the new soil-testing service.

This service was guided by the belief that limestone, hydrated lime, or quicklime fought soil acidity by counteracting the high concentration of hydrogen ions in the leached soil. The ease and speed with which acidity could be detected and measured encouraged widespread testing of soils—we discovered soil acidity everywhere! We likewise discovered that in acid soils productivity was, in general, lower as the degree of acidity was higher. From this we concluded that the presence of large amounts of hydrogen was the cause of poor crops. So we began fighting the acidity by neutralizing the hydrogen ions with carbonate of calcium.

We are just now coming around to a better understanding of how Nature grew crops on acid soils before we did. At the same time, we are beginning to understand what limestone really does when it makes better crops.

For the study of the physiology of plants, and of the colloidal behavior of the clays which grow them, indicates not only that soil acidity is not detrimental, but is in reality beneficial to growth!

Heavy liming drives out not only acidity. It eventually removes all other fertility and may load the soil so heavily with calcium that only that element is offered as plant nourishment. Plants will then, though growing on a neutral soil, starve for additional nutrients. Neutralizing soils by calcium saturation does not, therefore, make them productive, for this is the condition of the semiarid soils of some of our western states.

Calcium has been a good fertilizer for legumes on acid soils for some years. It has served directly as a nutrient, and it has served indirectly by helping other nutrients, as well as nitrogen, to get into the plant roots more abundantly. But once the need of leached soils for calcium has been met, the need for other nutrients becomes evident—potassium, for instance, and nitrogen. Thus fertilizers are coming into prominence for use on soils which a few years ago were treated only with limestone. Perhaps these are the facts behind the age-old rhyme that "lime and lime without manure, makes father rich but son poor."

Soil acidity, therefore, is not the sole problem in growing legumes. The production of these crops is a matter of ample soil fertility among which calcium from lime is only one nutrient. Our soils need a well-balanced supply of all plant food elements to remain productive.

CHAPTER 36

Nodulation Modifies Nutrient Intake from Colloidal Clay by Soybeans

THE TERM, "the living soil", is an age-old expression, but just what it connotes in the minds of different soil scientists or in our own thinking we are not sure. The legume bacteria represent an introduction of life into the soil. On my coming to the University of Missouri (1916) there was plenty of tight clay soil from northeast to southwest Missouri, so that about a fourth of the land was "dead" soil. My purpose was to make it a "living soil" and to take nitrogen from the air to accomplish that. Now, what is a "living soil?"

It was the Missouri soils' shortage of nitrogen for more crop production that brought me to Missouri. It was for crops richer in nitrogen, the symbol of foods rich in proteins, that concerned us with nitrogen—even if we had to try to take elemental nitrogen out of the air by means of symbiotic bacteria producing nodules on legume roots, feeding by those roots the extra nitrogen into the plant proteins, and thus giving protein-rich feeds for animal growth and reproduction rather than carbohydrate-rich feeds serving mainly for gain in weight as fattening.

Speaking of protein, nitrogen is a symbol of it, composed as it is of what is called "amino" acids. Amino is a chemical symbol of N plus two hydrogens tied to one carbon, in a chain close to a so-called "carboxyl" group, $-C\lessgtr^O_{OH}$, the mark of an acidic reaction, the amino acids of carbon chains of varied length and structure.

It is a protein that can be living, growing, protecting itself from attack and destruction by lower forms of life. In recent years we have learned, for plants, that if we balance their nutrition for what may be called a "balanced plant diet" in terms of about a dozen and a half natural elements, the plants protect themselves against fungus diseases and against leaf-eating insects. There is no need for poisonous sprays when the plants make their own necessary protective chemicals, or proteins, within their own body to give themselves immunity to microbial and fungus diseases and to attacks by many kinds of insects destroying the plants themselves.

When man manages the growing of crops for his foods and feeds for livestock, but diseases and insects destroy the crops, we do not ask ourselves, "Before man came on the scene, how did the Creator manage the crops to have them protect themselves to survive and be here for man's adoption and modification as his own food for survival?" Isn't it possible that continued cropping and fertility exhaustion from the soil have weakened the plant's nutrition for good health, correspondingly growing less protein but more carbohydrate so that plants are too poorly nourished to defend themselves? Are not such poorly nourished plants less nutrition for us as food and for ourselves to be healthy in self-defense but more subject to human ailments? If our own feeds are grown on soils sadly exhausted of their own once prime fertility, primitive man may have been initially much healthier than we moderns are.

When we consider the elements which plants use in building themselves by growth carried out by proteins, we listed initially 10, later about a dozen and a half of the earth's initial elements. Those were, namely; carbon and nitrogen from the atmosphere; oxygen and hydrogen from the water. Then, we have the soil-borne mineral elements, or the cations as alkaline earth elements: calcium and magnesium from limestone; potassium and sodium, the alkalis; then anions nitrogen, phosphorus, sulphur, and carbon; then trace elements manganese, copper, zinc, boron, molybdenum, chlorine and possibly others. The "trace" elements, as a soil deficiency, have become decisively essential since they have become connected with human deficiencies as elements in body processes and certain deficiency diseases like "brucellosis."

Plan and Methods of Study

Using the colloidal clay technique with the colloidal clay carrying the nutrient cations and some anions, adsorbed on the colloid in specific amounts, soybean seeds were the only source of nitrogen to test the ability of the plants, innoculated with legume bacteria, to fix atmospheric nitrogen. By utilizing a series of graduate students, during several years, working with the colloidal clay technique, we had finally arrived at enough experience to use the colloidal clay, with acid-washed quartz sand, as plant diets to vary calcium, magnesium, potassium, as hydroxides, and phosphorus as calcium hydrogen phosphate, all titrated on the acid clay (pH 3.6) in suitably varied quantities as plant diets for this study.

By means of two soybean series, one sterile of legume bacteria, and the other innoculated with laboratory Rhizobia culture for soybeans, the changed plant physiology demonstrated what one microbial life form in the soil could accomplish in the phenomenon of ion exchange between the plant roots and the colloidal complex of the soil. The colloidal complex had initially been made the equivalent of sterile soil by electrodialysis during several days. By this means we were able to demonstrate that the root of a legume plant is a decidedly different force in exchanging ions with the soil than is the root of a non-legume plant.

We aimed to learn several facts about legume plants. We used as possible postulates for the research the following:

1. We already knew that a yield of larger crop mass is not necessarily proof of crops' delivery of more food value in either protein or minerals.

2. Is what might be called a "living soil" in terms of more microbial life in root nodules a modification of the plant's larger, possibly better balanced nutrition, especially relative to protein production by more mineral nutrient intake?

3. How effective is proteinaceousness of the plant's roots as a help in its taking more inorganic nutrient elements from the exchangeable supply adsorbed on the colloidal complex?

4. Do different quantities of cations on the clay favor, or hinder, each other's services in plant nutrition; e.g., is magnesium as an excess disturbing to calcium?

5. Does potassium, as an increased carbohydrate synthesizer by the plant, serve to supply it with more energy for its nitrogen fixation?

6. Do proteinaceous roots suggest plants of more nutritional value as food by intake of more inorganic fertility?

Other postulates might have been added.

Two levels of calcium, 10 and 20 M.E. per plant were used, and coupled with each of those were three levels of potassium, 5, 10, and 15 M.E. per plant, thus varying both calcium and potassium. For magnesium and phosphorus the constants of 10 M.E. for the former and 7.5 M.E. for the

Table 1

Ions Added to Clay Cultures by Titration.

Culture	Ions added, M.E.				
no.	K	Ca	Mg	P	Ba
1	5	10	10	7.5	25*
2	10	10	10	7.5	20
3	15	10	10	7.5	15
4	5	20	10	7.5	15
5	10	20	10	7.5	10
6	15	20	10	7.5	5

*Barium added for series A, non-nodulated, was 5 M.E. higher in every culture than was used in series B, nodulated. Barium was added to make the final clay nearly neutral.

latter were used in both series. The M.E. of barium for the first potassium series of 5, 10, 15 M.E. and for the constant 10 M.E. series of calcium were 25, 20, and 15 M.E.; but were 15, 10, and 5 M.E. of barium for the second potassium series combined with 20 M.E. of calcium. Table 1 gives the details of the initial plan of the M.E. of nutrients titrated on the clay. The clay mixed with quartz sand was the growth medium in which one series (A) was non-nodulated and the other (B) was nodulated. Both crops were started in May, the (A) in 1941 and the (B) crop in 1942.

Results

Nitrogen in the Crops. The non-nodulated crop's contents of nitrogen was only that offered initially to the seed. The percentages of nitrogen in the dry matter of the crop were 1.50 as a minimum and 2.66 as a maximum while the corresponding figures for the nodulated crop (B) were 3.24 and 4.00. The average figures for the six cultures in duplicate in each of these two series were 1.91 for the former and 3.50 percent of nitrogen for the latter. The average values for total nitrogen per 50 plants were 349.7 mgms for the non-nodulated (A) crop and 449.7 mgms for the plants with nodules. The ratios for the percentages are A:B::1:1.8 and for the totals of nitrogen their ratios were A:B::1:1.2 with the increases due to the use of the extra atmospheric nitrogen. This meant that the nodulated crop was 80% more proteinaceous. This test demonstrated that protein on the inside of the root

Table 2
Crop Weights According as Roots Bore Nodules or None Under the Different Soil Treatments

Culture no.	M.E. offered	Nodulation	Tops, gms	Roots, gms	Total, gms	Ratio of tops/roots
	K	Ca				
1	5	10	+	7.65	2.30	9.90	3.3
			−	8.03	4.82	12.85	1.6
2	10	10	+	9.14	2.26	11.40	4.0
			−	14.07	5.71	19.79	2.4
3	15	10	+	11.17	3.09	14.26	3.6
			−	13.81	6.07	19.88	2.2
4	5	20	+	10.23	2.96	13.20	3.4
			−	13.06	5.89	18.95	2.2
5	10	20	+	10.78	3.16	13.94	3.4
			−	16.01	6.03	22.04	2.6
6	15	20	+	11.92	3.33	15.25	3.5
			−	16.27	6.15	22.42	2.6
Total crop weights			+	60.90	16.91	77.97	3.5*
			−	81.27	34.68	115.95	2.3*

Means.

as a colloid itself might be a factor modifying the exchange through the root membrane with the soil colloidal complex on the exterior of the root. The "living soil" via added living legume bacteria made a big difference.

Weights of the Crop. Quite contrary to expectation, the weights of the non-nodulated soybean crop, which was behaving as a non-legume with reference to its nitrogen, were much larger than those of the nodulated crop (reported as Table 2). This occurred when both were growing on the same supply of available nutrients adsorbed on the colloidal clay. Here then, the mass of plant growth was almost 50% larger in total when the series was behaving as a non-legume.

More significant, however, is the fact that the nodulated crop had contact with the same amount of clay and total nutrients, a total root mass that was only half, and less, that of the non-nodulated crop. Nevertheless, its ratio of tops to roots of the latter was 2.31 while for the crop behaving as a legume, the tops had 3.53 times as much mass as the roots.

This feature deserves emphasis, namely, that the root mass of the nodulated crop was 50% more efficient in producing mass of top as related to mass of roots. If we can assume that the larger root mass represented correspondingly larger total root surface for clay contact, and ionic exchange functions with it, then it is immediately evident that the nodulated root, which is also the more proteinaceous root, is more effective in producing mass of top per unit mass and surface of root. If the legume plant carries in addition more nutrients taken from the soil, as is common for it, then the root of the leguminous plant must also be a more efficient physio-chemical system for the movement of ions from the colloidal clay complex through its wall into the interior of the root.

Potassium, Calcium and Magnesium in the Crops. The fact that the roots of the nodulated soybean plants were more active in moving nutrient ions into themselves from the adsorption atmosphere of the colloidal clay is evident from the data for concentrations and totals of the three nutrients, potassium, calcium and magnesium, in the two crop series given in Table 3.

Perhaps the most interesting fact is the much higher concentration of potassium in the nodulated crop. As an average of the six treatments, this was 3.36% of the plant dry matter for the nodulated crop and only 1.92% for that not nodulated. The total potassium in the nodulated crop was also larger in every treatment in spite of the fact that the mass of the crop was smaller.

As for the calcium, the concentration of this element showed no regular variation in either the nodulated or non-nodulated crop, save as the soils offer increased. The total in the nodulated crop increased consistently as more potassium was offered and taken at either level of calcium supplied. In the non-nodulated crop at 10 M.E. of calcium, the totals were all very similar but at 20 M.E. of calcium they decreased as more potassium was taken. Nevertheless, at the 20 M.E. level of calcium this larger supply resulted in reduced concentration of potassium in the plants at all levels of the potassium supply. Here, then, the increasing intake of potassium by the non-legume suggests an excluding effect by potassium on the calcium, and the higher calcium similarly on the potassium when both were on the clay in exchangeable forms.

The concentrations of magnesium were higher in every case for the nodulated crop. At the 10 M.E. of calcium there was a decrease in concentration of magnesium with increased concentration of potassium in the crop whether behaving as a legume or non-legume. In the non-nodulated

Table 3

Concentrations and Totals of Potassium, Calcium, and Magnesium
in the Crops According as the Roots Bore Nodules or None Under
the Different Soil Treatments

Culture no.	Nodulation	Potassium %	Potassium Mgms	Calcium %	Calcium Mgms	Magnesium %	Magnesium Mgms
1	+	2.85	282	0.40	39	0.58	58
	−	1.83	234	0.43	55	0.38	59
2	+	3.87	442	0.53	47	0.45	52
	−	2.07	408	0.29	56	0.28	55
3	+	4.34	620	0.38	54	0.35	51
	−	2.41	479	0.26	52	0.21	46
4	+	2.13	280	0.70	92	0.66	88
	−	1.33	251	0.60	114	0.36	68
5	+	3.30	460	0.70	98	0.46	65
	−	1.80	398	0.51	111	0.24	55
6	+	3.96	600	0.67	101	0.38	58
	−	2.10	470	0.39	86	0.27	60

plants to which 20 M.E. of calcium were available, the decrease in magnesium concentration was not as regular.

The largest total amount of magnesium was in the nodulated crop given the maximum of calcium and minimum of potassium. The lowest total amount of magnesium was in the non-nodulated crop given the minimum of calcium and the maximum of potassium. The fuller significance of these facts must await later discussion.

Efficiency of Use by Nodulated and Non-Nodulated Plants of Potassium, Calcium, and Magnesium Adsorbed on the Clay. In order to enhance appreciation of the larger movements of plant nutrients into the roots in consequence of their proteinaceousness, the total amounts of the potassium, calcium, magnesium taken by the plants were calculated as percentages of the supplies offered on the clay. The data are assembled in Table 4.

Table 4

Efficiencies with Which the Potassium, Calcium, and Magnesium were Taken According as the Roots Bore Nodules or None*

Culture no.	Nodulation	Potassium, %	Calcium, %	Magnesium, %
1	+	76	18	44
	−	64	26	45
2	+	78	22	39
	−	73	26	42
3	+	81	26	38
	−	63	24	35
4	+	76	22	67
	−	69	27	51
5	+	81	24	49
	−	71	27	41
6	+	79	25	44
	−	62	27	46

* Percentage of offered supply taken by crop.

Again the high efficiency with which the potassium moved into the crop, and the higher efficiency for the nodulated crop, are outstanding. This naturally raises the question whether this larger amount of potassium means more carbohydrate synthesis for its use in plant respiration and synthesis of protein. Certainly, the more proteinaceous roots were more efficient in encouraging potassium entrance, when as an average 78.5% of the total on the clay was taken in contrast to 67.0% taken by the non-nodulated, less proteinaceous roots.

The plant's efficiency of consumption of calcium by the non-nodulated crop was not responsive to potassium differences. It was higher, in general, namely, 26.5%, as the mean, than for the nodulated crop (mean 23.0%). In the nodulated crop, increasing amounts of potassium meant higher efficiency in the movement of calcium into the plants, but mainly at the lower level of calcium.

In general, the efficiency of magnesium utilization declined as more potassium was offered and there was a suggestion of less efficient use by the non-nodulated crop.

Phosphorus, Silicon and Barium in the Crops. The concentration of phosphorus in the crops, whether nodulated or not, responded inversely to the concentrations of the potassium, more particularly when only 10 M.E. of calcium were available. This is shown in Table 5. The concentrations in the nodulated crop were always higher than those in the corresponding treatments of the non-nodulated crop. The total amounts of phosphorus in the crops given 10 M.E. of calcium and nodulated increased as more potassium was offered. Without nodulation at both calcium levels, and with nodulation at the higher calcium level, this relation did not suggest itself.

These facts suggest that for the nodulated legume root, the increasingly added potassium encourages increased intake of phosphorus from a constant supply in the soil where the calcium supply is moderate or low, but not when this is more liberal.

The concentration of silicon, even more pronouncedly than that of phosphorus, showed an inverse relation to the concentration of the potas-

Table 5

Concentrations and Total of Phosphorus, Silicon, and Barium in the Crops According as the Roots Bore Nodules or None Under the Different Soil Treatments

Culture no.	Nodulation	Phosphorus		Silicon		Barium	
		%	Mgms	%	Mgms	%	Mgms
1	+	0.45	44	2.54	251	1.52	151
	−	0.42	54	2.28	293	1.09	141
2	+	0.42	48	2.15	246	0.65	74
	−	0.34	64	1.24	245	0.47	96
3	+	0.38	54	1.46	208	0.28	39
	−	0.29	59	1.10	219	0.26	51
4	+	0.38	50	1.60	211	0.36	47
	−	0.32	61	1.13	214	0.50	95
5	+	0.32	46	1.08	151	0.22	30
	−	0.27	61	0.95	209	0.17	37
6	+	0.33	50	0.81	124	—	—
	−	0.29	64	0.91	193	0.15	32

sium. Potassium, therefore, suggests itself as having an excluding effect on silicon. Calcium classifies in the same category since at 20 M.E. the concentrations of silicon were roughly only about one-half those at 10 M.E. of calcium. Increasing the potassium from 5 to 15 M.E. shifted the silicon concentration from 2.54 to 1.46% for the nodulated crop and from 2.28 to 1.10% for the non-nodulated, both grown with 10 M.E. of calcium. With 20 M.E. of calcium, the corresponding shifts were from 1.60 to 0.81 and from 1.13 to 0.91 respectively with increase in potassium offered. The nodulation permitted a higher concentration of silicon.

When the totals of silicon are considered, there was more of it in the non-nodulated or heavier crop. The increasing potassium and the increasing calcium both served to demonstrate their effects of excluding the silicon, or the equivalent of nourishing the plant so that a different physio-chemical situation in the root meant less movement of silicon into it.

The concentrations and totals of barium followed the amounts present in the soil and did not relate themselves in any recognized way to any physiological factors. The non-nodulated series originally given 5 M.E. more of barium to each culture had more total barium in the crop. Barium suggests itself as striking up a kind of an equilibrium between that within and that without the plant.

Efficiency of Use by the Nodulated and Non-nodulated Plants of Phosphorus and Barium Adsorbed on the Clay. The same supply of phosphorus on the clay was used more efficiently by the nodulated crop grown with 10 M.E. of calcium as more potassium was applied. This is shown in Table 6.

There is a suggestion of a similar condition for the non-nodulated crop. At the higher levels of calcium, namely 20 M.E. there were no distinct suggestions. It is interesting to note that from 40 to 55% of the offered phosphorus found its way into the crops, and that, in general, the figure was higher on the non-nodulated crop.

That the nodulated crop which was synthesizing more nitrogen into more protein should use less phosphorus from the soil supply suggests that the non-legume was building phosphorus into compounds other than proteins or was merely moving the phosphorus into the crop as a deposition in some inorganic or less complex organic form.

Table 6

Efficiencies with Which the Phosphorus and Barium were Taken as the Roots Bore Nodules or None*

Culture no.	Nodulation	Phosphorus, %	Barium, %
1	+	39	11
	−	47	8.2
2	+	42	7.2
	−	56	6.9
3	+	47	5.8
	−	52	5.1
4	+	44	6.9
	−	54	9.2
5	+	40	8.8
	−	53	5.4
6	+	44	—
	−	56	4.7

*Percentage of offered supply taken by crop.

Summary

In summary, the soybean crops grown with different soil treatments pointed out that the nodulated crops with their more proteinaceous roots represent these as different physio-chemical systems when tested against the colloidal clay than are the roots of non-nodulated soybeans. When the concentrations and totals in the crops of the originally adsorbed ions on the clay are considered, the nodulated crop demonstrated more regularities and consistent relations between those within and those outside the crop roots.

Even though the non-nodulated crop masses were larger, the nodulated crops were higher in concentrations and totals of potassium, in concentrations of calcium, of magnesium, and of phosphorus; but lower in totals of the non-nutrient silicon. In terms of the ingo of exchangeable ions into the crop from the clay, higher percentages of the potassium and magnesium were taken in consequence of nodulation. Calcium and phosphorus in totals moved into the non-nodulated crop as readily as into the nodulated crop.

These results suggest that the composition of the legume forage, in terms of several of the mineral nutrient elements from the soil, is different because the *protein nature of the root makes this part of the plant a different physio-chemical system in relation to the colloidal complex of the soil for its intake*. Plant nutrition as a movement of adsorbed ions from the clay into the root is not only a matter of kinds and amounts of ions on the clay and the total clay in the soil, but also a matter of the physiology of the particular root as well.

CHAPTER 37

Vegetable Crops in Relation to Soil Fertility — Calcium Contents of Green Leafy Vegetables

GREEN LEAFY VEGETABLES are recognized as important foods in the human diet. As providers of minerals and vitamins they are among the "protective" foods recommended by nutritionists. Attention has been called by Kohman, Sherman, and Wittwer to important nutritional differences between certain greens of the mustard family (kale, mustard greens, and turnip tops) and those of the goosefoot family (spinach, Swiss chard, beet greens, and New Zealand spinach). The superiority of greens of the mustard group may be ascribed to their contributions of calcium and ascorbic acid.

The importance of soil fertility as a determiner of "nutritive quality" in crops has been emphasized in a review by Beeson. More recent reports of Holmes, Crowley, and Kuzmeski; Lucas, Scarseth, and Sieling; Sheets, McWhirter, *et al.*; and Speirs, Anderson, *et al.* have continued to focus attention on this subject.

This report deals with comparative calcium values of some important green leafy vegetables, which were grown during the winter under controlled conditions in the greenhouse and with colloidal clay cultures.

Experimental Procedure

The clay-culture technique of growing plants, using variable levels of calcium and nitrogen, was utilized. For a source of colloidal material the clay subsoil of Putnam silt loam was selected. This native material, leached of its exchangeable nutrients, has an exchange capacity of 28 milliequivalents per 100 grams, 12 of which are hydrogen. By replacing the adsorbed hydrogen with cationic nutrients and blending the clay with pure white, quartz sand, a clay-sand mixture results having the semblance of natural soil. The details of preparing the clay and adding the nutrients have been adequately described by Albrecht and Schroeder.

In these studies a series of treatments was prepared by supplying calcium and nitrogen levels each of 5, 10, 20, and 40 milliequivalents (m.e.) with all possible combinations of the two nutrients. Other ions were held constant for all treatments. The nutrient salt combinations and quantities of clay used to provide the 16 nutrient levels are presented (Table 1). The pH values of the cultures approximated 6.8.

The vegetables were grown in one-gallon glazed crocks with 10 replicates for each treatment. Seedling plants were allowed to develop for a period of 60 to 90 days depending on the crop. At the proper stage of maturity the tops were harvested and the fresh and dry weights recorded. After being shredded in a Wiley mill and finely ground in a Merker mill, the dried material was suitable for analyses. Chemical determinations for calcium and magnesium were made according to the official A.O.A.C. methods. Oxalate was measured according to Pucher, Wakeman, and Vickery.

Results and discussion

The fresh weights of all the crops as influenced by the variable calcium and nitrogen are presented (Table 2). For all these vegetables the response to nitrogen was more marked than that for calcium. With New Zealand spinach and kale the calcium level in the cultures had practically no influence on the production of vegetation; whereas with spinach, chard, and mustard greens a pronounced interaction of calcium with nitrogen was noted. The amount of total vegetation produced varied with the crop and not with the botanical family to which it belonged. Yields of fresh material in spinach and beet greens were about half those for chard, turnip greens, New Zealand spinach, and kale. This would indicate that the latter collection of crops from the two families is not as exacting in the requirements for a high nutrient level in the soil as are spinach and beets, both of the goosefoot family. The yields, therefore, did not differentiate the two families.

The calcium contents of the crops, expressed in percentage compositions of dry weights, are assembled (Table 3) and portrayed graphically, as influenced by the calcium supplied in the clay cultures (Fig. 1). Marked differences in calcium values between greens of the mustard and goosefoot families are evident. In no case, regardless of the supply of exchangeable calcium in the soil, does the highest figure for the goosefoot greens

Table 1

Amounts of Nutrient Salts and Clay Used in Providing Four Levels Each of Calcium and Nitrogen

Treatment No.	Variables (m.e.)		Salts used and milliequivalents of ions										Clay per plant (gm.)
	Ca	N	Ca–Ac		NH_4–NO_3		K_2H–PO_4		K–Ac		Mg–SO_4		
1..........	40	40	40	40	20	20	13.3	20	6.7	6.7	6	6	717
2..........	40	20	40	40	10	10	13.3	20	6.7	6.7	6	6	633
3..........	40	10	40	40	5	5	13.3	20	6.7	6.7	6	6	592
4..........	40	5	40	40	2.5	2.5	13.3	20	6.7	6.7	6	6	571
5..........	20	40	20	20	20	20	13.3	20	6.7	6.7	6	6	550
6..........	20	20	20	20	10	10	13.3	20	6.7	6.7	6	6	467
7..........	20	10	20	20	5	5	13.3	20	6.7	6.7	6	6	425
8..........	20	5	20	20	2.5	2.5	13.3	20	6.7	6.7	6	6	404
9..........	10	40	10	10	20	20	13.3	20	6.7	6.7	6	6	467
10..........	10	20	10	10	10	10	13.3	20	6.7	6.7	6	6	383
11..........	10	10	10	10	5	5	13.3	20	6.7	6.7	6	6	342
12..........	10	5	10	10	2.5	2.5	13.3	20	6.7	6.7	6	6	321
13..........	5	40	5	5	20	20	13.3	20	6.7	6.7	6	6	425
14..........	5	20	5	5	10	10	13.3	20	6.7	6.7	6	6	342
15..........	5	10	5	5	5	5	13.3	20	6.7	6.7	6	6	300
16..........	5	5	5	5	2.5	2.5	13.3	20	6.7	6.7	6	6	279

Table 2

Yields of Green Leafy Vegetables Grown at Variable Levels of Calcium and Nitrogen

Treatment No.	Variables (m.e.) Ca	N	Fresh weight (gm. per 10 plants) Spinach (Bloomsdale L. standing)	Swiss chard (Lucullus)	Beet greens (Detroit Dark Red)	New Zealand spinach	Mustard greens (Fla. Broadleaf)	Turnip greens (Shogoin)	Kale (Blue Scotch Curled)
1............	40	40	234	635	264	468	341	429	523
2............	40	20	171	486	154	422	270	342	308
3............	40	10	85	233	72	268	179	187	163
4............	40	5	37	180	46	142	77	94	66
5............	20	40	321	487	276	280	268	411	544
6............	20	20	220	694	160	368	274	338	370
7............	20	10	109	243	95	231	177	193	146
8............	20	5	65	134	48	123	103	112	71
9............	10	40	179	392	226	461	235	356	468
10............	10	20	229	334	132	325	279	307	351
11............	10	10	139	215	90	219	182	165	192
12............	10	5	115	117	66	122	99	92	90
13............	5	40	129	32	192	466	254	310	558
14............	5	20	205	213	186	392	284	269	401
15............	5	10	153	172	124	159	212	178	223
16............	5	5	60	105	69	99	97	83	88

Table 3

Calcium Contents of Green Leafy Vegetables Grown at Variable Levels of Calcium and Nitrogen

Treatment No.	Variables (m.e.)		Contents of calcium on a dry-weight basis						
	Ca	N	Spinach	Swiss chard	Beet greens	New Zealand spinach	Mustard greens	Turnip greens	Kale
			pct.		pct.	pct.	pct.	pct.	pct.
1.................	40	40	0.71	1.03	.76	.46	1.78	2.56	3.10
2.................	40	20	0.80	0.89	.52	.54	1.74	2.70	2.44
3.................	40	10	1.13	0.89	.92	.57	1.70	2.64	2.26
4.................	40	5	1.23	0.75	.86	.62	1.82	2.58	4.08
Average...........	...	...	0.97	0.89	.77	.55	1.76	2.62	2.97
5.................	20	40	0.69	0.78	.60	.66	1.64	2.42	2.46
6.................	20	20	0.64	0.68	.74	.48	1.60	1.91	2.24
7.................	20	10	0.75	0.72	.92	.55	1.38	2.32	1.75
8.................	20	5	0.86	0.78	.92	.63	1.54	2.56	3.20
Average...........	...	...	0.74	0.74	.80	.58	1.54	2.30	2.41
9.................	10	40	0.64	0.60	.86	.46	1.41	2.14	2.26
10................	10	20	0.64	0.78	.56	.60	1.26	1.82	1.60
11................	10	10	0.66	0.82	.66	.52	1.07	2.16	1.38
12................	10	5	0.86	0.75	.76	.58	1.57	2.20	1.34
Average...........	...	...	0.70	0.74	.71	.54	1.33	2.08	1.65
13................	5	40	0.79	0.49	.56	.55	1.50	2.22	1.98
14................	5	20	0.59	0.82	.48	.53	1.25	2.00	1.48
15................	5	10	0.68	0.66	.56	.51	0.99	2.26	1.38
16................	5	5	0.62	0.55	.52	.51	1.24	2.04	1.66
Average...........	...	...	0.67	0.63	.53	.53	1.25	2.13	1.63

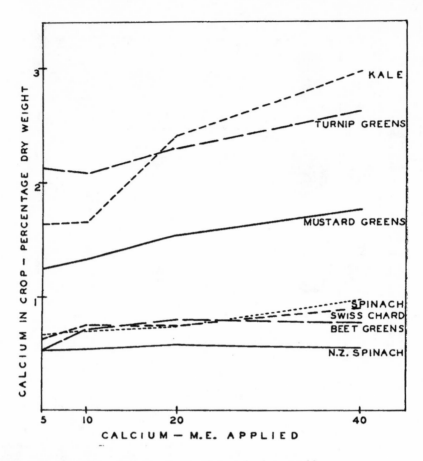

Fig. 1. Comparative calcium contents of green leafy vegetables.

(spinach in this case) equal the lowest graphical value for any of the mustard group. Thus the amounts of dietary calcium supplied by the greens of the two families are widely different.

As a result of increasing the calcium supply in the soil there were corresponding improvements in concentrations of calcium in the plant tissue. However, the increase in nutritional value in this respect was more pronounced in the mustard family. Of significance in this group was the betterment of quality, as concentrations of calcium in these vegetables, that was possible by additions of this nutrient element to the soil without any obvious external change in the appearance of the crop. Kale was one of the most responsive plants to an increased calcium supply, in so far as this altered its chemical composition, yet was influenced the least in its

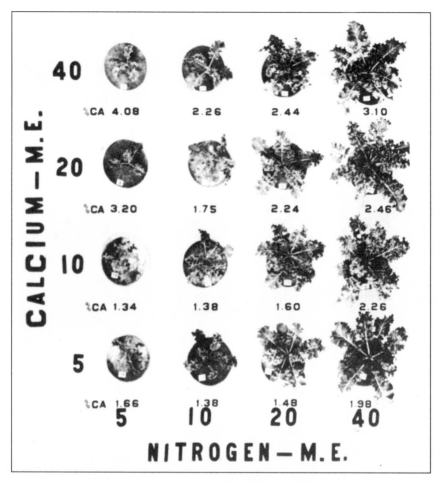

Fig. 2. Kale plants and their calcium contents when grown at variable levels of nitrogen and calcium. (Small numbers beneath each plant indicate the percentage in the crop on a dry-weight basis.)

vegetative growth by the same nutrient. The calcium content was almost doubled without any apparent change in vegetative growth or appearance (Fig. 2).

These differences in calcium concentrations of the green leafy vegetables are greatly magnified when one considers differences in their nutritional availability. According to Fairbanks and Mitchell, Fincke and Sherman, Kohman, Speirs, and Tisdall and Drake the calcium of spinach, Swiss chard, beet greens, and New Zealand spinach cannot be utilized in

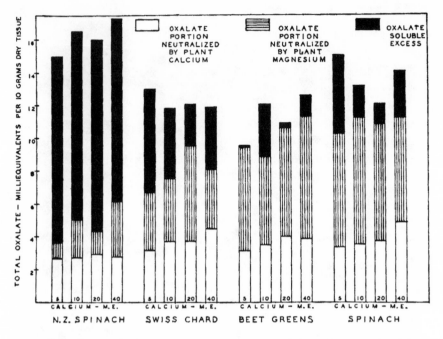

Fig. 3. Probable disposition of oxalate in New Zealand spinach, Swiss chard, beet greens, and spinach when grown at variable levels of calcium.

the diet because of the large amounts of oxalic acid present which combine with the plants' calcium and also with their magnesium to form insoluble and indigestible oxalates. In sharp contrast, according to the same investigators, the calcium of mustard greens, turnip tops, and kale is almost completely utilizable since these plants are practically free of oxalates.

With reference to spinach, Schroeder and Albrecht compared its nutritive quality when grown at variable levels of calcium in an acid soil (pH 5.2) and in another approaching neutrality (pH 6.8). The outstanding features of their experiments were the higher concentrations of oxalate, calcium, and magnesium shown to be in the plants grown on the soil at a pH of 5.2. For this acid soil at all calcium levels the two bases, added together, were present in the crop in more than sufficient quantities to neutralize all the oxalic acid. The plants grown in near neutral soils (pH 6.8), however, failed to absorb sufficient calcium and magnesium for complete neutralization of their oxalate contents. Under the neutral conditions, increased calcium applications to the soil also failed to alter appreciably the concentration of calcium in the plant. In the experiments reported herein the clay cultures were prepared with pH values comparable to those approaching neutrality as used by Schroeder and Albrecht. Therefore, high oxalate concentrations in relation to those of calcium and magnesium in the crops were anticipated.

The total oxalates produced, including those portions neutralizable by the plants' calcium and magnesium as well as those in excess, are portrayed (Fig. 3) for the four crops of the goosefoot family. Expressed as milliequivalents per 10 grams of dry plant tissue, stoichiometrically the oxalate exceeded by several times the calcium at all fertility levels. Under the conditions of these experiments not one of the four crops contained sufficient calcium, or even enough calcium and magnesium combined, to neutralize all its oxalic acid. The condition of complete neutralization was most nearly approached in beet greens and spinach. According to the chart New Zealand spinach, Swiss chard, beet greens, and spinach could contribute no dietary calcium. In addition, some excess oxalate was always present beyond the quantities possible of neutralization by the plants' bases. If one were to neutralize completely the oxalate of New Zealand spinach by calcium it would require from four to six times as much as the plant itself contains.

The effect on oxalate production of increasing the soil's calcium supply was not appreciable. It has been shown by Wittwer, Albrecht, and Goff that altering the level of soil nitrogen does, however, influence oxalate synthesis. It is of interest that the undesirable effects of excess, soluble oxalates in the goosefoot family were not overcome by the mere addition of more calcium to the clay media, and that in no case could all the oxalate be neutralized even when both the plants' magnesium and calcium were considered for that end.

Conclusions

The comparative calcium contents of spinach, Swiss chard, beet greens, New Zealand spinach, mustard greens, turnip tops, and kale were ascertained by analyzing the crops, each grown under controlled greenhouse conditions in colloidal clay cultures.

Increasing the calcium supply in the substrate enhanced, in general, the calcium concentrations in the crops.

The members of the mustard family (turnip greens, kale, mustard greens) had a much higher percentage of calcium than those of the goosefoot family (spinach, Swiss chard, beet greens, and New Zealand spinach).

The differences in calcium contributions to the human diet by the two plant families were magnified by the high oxalate content in the goosefoot greens. When this oxalate was expressed on a chemically equivalent basis, it was present in sufficient quantities to neutralize and thereby make insoluble and indigestible all the calcium and magnesium in these greens and to leave excess oxalate for dietary removal of calcium derived from other foods consumed with them.

AFTERWORD

The previous few pages have cleared up at least one point. It is impossible to take calcium and sequester it under a subject head without reference to the other volumes of the Albrecht message.

Proper calcium levels help plants form better root systems for the root-bed, stems and leaves for efficient use of sunlight energy, water, carbon dioxide, nitrogen and mineral nutrients. They reduce the toxicity of several soil constituents and combinations.

A comment for this section has been promised for enlargement of the subject, and perhaps a demurrer for our times.

In *"Understand the Calcium Process in American Agriculture,"* published in Biodynamics Quarterly, Spring 1991, Walter Goldstein wondered in print silence whether the cation balances told the whole story, certainly Carey A. Reams would have entertained such a question, and Rudolf Steiner circulated his insight even while Albrecht was conducting scientific tests. Steiner was a clairvoyant, and yet he advised his followers to "experiment, experiment." The biodynamic system that emerged from his insight has been ratified by followers who have added paragraphs and chapters to the calcium connection. The literature is massive.

Whatever, any analysis has to start with analysis, seedbed and root-bed preparation, seed selection, and then it has to move into tillage, crop maintenance, foliar support nutrition, harvesting and storage. All seem to depend on the calcium connection. When the foundation of this sequence is short-circuited, rescue chemistry hopes to pull the farmer's chestnuts out of the fire. All this fails largely because the calcium connection hasn't been made in the first place. It is no accident that weed crops and subsoils connect. Weeds that best proliferate under anaerobic conditions—foxtail, tall panicum—arrive when there is a calcium disconnect. Yet calcium levels without the tolerance levels Albrecht prescribed improve soil texture, phosphorus and micronutrient availability, thus improve the environment for microorganism and aid the growth of both symbiotic and non-symbiotic nitrogen-fixing bacteria.

Calcium thus remains a backbone consideration in any volume of *The Albrecht Papers*. It was therefore the goal of this volume to help farmers fine-tune their thinking on the subject before moving on.

The ideas proposed here are further enlarged in *The Pfeiffer Papers,* in *The Enlivened Rock Powders* (by Harvey Lisle) and in *A Biodynamic Farm* (by Hugh Lovel). Albrecht followed the work of Pfeiffer, a student of Steiner, with keen interest, much as he followed *Biological Transmutations* (by Louis Kervran), until nature closed down that interest with his death in 1974.

Absorb the rest of these papers and learn for yourself.

—*Charles Walters, Editor*

BIBLIOGRAPHY

Physical Importance of Calcium in Legume Inoculation.

Alway, F. J., and Ness, G. H., Inoculation of alfalfa on lime-deficient sandy soils; soil transfer vs. use of cultures. Minn. Agric. Exp. Sta. Tech. Bul. no. 46. 1927.

Bradfield, R., A simplified cell for determining the electro-dialyzable base content of soils and permutits. Jour. Amer. Soc. Agron. 19:1015–1021, 1927.

Bryan, O. Co., Effect of acid soils on nodule-forming bacteria. Soil Sci. 15: 37–40, 1923.

Bryan, O. Co., Effect of different reactions on the growth and nodule formation of soy beans. Soil Sci. 13: 271–287, 1928.

Chambers, R., and Rezzinkoff, P., The action of the chlorides of sodium, potassium, calcium, and magnesium on the protoplasm of Amoeba proteus. Jour. Gen. Phys. 8: 369–401, 1926.

Day, Dorothy, Some effects on Pisum salivum of a lack of calcium in the nutrient solution. Science 68: 426–427, 1928.

Falk, I. S., The role of certain ions in bacterial physiology. Abst. Bact. 7: 35–50; 87–105; 135–147, 1923.

Fellers, C. R., The effect of inoculation, fertilizer treatment and certain minerals on the yield, composition, and nodule formation of soy beans. Soil Sci. 6: 81–130, 1918.

Hellriegel, H., Methods of sterilized sand cultures employed at the Bernburg Experiment Station. Exp. Sta. Rec. 5: 835–854, 1894.

Hotchkiss, Margaret, Studies on salt action. VI. The stimulating and inhibitive effect of certain cations upon bacterial growth. Jour. Bact. 8: 141–162, 1923.

Karraker, P. E., Production of nodules on different parts of the root system of alfalfa growing in soils of different reactions. Soil Sci. 24: 103–109, 1927.

Machinda, S., ueber den Einfluss von Kalk-und Magnesia-salzen auf manche Taetigkeiten von Mikroben. Bul. Exp. Sta. Nishigahara, Japan. 1–12. Cited by Falk, I. S., Abst. Bact. 7: 96, 1923.

McCrudden, F. H., The quantitative separation of calcium in the presence of magnesium and phosphates. Jour. Biol. Chem. 7: 83–100, 1907. 10: 187–199, 1910.

Scanlan, R. W., Calcium as a factor in soy bean inoculation. Soil Sci. 25: 313–327, 1928.

Truog, E., Soil acidity. I. Its relation to the growth of plants. Soil Sci. 5: 169–195, 1918.

Winslow, C. E. A., and Falk, I. S., Studies on salt action. I,II. Proc. Soc. Exp. Biol. Med. 15: 67–68; 131–134, 1927.

Nutritional Role of Calcium in Plants. I. Prominent in the Non-Legume Crops, Sugar Beets.

Albrecht, William A., Nitrogen fixation as influenced by calcium. Proc. Sec. Intern. Congr. Soil Sci. Leningrad-Moscow Third Com. 3, 29–39 (1930).

Albrecht, William A., Inoculation of legumes as related to soil acidity. J. Am. Soc. Agron. 33, 153–155 (1941).

Albrecht, William A., Some soil factors in nitrogen fixation by legume. Trans. Soc. Soil Sci. New Brunswick, N. J. R. 71–84, (1939).

Albrecht, William A., Calcium as a factor in seed germination. J. Am. Soc. Agron. 33, 153–155, (1941).

Albrecht, William A., It's the calcium, not the alkalinity. Soybean Digest, September, 1941.

Albrecht, William A., The fertility problem of Missouri soils. Proc. Missouri State Hort. Soc. Nov. 30, 1942, pp. 94–100.

Albrecht, William A., Relative effectiveness of coarsely ground and finely pulverized limestone. Soil Sci. 61, 265–261, (1946).

Albrecht, William A., Colloidal clay cultures: Properties of the clay and procedures in its use as a plant growth medium. Soil Sci. 62, 23–21, (1946).

Albrecht, William A., Soil fertility in its broader implications. Missouri Agr. Expt. Sta. Research Bull. 765, 72–88 (1961) (Bibliography).

Anonymous, Lime soil to feed crops — not to remove soil acidity. Missouri Farm News Service May 5, 1954.

Ferguson, Carl E. (W. M. A. Albrecht). Nitrogen fixation and soil fertility exhaustion by soybeans under different levels of potassium. Missouri Agr. Expt. Sta. Research Bull. 330, 9 (1940).

Harris, J. E., Soil acidity. Michigan Agr. Coll. Expt. Sta. Tech. Bull. 19 (1914).

Preston, R. D., Structure of plant polysaccharides. Endeavor 23, 153–160 (1964).

Soil Acidity as Calcium (Fertility) Deficiency.

Albrecht, W. A., and Franklin L. Davis. Relation of calcium to nodulation of soybean on acid and neutral soils. Soil Science 28: 261–279, 1929.

Albrecht, W. A., and F. I., Davis. Physiological importance of calcium in legume inoculation. Botanical Gazette 88: 310–321, 1929.

Albrecht, W. A. Inoculation of legumes as related to soil acidity. Jour. Amer. Soc. Agron. 25: 512–522, 1933.

Albrecht, W. A. Drilling fine limestone for legumes. Missouri Agr. Expt. Sta. Bul. 367, 1936.

Albrecht, W. A., Ellis R. Graham, and Carl E. Ferguson. Plant growth and the breakdown of inorganic soil colloids. Soil Science 47: 455–458, 1939.

Albrecht, W. A., and R. A. Schroeder. Plant nutrition and the hydrogen ion. I. Plant nutrients used most effectively in the presence of a significant concentration of hydrogen ions. Soil Science 52: 313–327, 1942.

Albrecht, W. A. Colloidal clay cultures: Preparation of the clay and procedures in its use as a plant growth medium. Soil Science 62: 23–31, 1946.

Albrecht, W. A. Plant nutrition and the hydrogen ion, V. Relative effectiveness of coarsely ground and finely pulverized limestone. Soil Science 61: 265–271, 1946.

Albrecht, W. A. Nutrition via soil fertility according to the climate pattern. British Commonwealth Scientific Official Conference. Proceedings Specialist Conference in Agriculture, Australia, 1949. Plant and animal nutrition in relation to soil and climatic factors. His Majesty's Stationery Office 1951.

Ferguson, Carl E., and W. A. Albrecht. Nitrogen fixation and soil fertility exhaustion by soybeans under different levels of potassium. Missouri Agr. Expt. Sta. Res. Bul. 330, 1–52, 1941.

Graham, Ellis R. Soil development and plant nutrition, I. Nutrient delivery to plants by the sand and silt separates. Proc. Soil Sci. Sec. Amer. 6: 259–261, 1941.

Graham, Ellis R. Calcium transfer from mineral to plant through colloidal clay. Soil Science 51: 650–671, 1941.

Graham, E. R. and W. L. Baker. Ionic saturation of plant roots with special reference to hydrogen. Soil Science 72: 435–441, 1951.

Horner, Glenn M. Relation of degree of base saturation of a colloidal clay by calcium to growth, nodulation and composition of soybeans. Missouri Agr. Expt. Sta. Res. Bul. 232: 1–36, 1936.

Hutchings, Theron B. Relation of phosphorus to growth, nodulation and composition of soybeans. Missouri Agr. Expt. Sta. Res. Bul. 243: 1–47, 1936.

Miller, M. F. Testing soils for acidity by the modified Comber method. Missouri Agr. Extension Service Cir. 339, 1936.

Schroeder, R. A., and W. A. Albrecht. Plant nutrition and the hydrogen ion. III. Soil calcium and the oxalate content of spinach. Bul. Torrey Bot. Club 69: 561–568, 1912.

Interrelationships of Calcium, Nitrogen and Phosphorus in Vegetable Crops.

Albrecht, W. A. Physiology of root nodule bacteria in relation to fertility levels of the soil. Prec. Soil Sci. Soc. Amer. 2: 315–327.

Albrecht, W. A, and McCalla, T. M. The colloidal clay fraction of soil as a cultural medium. Amer. Jour. Bot. 25: 403–407, 1938.

Albrecht, W. A, and Schroeder, R. A. Colloidal clay culture for refined control of nutritional experiments with vegetables. Proc. Amer. Soc. Hort. Sci. 37: 689–692, 1939.

Brown, D. S. The growth and composition of tree tops of peach trees in sand culture in relation to nutrient-element balance. West Virginia Agr. Exp. Sta. Bull. 322, 1945.

Converse, C. D., Gammon, N., and Sayre, J. D. The use of ion exchange materials in studies on corn nutrition. Plant Physiol. 18: 114–121, 1943.

Cooper, H. P. Ash constituents of pasture grasses, their standard electrode potentials and ecological significance. Plant Physiol. 5: 193–214, 1930.

Comie, G. A. Factors inducing mineral deficiency symptoms on the potato plant. Ann. Appl. Biol. 29: 330–400, 1942.

Cullinan, F. P., and Batjer, L. P. Nitrogen, phosphorus, and potassium interrelationships in young peach and apple trees. Soil Sci. 55: 49–60, 1943.

Davidson, O. W., and Blake, M. A. Nutrient deficiencies and nutrient balance with the peach. Proc. Amer. Soc. Hort. Sci. 55: 339–346, 1937.

Graham, E. R., and Albrecht, W. A. Nitrate absorption by plants as an anion exchange phenomenon. Amer. Jour. Bot. 30: 193–198, 1943.

Hamner, C. I. Growth responses of Biloxi soybeans to variations in relative concentrations of phosphate and nitrate in the nutrient solution. Bot. Gaz. 101: 637–649, 1940.

Hoagland, D. R. Lectures on the inorganic nutrition of plants. Chronica Botanica Co. Waltham, Massachusetts. 164–169, 173–177, 1944.

Hutchings, T. B. Relation of phosphorus to growth, nodulation and composition of soybeans. Missouri Agr. Exp. Sta. Res. Bull. 232, 1936.

Jenny, H., and Overstreet, R. Cation exchange between plant roots and soil colloids. Soil Sci. 47: 257–272, 1939.

Jenny, H. Adsorbed nitrate ions in relation to plant growth. Jour. Colloid Sci. 1: 33–47, 1946.

Lagatu, H., and Maume, L. 'Etudde, par l'analyse periodique des ferilles, de Pinfloence des engrais de chaux, de magnesie et de potasse sur la vigne. Compt. Rend. 179: 932–934, 1924.

Loehwing, W. F. Calcium, potassium and iron balance in certain crop plants in relation to their metabolism. Plant Physiol. 3: 261–175, 1928.

Lundegardh, H. The influence of the soil upon the growth of the plant. Soil Sci. 40: 89–101, 1935.

McKinney, H. H. Soil factors in relation to incidence and symptom expression of virus diseases. Soil Sci. 61: 95–100, 1946.

Phillips, T. G., Smith, T. O., and Hepler, J. R. Some effects of potassium and nitrogen on the composition of the tomato plant. New Hampshire Agr. Exp. Sta. Tech. Bull. 73, 1939.

Reeve, Eldrow, and Suive, J. W. Potassium-boron and calcium-boron relationships in plant nutrition. Soil Sci. 57: 1–14, 1944.

Richards, E. J. Mineral nutrition of plants. Ann. Rev. Biochem. 13: 611–630, 1944.

Schroeder, R. A., and Albrecht, W. A. Plant nutrition and the hydrogen ion: H-Potato scab. Soil Sci. 53: 481–488, 1942.

Shive, J. W. A three-salt nutrient solution for plants. Amer. Jour. Bot. 2: 157–160, 1915.

Thomas, W. Balanced fertilizers and Liebigs' law of the minimum. Science n. s. 70: 382–384, 1929.

Shive, J. W. The conception of balance with respect to the absorption of nitrogen, phosphorus and potassium by plants and the influence of the level of nutrition. Science n. s. 72: 425–427, 1930.

Shive, J. W. The reciprocal effects of nitrogen, phosphorus, and potassium as related to the absorption of these elements by plants. Soil Sci. 33: 1–20, 1932.

Wadleigh, C. H. Influence of varying cation proportions upon the growth of young cotton plants. Soil Sci. 48: 109–120, 1939.

Walker, J. C. Soil management and plant nutrition in relation to disease development. Soil Sci. 61: 47–54, 1946.

Walker, J. C., and Foster, R. E. Plant nutrition in relation to disease development. III. Fusarium wilt of tomato. Amer. Jour. Bot. 33: 29–264, 1946.

Waugh, J. G., Cullinan, F. P., and Scott, D. H. Response of young peach trees in sand culture to varying amounts of nitrogen, potassium, and phosphorus. Proc. Amer. Soc. Hort. Sci. 37: 95–96, 1940.

Wittwer, S. H., Schroeder, R. A., and Albrecht, W. A. Vegetable crops in relation to soil fertility. II. Vitamin C and nitrogen fertilizers. Soil Sci. 59: 329–336, 1945.

Wittwer, S. H., Albrecht, W. A., and Goff, H. R.

Plants and the Exchangeable Calcium of the Soil.

Albrecht, W. A. 1933. Inoculation of legumes as related to soil acidity. Jour. Amer. Soc. Agron. 25: 512–522.

Albrecht, W. A. and F. L. Davis. 1937. Physiology of root nodule bacteria in relation to fertility levels of the soil. Soil Sci. Soc. Proc. 2: 315–327.

Albrecht, W. A. 1939. Some soil factors in nitrogen fixation by legumes. Intern. Soc. Soil Sci. Third Com. Trans. U. S. A. Vol. A.

Albrecht, W. A. 1940. Calcium-potassium-phosphorus relation as a possible factor in ecological array of plants. Jour. Amer. Soc. Agron. 32.

Albrecht, W. A. and H. Jenny. 1931. Available soil calcium in relation to "damping off" of soybeans. Bot. Gaz. 92: 263–278.

Albrecht, W. A. and T. M. McCalla. 1938. The colloidal clay fraction of soil as a cultural medium. Amer. Jour. Bot. 25: 403–407.

Albrecht, W. A. and R. A. Schroeder. 1939. Colloidal clay culture for refined control of nutritional experiments with vegetables. Proc. Amer. Soc. for Hort. Sci. 37: 689–692.

Graham, Ellis R. 1938. Magnesium as a factor in nitrogen fixation by soybeans. Missouri Res. Bull. 288.

Horner, Glenn M. 1935. Relation of the degree of base saturation of a colloidal clay by calcium to the growth, nodulation and composition of soybeans. Missouri Res. Bull. 232.

Nutchings, Theron B. 1936. Relation of phosphorus to growth, nodulation and composition of soybeans. Missouri Res. Bull. 243.

Jenny, Hans and R. Overstreet. 1939. Contact interchange between plant roots and soil colloids. Soil Sci. 47: 257–272.

McCalla, Thomas M. 1937. Behavior of legume bacteria in relation to the exchangeable calcium and hydrogen ion concentration of the colloidal clay fraction of the soil. Missouri Res. Bull. 256.

McCalla, Thomas M. 1930. Physico-chemical behavior of soil bacteria in relation to the soil colloid. Jour. of Bact. 40: 33–43.

Ravikovitch, S. 1934. Anion exchange. I. Adsorption of the phosphoric acid by soil. Soil Sci. 38: 219–239. II. Liberation of the phosphoric acid adsorbed ions by soils. Soil Sci. 38: 279–290.

True, R. H. 1921. The function of calcium in the nutrition of seedlings. Jour. Amer. Soc. Agron. 13: 91–107.

Calcium Saturation and Anaerobic Bacteria as Possible Factors in Gleization.

Joffe, J. S. 1936 Pedology, pp. 328–344. Rutgers University Press, New Brunswick, N. J.

Albrecht, W. A. 1938 Nitrate production in soils as influenced by cropping and soil treatments. Missouri Agr. Exp. Sta. Res. Bul. 294.

Wilde, S. A. 1940 Classification of gley soils for the purpose of forest management and reforestation. Ecology 21: 34–44.

Calcium and Hydrogen-Ion Concentration in the Growth and Inoculation of Soybeans.

Albrecht, W. A., and Davis, Franklin L. Relation of calcium to the nodulation of soybeans on acid and neutral oils. Soil Science, 28: 261–279, 1929.

Albrecht, W. A., and Davis, Franklin L., Physiological importance of calcium in legume inoculation. Bot. Gaz., 88: 310–321, 1929.

Albrecht, W. A. Nitrogen fixation as influenced by calcium. Proc. 2d Intern. Soil Congress. To be published.

Gedrotz, K. K. Exchangeable cations of the soil and the plant. I. Relation of plant to certain cations fully saturating the soil. Exchange capacity. Soil Science, 32: 51–64, 1931.

Scanlan, Robert W. Calcium as a factor in soybean inoculation. Soil Science, 25: 313–325, 1928.

Swanson, C. O., Gainey, P. L., and Latshaw, W. L. The calcium content of soil in relation to absolute reaction. Soil Science. 17: 181–191, 1924.

Growing Legumes on Acid Soils. The Rural New Yorker, November 2, 1946.

Relation of Calcium to the Nodulation of Soybeans on Acid Neutral Soils. Soil Science, volume 28, number 4, pp. 261–279, October 1929. Co-author, Franklin L. Davis.

Alway, F. J., and Ness, G. H. 1927 Inoculation of alfalfa on lime-deficient sandy soils; soil transfer vs. use of cultures. Minn. Agr. Exp. Sta. Tech. Bul. 46.

Bewley, W. F., and Hutchinson, H. B. 1920 On the changes through which the nodule organism (Ps. radicicola) passes under cultural conditions. Jour. Agr. Sci. 10: 144–161.

Bradfield, R. 1927 A simplified cell for determining the electro-dialyzable base content of soils and permutits. Jour. Amer. Soc. Agron. 19: 1015–1021.

Bryan, O. C. 1923 Effect of acid soils on nodule-forming bacteria. Soil Sci. 15: 37–40.

Erdman, L. W. 1926 Studies on inoculated soybeans: I. The importance of determining the number and size of soybean nodules for evaluating relative efficiencies of two or more cultures. Jour. Amer. Soc. Agron. 18: 799–804.

Fellers, C. R. 1927 The effect of inoculation, fertilizer treatment, and certain minerals on the yield, composition, and nodule formation of soybeans. Soil Sci. 6: 81–130.

Harper, H. J. and Murphy, H. F. 1928 Some factors which affect the inoculation of soybeans. Jour. Amer. Soc. Agron. 20: 959–974.

Jaeger, G. G. 1929 Rowan's new way of fattening land. Country Gent., p. 6, January, 1929.

Karraker, P. E. 1927 Production of nodules on different parts of the root system of alfalfa, growing in soils of different reactions. Soil Sci. 24: 103–109.

Lohnis, F., and Smith, N. R. 1916 Life cycles of the bacteria. Jour. Agr. Res. 6: 675–703.

McCool, M. M. (1927) Methods of applying lime. Jour. Amer. Soc. Agron. 19: 198–199.

Scanlan, R. W. (1928) Calcium as a factor in soybean inoculation. Soil Sci. 25: 313–327.

Thorton, H. G., and Gangulee, N. (1926) The life cycle of the nodule organism Bacillus radicicola (Beij) in soil and its relation to the infection of the host plant. Proc. Roy. Soc. (London) Ser. B. 99: 427–451.

Wilson, J. K. (1917) Physiological studies of B. radicicola of soybean and of factors influencing nodule formation. N. Y. (Cornell) Agr. Exp. Sta. Bul. 386.

Vegetable Crops in Relation to Soil Fertility — Calcium Contents of Green Leafy Vegetables.

Albrecht, W. A., and Schroeder, R. A., 1939. Colloidal clay culture for refined control of nutritional experiments with vegetables. Proc. Am. Soc. Hort. Sci. 37, 689–692.

Association of Official Agricultural Chemists, 1940. Official and Tentative Methods of Analyses. Fifth ed., 127–128.

Beeson, K. C., 1941. The mineral composition of crops with particular reference to the soils in which they were grown. U. S. Dept. Agr., Misc. Pub. 360.

Fairbanks, B. W., and Mitchell, H. H., 1938. The availability of calcium in spinach, in skim milk powder and in calcium oxalate. J. Nutrition 16, 79–89.

Fincke, M. L., and Sherman, H. C., 1935. The availability of calcium from some typical foods. J. Biol. Chem. 110, 421–428.

Holmes, A. D., Crowley, L. V., and Kuzmeski, J. W., 1945. Influence of supplementary calcium and magnesium fertilizers upon nutritive value of kale. Food Research 10, 401–407.

Kohman, E. F., 1939. Oxalic acid in foods and its behavior and fate in the diet. J. Nutrition 18, 233–246.

Lucas, R. E., Scarseth, G. D., and Sieling, D. H., 1942. Soil fertility levels as it influences plant nutrient composition and consumption. Indiana Agr. Expt. Sta. Bull. 468.

Pucher, G. W., Wakeman, A. J., and Vickery, H. B., 1941. Organic acids in plant tissues. Ind. Eng. Chem., Anal. Ed. 13, 241–246.

Schroeder, R. A., and Albrecht, W. A., 1942. Plant nutrition and the hydrogen ion. III. Soil calcium and the oxalate content of spinach. Bull. Torrey Botan. Club 69, 561–568.

Sheets, O. A., McWhirter, L., Anderson, W. S., Gieger, M., Ascham, L., Cochran, H. L., Spiers, M., Reder, R., Edmond, J. B., Lease, E. J., Mitchell, J. H., Fraps, G. S., Whitacre, J., Yarnell, S. H., Ellett, W. B., Moore, R. C. and Zimmerley, H. H., 1944. Effect of fertilizer, soil composition, and certain climatological conditions of the calcium and phosphorus content of turnip greens. J. Agr. Res. 68, 145–190.

Sherman, H. C., 1944. Principles of nutrition and nutritive value of food. U. S. Dept. Agr., Misc. Pub. 564.

Speirs, M., 1939. The utilization of calcium in various greens. J. Nutrition 17, 557–564.

Albrecht, W. A. Anderson, W. S., Gieger, M., McWhirter, L., Sheets, O. A., Reder, R., Edmond, J. B., Lease, E. J., Mitchell, J. H., Fraps, G. S., Whitacre, J., Yarnell, S. H., Ellett, W. B., Moore, R. C., Zimmerley, H. H., Ascham, L., and Cochran, H. L., 1944. Effect of fertilizer and environment on the iron content of turnip greens. Southern Cooperative Series, Bull. 2.

Tisdall, F. F., and Drake, T. G. H., 1938. The utilization of calcium. J. Nutrition 16, 613–620.

Wittwer, S. H., 1945. Some nutritional aspects of green leafy vegetables. Sci. Monthly 61, 71–73.

Wittwer, S. H., Albrecht, W. A., and Goff, H. R., 1946. Vegetable crops in relation to soil fertility. III. Oxalate content and nitrogen fertilization. Food Research 11, 54–60.

Publisher's Note:

This bibliography contains reference works that Dr. William A. Albrecht used for research when working on many of the papers contained in this book. Some selections are not available from works that have been obtained from Dr. Albrecht's personal papers.

INDEX

Also from Acres U.S.A.

Hands-On Agronomy

BY NEAL KINSEY & CHARLES WALTERS

 The soil is more than just a substrate that anchors crops in place. An ecologically balanced soil system is essential for maintaining healthy crops. This is a comprehensive manual on soil management. The "whats and whys" of micronutrients, earthworms, soil drainage, tilth, soil structure and organic matter are explained in detail. Kinsey shows us how working with the soil produces healthier crops with a higher yield. True hands-on advice that consultants charge thousands for every day. Revised, third edition. *Softcover, 352 pages. ISBN 0-911311-59-9*

Hands-On Agronomy Video Workshop

DVD Video Workshop

BY NEAL KINSEY

 Neal Kinsey teaches a sophisticated, easy-to-live-with system of fertility management that focuses on balance, not merely quantity of fertility elements. It works in a variety of soils and crops, both conventional and organic. In sharp contrast to the current methods only using N-P-K and pH and viewing soil only as a physical support media for plants, the basis of all his teachings are to feed the soil, and let the soil feed the plant. The Albrecht system of soils is covered, along with how to properly test your soil and interpret the results. *80 minutes.*

The Secret Life of Compost

BY MALCOLM BECK, WITH COMMENTARY BY CHARLES WALTERS

 We don't need to poison the earth in order to grow better food, and what is harmful to the environment when improperly disposed of often can be turned back to the soil in a beneficial way through composting — if you know how. Here's how. Malcolm Beck's Garden-Ville is one of the largest commercial composting operations in the country. He shares his insight into the processes of decay that can transform everything from lawn trimmings to sewer sludge into life-giving earth. Coupled with Beck's insight into nature and practical advice are remarks from Charles Walters, author and founder of *Acres U.S.A. Softcover, 150 pages. ISBN 0-911311-52-1*

To order call 1-800-355-5313 or order online at www.acresusa.com

Agriculture in Transition

BY DONALD L. SCHRIEFER

Now you can tap the source of many of agriculture's most popular progressive farming tools. Ideas now commonplace in the industry, such as "crop and soil weatherproofing," the "row support system," and the "tillage commandments," exemplify the practicality of the soil/root maintenance program that serves as the foundation for Schriefer's highly-successful "systems approach" farming. A veteran teacher, lecturer and writer, Schriefer's ideas are clear, straightforward, and practical. *Softcover, 238 pages. ISBN 0-911311-61-0*

From the Soil Up

BY DONALD L. SCHRIEFER

The farmer's role is to conduct the symphony of plants and soil. In this book, learn how to coax the most out of your plants by providing the best soil and removing all yield-limiting factors. Schriefer is best known for his "systems" approach to tillage and soil fertility, which is detailed here. Managing soil aeration, water, and residue decay are covered, as well as ridge planting systems, guidelines for cultivating row crops, and managing soil fertility. Develop your own soil fertility system for long-term productivity. *Softcover, 274 pages. ISBN 0-911311-63-7*

Science in Agriculture

BY ARDEN B. ANDERSEN, PH.D., D.O.

By ignoring the truth, ag-chemical enthusiasts are able to claim that pesticides and herbicides are necessary to feed the world. But science points out that low-to-mediocre crop production, weed, disease, and insect pressures are all symptoms of nutritional imbalances and inadequacies in the soil. The progressive farmer who knows this can grow bountiful, disease- and pest-free commodities without the use of toxic chemicals. A concise recap of the main schools of thought that make up eco-agriculture — all clearly explained. Both farmer and professional consultant will benefit from this important work. *Softcover, 376 pages. ISBN 0-911311-35-1*

Bread from Stones

BY JULIUS HENSEL

This book was the first work to attack Von Liebig's salt fertilizer thesis, and it stands as valid today as when first written over 100 years ago. Conventional agriculture is still operating under misconceptions disproved so eloquently by Hensel so long ago. In addition to the classic text, comments by John Hamaker and Phil Callahan add meaning to the body of the book. Many who stand on the shoulders of this giant have yet to acknowledge Hensel. A true classic of agriculture. *Softcover, 102 pages. ISBN 0-911311-30-0*

To order call 1-800-355-5313 or order online at www.acresusa.com

The Secret Life of Compost

BY MALCOLM BECK, WITH COMMENTARY BY CHARLES WALTERS

 We don't need to poison the earth in order to grow better food, and what is harmful to the environment when improperly disposed of often can be turned back to the soil in a beneficial way through composting — if you know how. Here's how. Malcolm Beck's Garden-Ville is one of the largest commercial composting operations in the country. He shares his insight into the processes of decay that can transform everything from lawn trimmings to sewer sludge into life-giving earth. Coupled with Beck's insight into nature and practical advice are remarks from Charles Walters, author and founder of *Acres U.S.A. Softcover, 150 pages. ISBN 0-911311-52-1*

Fletcher Sims' Compost

BY CHARLES WALTERS

 Covers the optimal conditions for converting plant and animal wastes into compost by balancing the correct ratio of raw materials, using the correct microorganisms and moisture content, proper pile or windrow construction, and efficient mixing. Fletcher Sims, the Dean of Composters, has elevated the "art" of good composting to a "science." Explains not only the complexities of commercial-scale compost production, but also the benefits of the use of this gentle fertilizer. A book that really draws you in, it is a combination of a biography and technical guide written by the founder of *Acres U.S.A. Softcover, 247 pages. ISBN 0-911311-43-2*

A Farmer's Guide to the Bottom Line

BY CHARLES WALTERS

 This book is the culmination of Walters' lifetime of experience, written in his honest, straight-ahead style, outlining how the small farmer-entrepreneur can find his way to a profitable bottom line. The book provides how-to information on each step from planning to implementation of business practices for the eco-friendly farm and includes examples of people who are making a living, and a profit, by demanding a fair price for their labor. Whether you are considering taking up farming as an occupation or just interested in the economics and history of farming, this book is a must-read. *Softcover, 212 pages. ISBN 0-911311-71-8*

How to Grow World Record Tomatoes

BY CHARLES H. WILBER

 For most of his 80+ years, Charles Wilber has been learning how to work with nature. In this almost unbelievable book he tells his personal story and his philosophy and approach to gardening. Finally, this Guinness world record holder reveals for the first time how he grows record-breaking tomatoes and produce of every variety. Detailed step-by-step instructions teach you how to grow incredible tomatoes — and get award-winning results with all your garden, orchard, and field crops! Low-labor, organic, bio-intensive gardening at its best. *Softcover, 132 pages. ISBN 0-911311-57-2*

How to Grow World Record Tomatoes

BY CHARLES H. WILBER

 For most of his 80+ years, Charles Wilber has been learning how to work with nature. In this almost unbelievable book he tells his personal story and his philosophy and approach to gardening. Finally, this Guinness world record holder reveals for the first time how he grows record-breaking tomatoes and produce of every variety. Detailed step-by-step instructions teach you how to grow incredible tomatoes — and get award-winning results with all your garden, orchard, and field crops! Low-labor, organic, bio-intensive gardening at its best. *Softcover, 132 pages. ISBN 0-911311-57-2*

Weeds: Control Without Poisons

BY CHARLES WALTERS

 For a thorough understanding of the conditions that produce certain weeds, you simply can't find a better source than this one — certainly not one as entertaining, as full of anecdotes and homespun common sense. It contains a lifetime of collected wisdom that teaches us how to understand and thereby control the growth of countless weed species, as well as why there is an absolute necessity for a more holistic, eco-centered perspective in agriculture today. Contains specifics on a hundred weeds, why they grow, what soil conditions spur them on or stop them, what they say about your soil, and how to control them without the obscene presence of poisons, all cross-referenced by scientific and various common names, and a new pictorial glossary. *Softcover, 352 pages. ISBN 0-911311-58-0*

The Biological Farmer

A Complete Guide to the Sustainable
& Profitable Biological System of Farming

BY GARY F. ZIMMER

 Biological farmers work with nature, feeding soil life, balancing soil minerals, and tilling soils with a purpose. The methods they apply involve a unique system of beliefs, observations and guidelines that result in increased production and profit. This practical how-to guide elucidates their methods and will help you make farming fun and profitable. *The Biological Farmer* is the farming consultant's bible. It schools the interested grower in methods of maintaining a balanced, healthy soil that promises greater productivity at lower costs, and it covers some of the pitfalls of conventional farming practices. Zimmer knows how to make responsible farming work. His extensive knowledge of biological farming and consulting experience come through in this complete, practical guide to making farming fun and profitable. *Softcover, 352 pages. ISBN 0-911311-62-9*

Alternative Treatments for Ruminant Animals

BY PAUL DETTLOFF, D.V.M.

Drawing on 36 years of veterinary practice, Dr. Paul Dettloff presents an natural, sustainable approach to ruminant health. Copiously illustrated chapters "break down" the animal into its interrelated biological systems: digestive, reproductive, respiratory, circulatory, musculoskeletal and more. Also includes a chapter on nosodes, with vaccination programs for dairy cattle, sheep and goats. An information-packed manual from a renowned vet and educator. *Softcover, 260 pages. ISBN 0-911311-77-7*

Grass, the Forgiveness of Nature

Exploring the miracle of grass, pastures & grassland farming

BY CHARLES WALTERS

What is the most important plant in the world? In terms of nutritive content, function within the ecosystem, and even medicinal properties, the answer to this question may very well be *grass*. In this wide-ranging survey of grass forages and pastureland, Charles Walters makes the case that grass is not just for cows and horses — that in fact it is the most nutritious food produced by nature, as well as the ultimate soil conditioner. You will learn from traditional graziers who draw on centuries of wisdom to create beautiful, lush, sustainable pastures, as well as cutting-edge innovators who are using such methods as biodynamics and sea-solids fertilization to create some of the healthiest grasslands in the world. Leading agronomists not only explain the importance of grasses in our environment, they also share practical knowledge such as when to look for peak levels of nutrition within the growing cycle and how to use grass to restore soil to optimum health. A must-read for anyone interested in sustainable, bio-correct agriculture, this information-packed volume is a comprehensive look at an essential family of plants. *Softcover, 320 pages. ISBN 0-911311-89-0*

Soil, Grass & Cancer

BY ANDRÉ VOISIN

Almost a half-century ago, André Voisin had already grasped the importance of the subterranean world. He mapped the elements of the soil and their effects on plants, and ultimately, animal and human life as well. He saw the hidden danger in the gross oversimplification of fertilization practices that use harsh chemicals and ignore the delicate balance of trace minerals and nutrients in the soil. With a volume of meticulously researched information, Voisin issues a call to agricultural scientists, veterinarians, dietitians and intelligent farmers to stand up and acknowledge the responsibilities they bear in the matter of public health. He writes as well to the alarmed consumer of agricultural products, hoping to spread the knowledge of the possibilities of protective medicine — part of a concerted attempt to remove the causes of ill health, disease and, in particular, cancer. *Softcover, 368 pages. ISBN 0-911311-64-5*

The Keys to Herd Health

BY JERRY BRUNETTI

Whether dairy or beef, a healthy herd begins in such keystone concepts as biodiversity on the farm, acid/alkali balance in feedstuffs, forage quality, and more. In this accessible video, eco-consultant and livestock feed specialist Jerry Brunetti details the keynote essential for successful livestock operation. A popular speaker at eco-farming events across North America, Brunetti explains the laws of nature in terms farmers can embrace, and doles out specific steps you can utilize on your farm right away — all in a convenient video format that you can watch and review whenever you like. *VHS & DVD format.*

Holistic Veterinary Care

BY JERRY BRUNETTI & HUBERT J. KARREMAN, V.M.D.

Dr. Hubert J. Karreman, author of the compendium *Treating Dairy Cows Naturally,* is joined by renowned animal nutrition expert Jerry Brunetti to present an overview of the strategies and tools available for successful holistic herd health management. The emphasis is on natural alternatives for the treatment of common dairy cow problems, including complications in reproduction, birth and lactation. This video will provide you with a basic understanding of the power and the limitations of herbs, how to treat the whole cow, and how to build a herbal medicine kit for your farm. Drawing on actual case studies, which are examined, diagnosed, and treated using holistic protocols, this video serves as a virtual hands-on course in holistic herd health that will prove invaluable to every dairy producer, from the micro-scale family farmer to commercial-scale operations. *VHS & DVD format.*

The Other Side of the Fence — Historic Video

WITH WILLIAM A. ALBRECHT, PH.D.

Professor William A. Albrecht's enduring message preserved and presented for future generations. In this 1950s-era film, with introductory and closing remarks by Acres U.S.A. founder Charles Walters, Prof. Albrecht explains the high cost of inadequate and imbalanced soil fertility and how that "dumb animal," the cow, always knows which plant is the healthier, even though we humans don't see a difference with our eyes. A period film that is dated in style but timeless in message. Perfect for your group gathering. *VHS & DVD format, 26 minutes.*

To order call 1-800-355-5313 or order online at www.acresusa.com